To the great sea novels of World War II—*The Caine Mutiny, The Cruel Sea* —comes the German counterpart, *Sharks and Little Fish*.

Through the experiences of his central character, the 17-year-old Hans Teichmann, Wolfgang Ott has created an unforgettable picture of what the war was like for the young Germans who fought in the submarines. From the harsh discipline of the barracks, the barroom brawls and drunken revels in brothels, to the appalling ruthlessness of sea war and the terror of men trapped at the bottom of the ocean while the killer destroyers cruise slowly above—Ott spares his readers nothing of what he saw and endured himself as a submarine ensign in World War II.

This is fiction of stunning power, a novel with the authority of a documentary, "a true and terrible book—a punishment and a revelation." (*The New York Times*.)

INTERNATIONAL ACCLAIM FOR A WAR NOVEL OF STUNNING POWER:

"Not only the first, but probably the unsurpassable denunciation of the German Navy and submarine warfare."

—Hans Hellmut Kirst

"There is no other book in German literature that can compare with this one in 'hardness.' "

—*Der Tag,* Berlin

"As uncompromising, vivid and unfalsified an account of wartime naval life as has appeared. . . . In every way this is a war novel of unusual quality."

—*Times Literary Supplement,* London

"A work of extraordinary power . . . a more relentless exposure of war and the brutality of German naval discipline could not be imagined."

—Orville Prescott, *The New York Times*

"For all his crudities, novelist Ott has made a case against war that is as powerful as anything in a recent novel."

—*Time* Magazine

"One can well understand the furor that arose in Germany when *Sharks and Little Fish* first appeared, for rarely has such a bitter, powerful indictment of the German people been put on paper . . . a brutal story that will leave the reader gasping."

—*New York Herald Tribune*

SHARKS AND LITTLE FISH

Wolfgang Ott

BALLANTINE BOOKS • New York

Original title: *Haie und kleine Fische*
Albert Langen—Georg Mueller Verlag, Muenchen

Translation by Ralph Manheim

Library of Congress Catalog Card No. 57-10236

This edition published by arrangement with Pantheon Books

First Printing: November, 1966
Second Printing: December, 1971

Cover art by Bob Schultz

Printed in the United States of America

BALLANTINE BOOKS, INC.
101 Fifth Avenue, New York, New York 10003
An Intext Publisher

SHARKS
AND
LITTLE
FISH

1

They lodged in the crew's quarters. Their bunks were on the
port side, and Stollenberg was above Teichmann. He sat on
the edge of his bunk and pulled on his socks; his feet were
clean and his socks were darned. Teichmann told him to get
his sweaty feet out of there.

Setting one foot on the edge of Teichmann's bunk, Stollenberg climbed down and sat on the bench across the compartment.

Teichmann watched him as he shook the cockroaches out
of his sea boots, felt inside to make sure there were none
left, pulled on the boots, went to the bread locker, cut off a
slice from the stalest loaf, fished the roaches out of the jam
pot with his knife, spread a thick layer of red jam on his
bread, and bit into it.

Teichmann turned over to the wall.

"Come peel potatoes, it's almost eight," said Stollenberg
with his mouth full.

Teichmann lay still.

"All right, it's rough," said Stollenberg. "But get moving."

Teichmann lay still. It annoyed him that Stollenberg
should be such an eager beaver: only six months ago he was
sitting next to me in school, and when he was called on and
he got stuck I prompted him; he helped me too when I got
stuck, but I did it more often and what's more I gave him
better steers. He was no shining light, and now he acts as if
he's at home here and ...

"Come along, sailor, time to take a leak," said Heyne,
poking him in the small of the back.

The crew stood on the lee side of the top deck, peeling
potatoes. Pitt spat into the air, and the wind carried his
spittle overboard. His second day on board, when he was sea-

7

sick, Teichmann had spat; the wind had come from forward, and the spit had splashed on the porthole of the charthouse under the bridge, where the mate was mulling over the course. Teichmann wished Pitt's spit would land there sometime, but the spit and the wind wouldn't do him that favor. He remembered how they'd beaten him up, with Pitt in the lead; he'd been too seasick to fight back and they had fixed for Stollenberg and Heyne to be on watch so they couldn't help him.

A beating was something new to him. He was powerfully built, but only from the waist up. He had a big broad chest and long muscular arms with fists that could punch quickly and accurately, but his thighs and legs were lean and wiry and looked frail at the joints. He was almost six feet tall, and when he walked he stooped forward a bit, as though he had difficulty in holding up his massive frame. With his long arms, he looked like an orangoutang, except that he had a nice face.

Pitt had advised him to face into the weather, so the wind would blow into his mouth and keep his food down. But it came up just the same and blew round their ears. That night he had to wash their stinking dungarees, including several sets belonging to men who hadn't even been on deck when he had thrown up, and when he bitched, they beat him up. He'd been pretty seasick. Not like the landlubbers that imagine they are seasick when they take a boat from Cuxhaven to Helgoland and lean over the rail and throw up. At first he'd done that too, but later on his stomach was empty and nothing came up but bile. It was like that for a week; he lay all doubled up in his bunk like an embryo, and he wouldn't have had the least objection to dying.

The potato pot was full. Teichmann carried it into the galley. In the doorway of the captain's cabin stood Dora, wearing a shirt and a pair of men's long pants.

"Come in, kid, and see an old woman crying."

He delivered the pot to the galley. On the way back he passed in front of the cabin again. This time Dora had on a green pullover. Her eyes were red, and the cabin reeked of perfume and alcohol.

8

"You scared of me, little fellow?"

"No, and I'm not so little, I'm almost six feet."

"Six feet tall, and sixteen years old."

"I'm going on seventeen."

"And what do you do when you're in Bremerhaven?"

"Just look around."

"I mean, have you got a girl-friend?"

"No."

"Then who do you go to see?"

"There's no shortage of dames."

"No, but the first time it oughtn't to be one of those."

"What do you mean, 'the first time?' "

"Oh, so you're that kind? Then you can have me too; I'm that kind too, or am I?"

"Of course."

"Yes, of course I am."

And then she said, "But you didn't have to say so. That wasn't nice."

"But it's the truth."

"Just the same, you didn't need to say so."

"But everybody on board knows it."

"What do they know? Do they know I had to twiddle my fingers for five years and live like a nun because my husband gave me a dose? Do they?"

"I didn't know that."

"It don't matter. So you won't come in? O.K. Nobody's forcing any favors on you. Shove off."

So that, thought Teichmann, is Dora. It was the first time she had spoken to him; up until then, he'd been air as far as she was concerned. All he had known was that the old man introduced her as his wife.

When the net was hauled in, it was full. The herring lay on deck three feet deep, thrashing around. The men shoveled them into their baskets and gutted them.

"What Dora needs is lot of good strong drink," said the mate that afternoon, when Teichmann had the wheel watch, "that's the best cure for hot pants. You can't imagine the way the broads were after me in the old days. But I never paid. The pleasure is mutual, I said. And they saw I was right.

9

Yes, my boy, that's the way to do." The mate stuck his little finger in his ear and shook the rest of his hand like a vibrator. Then he pulled a bottle from the inside of his jacket and drank.

"Have a drink?"

"I'm on watch."

"All right. Maybe it's better you don't drink. On account of the course. It's enough for me to be tight. What's your name?"

"Teichmann."

"I mean your first name."

"Hans."

"Well, Hans, get this. Liquor is the best cure for it. I wanted one in my day, superior article, get me, good family, that kind. But she didn't want me. So I just began to drink. Since then I've been able to shack up with any broad that comes my way, makes no difference. Push, pull, and there you have it. A simple mechanical process, understand, like you can read about in a manual on engines. None of your bilge about love, no duties, no obligations, nothing—push, pull, and so on. What's your name?"

"Hans."

"Well, Hans, get this. If you can't make it alone, take to the bottle, it's better than church—Periscope to port!"

He's seeing things, thought Teichmann, and kept to his course. The mate tore the wheel out of his hands and spun it hard astarboard.

"Take this through the speaking tube: To the commander. Periscope bearing three three zero. Range two zero zero."

Not wishing to spoil the fun, Teichmann passed the message on. A few seconds went by, then he heard the old man's voice through the speaking tube: "In the first place I'm not a commander, I'm just the captain of a God-fearing fishing boat; in the second place tell that mate to hit the sack and sleep it off. Got that?"

"Yes, captain."

"What did he say?"

"He says it's unlikely."

"I'll eat ten brooms if that wasn't the periscope of a submarine. I know them things from the world war. I was on a torpedo boat for three years. Oh hell, it's no skin off my ass."

Teichmann took the wheel and went back to the old course. The mate lit his cigar.

"Does the old man think I'm drunk?"

"No."

"If you'd said yes, there'd be nothing but a grease spot left of you."

"Think so?"

"Watch yourself, boy, when I'm drunk there's no telling what I'll do."

When he was relieved, Teichmann went to the charthouse and logged his course. The old man came into the charthouse, with the mate in his wake, waved a radio message in his hand, and said to the mate, "We're going to head full speed for the Norwegian coast, and then we'll make for home inside the three-mile limit."

"If you think . . ."

"Yes, I think. The English ultimatum means war. Isn't that clear to you? In Berlin they won't give a good God damn for that ultimatum . . ."

"Or in London for the three-mile limit."

"What's that? Great heavens, what was that?"

"My stomach, captain."

"I beg your pardon. Is that what the ultimatum does to you?"

"It's my stomach, captain."

"Well, don't be bashful."

"No, not me."

The old man figured the new course and plotted it on the chart. On his way out he said, "Mr. Mate, your manners are really terrible."

"I've got a sick stomach. That's what bloats me up."

"You and your stomach—it's just crap, that's what it is."

"I don't care for your choice of language. By the way, on my watch I sighted the periscope of a sub, but there was some drunken bum on your end of the speaking tube. I guess he forgot to give you the message."

The radio operator came in with a second message. The old man read it. "We're to put in at Hamburg and report to the head of the North Sea Naval Station; the crew is under orders. Pass that on to all hands, will you, mate."

"Is Dora part of the crew?"

"I shall notify my wife myself."

"Which one? The one in Bremen or the one on board?"

"Both. Anyway, I don't ask the marriage bureau for permission when I take a wife."

"But you might have asked your owner. So far he's never allowed anybody to take a woman on board."

"That's why I don't ask him. Any objection?"

"Not me."

Teichmann climbed up to the storeroom and filled his paint pot. Then he secured a line to the bosun's chair, and Stollenberg lowered him at the bow until he was on a level with the ship's name. Stollenberg made the ends of the line fast to the rail. Then he lowered the paint pot and brush and Teichmann began to paint over the *A* of *Albatross*.

"I wonder what headway Gerd's making with his old man," said Stollenberg. "He's been gone long enough. I don't take much stock in that undersecretary in the Ministry of Education."

"A little lower with the paint; that's it. In a minute we'll have to move the chair forward a bit."

"I can do it without your coming up."

"That I would like to see."

"Well, don't worry. It'll take a while before they can convert the *Albatross* into a minesweeper. Right now they haven't even got room for us at the dockyard. And say, did you hear, they want to fit us out with a gun and two machine guns, give us something to make a noise . . ."

"In case the English fleet deigns to waste ammunition on an old herring tub. . . ."

"They have other things to worry about. We've got a couple of big buckets, after all; you saw them on the way through Heligoland Bight. Looked pretty good, didn't they?"

"We'd be in good shape if we got assigned to a cruiser or something."

"A destroyer would be plenty good."

"Can you move me forward now without dropping me into the drink?"

Stollenberg hoisted the paint pot on board and untied one end of the line on the chair, turned the chair around, and secured the loose line forward of the other.

"Now you've got me ass backward," said Teichmann.

"Wait a minute."

Stollenberg untied the after line and gave the chair another turn, moving Teichmann about five feet. He was about to lower the paint pot when Heyne turned up and told them to come along.

They went to the crew's quarters, which were empty at this time of day. Heyne said, "Put your shore duds on and take your papers and all that crap; we're having dinner with my old man. Afterwards we can write our officer applications. It's the only way we'll ever get off this old rat barge."

"But we haven't any graduation papers."

"My undersecretary friend will attend to that; I've spoken to him on the phone. He was a fraternity brother of my father's, and he's got a son that wants to get a degree out of my father, and this son didn't invent gunpowder, understand? It's all perfectly simple. You've just got to put on the squeeze in the right spot."

"I doubt if it will work," said Stollenberg.

"I'll do anything to get off this God-damn herring tub," said Teichmann.

Heyne's father lived in a house in Blankenese. A sign at the garden gate announced: "Professor Friedrich Heyne."

"Your fingernails are in mourning," said Stollenberg.

"That's God's truth. But I couldn't get the tar off even with a knife," said Teichmann and thrust his hands into his pants pockets.

"I got mine off with gas," said Stollenberg. "And it wouldn't have hurt you to put on a clean shirt. You've got a button missing."

"Leave him alone," said Heyne. "It doesn't matter."

"Take my tie, then they won't see where the button should be."

Teichmann put on Stollenberg's tie.

"What about you?"

"I'll fix me a sports shirt effect."

"Very becoming," said Heyne.

They went through the garden. A girl opened the house door.

"This is Molly," said Heyne. "Her real name is Maria Holzner. I call her Molly because she's so nice and soft. Feel her, she's made of . . ."

"Why, Herr Heyne . . ."

"Don't give yourself airs."

Molly laughed and said, "My mother always told me to put on tin panties when the sailors come around."

"We've got a can opener," said Stollenberg, and when the girl looked at him he blushed.

They waited in a large living room. Heyne had gone into his father's study. Teichmann dropped into a chair and gazed at Hindenburg, Luther, and Tirpitz. Luther hung between the two warriors. Then he moved his chair over by the fish bowl that stood in one corner of the room and talked to the fishes. He stuck his finger in the water and laughed when the fishes bumped into it.

"What are you splashing around there for?" asked Stollenberg.

"It amuses me, and the little fishes like it too. They're bored to death. And now, my friends, we're going to make a storm, so you'll know there's a war on."

"In a minute you'll have fish all over the floor."

Heyne's father was the soul of politeness. Teichmann felt thin fingers when the professor gave him his hand. He noted that the professor was half a head shorter than his son. He had close-cropped, silvery-blond hair and an insignificant nose, turned up just a little at the end, and his eyes were light blue and watery. On the whole he seemed modest and almost shy. Teichmann looked at Gerd Heyne, with his

14

long black hair and his large, rather aquiline nose, and wondered how the professor had come by such a son.

"I am happy to meet Reinhold's friends. You are just in time for supper."

Teichmann had to bite his lips; he hadn't known that Gerd had another name, and it seemed to him that the professor might have called his one and only son something less ridiculous. Stollenberg chatted with the professor as if they had been old card partners, and when he spoke of Gerd, he said Reinhold. I still have a good deal to learn, Teichmann thought.

Grace was said before dinner; Teichmann wrapped his hands in his napkin. There were three others at table: a pastor by the name of Diebold and his wife, and the professor's sister, who was called Luise and was obviously a spinster. Teichmann thought the pastor's lips were too thick for his calling; aside from that he had a gentle, simple, and good-natured face and a suitable potbelly. His wife was extremely lively in conversation with the young men; she had a strange way of looking at her plate, and her dress was fairly modern. There was nothing to drink during the meal. At the end there was another prayer. Then the professor said, "May I invite the young gentlemen to our little gathering?"

"I'm sorry, Father, we can't. We have to get our papers ready."

The professor's sister was first to rise.

In the living room with the fish bowl some twenty persons were now sitting, as Teichmann could see through the half-open door. People getting along in years, conversing in soft tones.

"They're having a Bible hour," said Heyne on the way upstairs. "That's how old age has affected my father. He used to be different. In a minute they'll begin playing the harmonium and singing. Then one of them will deliver a sermon, and in the end they'll play the organ again."

"You get all sorts of things on this agony-box," said Stollenberg, turning the dials on the big radio-phonograph that Heyne had by his couch.

"Yes, I like to listen to good music. I guess you're just interested in the sports news?"

"I'm not as lowbrow as all that," said Stollenberg. Heyne put on a record, the death scene of the Czar in *Boris Godunov* with Chaliapin singing. Moussorgsky was his favorite composer, said Heyne—"so wonderfully vulgar."

"Who painted that?" asked Teichmann.

"Rembrandt, 'The Man in the Gold Helmet.' The original is in the Kaiser Friedrich Museum in Berlin. But it's a good copy."

"I don't know much about it. And who's that?"

"That's Schopenhauer."

"There's lice on your cactuses," said Stollenberg. "A little water wouldn't hurt them."

"What? What's that?"

"There's lice on your cactuses, can't you see?"

"Oh . . . it's perfectly possible. I don't know anything about them," said Heyne.

They wrote out their applications. As references Teichmann and Stollenberg put down Heyne's father, the minister, and Admiral Raeder. "They won't ask *him*," said Heyne.

"But they'll want to know about our graduation papers."

"Write in, 'Sent for.' "

"Nonsense. We'll never get them."

"I know. But you can write it in just the same. In wartime they have other things to think about, and that minister had better bestir himself if his son wants to be a Herr Doktor."

"It says you have to be seventeen to apply," said Teichmann, "and I'm only sixteen."

"The minister will take care of that," said Heyne. "You look twenty."

"And we'll get a first-class recommendation from our herring captain; we'll put that in right away," said Stollenberg.

Down below someone was playing the harmonium. And then they began to sing: "Now rest all forests, fields, and cities, now slumbers all the world. . . ." Heyne went down to the cellar and came back with three bottles of Beaujolais. They began to drink, and when the air-raid sirens started up, they didn't hear a thing. The singers down below kept right on too.

"That hymn has a lot of verses," said Teichmann, "I remember from when I was a kid."

"You must have a mighty good memory," said Heyne.

"Let's drown it out; I'll put on a record."

"Yes, put on something decent."

"No, something indecent."

Heyne put on a little record and turned the volume up high. A girl's voice sang, "What are you doing with your knee, dear Hans . . . "

"I'll go get Molly," said Heyne.

She joined in the drinking. She was dressed severely in a black dress with a white apron. When the singing resumed down below, Heyne put on dance records. Molly danced. Her movements were clumsy and uncertain and soon she fell flat, but it didn't hurt her; she was well upholstered. When she stood up and began on another drink, Heyne said, "You're boiled as it is. Better dance a little more, it'll sober you up."

She lifted up her skirt and tried to imitate a ballerina, but she kept falling down. Stollenberg couldn't take his eyes off her. Heyne smoked cigarettes and looked on indifferently as Molly stood up and fell down and stood up again and fell down again. When she fell a bit more heavily, he said, "Don't flop so loud, they're having church downstairs."

The sirens blew the all clear.

Teichmann opened a window. It had grown dark outside. The air was damp and sultry; it looked like rain. The people down below departed. When they were gone, the professor took a watering can and began to sprinkle his lawn.

"Should I take my clothes off?" asked Molly.

"You can wait," said Heyne.

In taking leave of them, Professor Heyne gave Stollenberg a tie. "Please don't misunderstand me; I just think it will be more becoming. And please take these little packages for comfort along the way."

Stollenberg put the tie right on. At the garden gate Heyne said, "Tomorrow morning I'll send the applications to Kiel;

we'll send the old man's recommendations later. I'll be on board by ten. Good night."

"Good night, all," said Teichmann.

When they were alone Stollenberg said, "I suggest we go see the ladies."

"Is that what Molly's gymnastics do to you?"

"Molly left me perfectly cold. I just don't see why we should look at the moon while Gerd is having himself a time."

"So it *is* Molly."

They rode out to the red-light district.

At first they had trouble getting their bearings. The whole place was dark, with the street lamps blacked out. The first house they tried was so crowded they would have had to stand in line, and they decided against that. "Come back in an hour, boys, there'll be room," the madam called after them.

"Can't wait that long," said Stollenberg, and managed not to blush.

"You seem to be in an awful hurry," said Teichmann, amazed at what a little red wine had done to Stollenberg. Outside the next house there was a group of seamen from the merchant marine—blockade runners, they said. They'd just come in from South America and now it was high time to do something for their health.

"Cut the bragging," said Teichmann.

"Who's bragging? We had to run away from English destroyers—twice."

"Must have been pretty slow destroyers," said Teichmann.

"Says you. We had to put on special emergency. One of the destroyers opened fire, but they didn't hit us."

"Your tub must have been mighty little if they didn't hit you," said Teichmann.

"You keep your dirty trap shut. She was plenty big. But the tonnage is secret."

"She was a rowboat," said Teichmann. "She was so small the Limeys couldn't even see you. They were just trying out their guns."

"Do you call a twelve-thousand-ton tanker a rowboat?"

"Oho! I thought the tonnage was secret."

Before the fight could start, Teichmann and Stollenberg moved on.

"If you're going to pick a fight with everybody we meet," said Stollenberg, "we'll never get our business done!"

In the next place they found seats at a small table. The girls were busy upstairs, and when one came down she was immediately taken over by one of the guests. Stollenberg ordered two schnapps, and when they came they were double.

"That's going to be expensive," said Teichmann.

"It's on me."

"Just the drinks?"

"No, both."

An old woman with two front teeth missing went from table to table saying if the gentlemen would just be patient for a moment, she had asked a colleague for reinforcements, and two very special young ladies were on their way; they were expected any minute.

To keep the customers' spirits up, a nude dancer appeared. But she was unavailable; the woman with the missing front teeth said no, she was sorry, her contract with the lady called only for artistic dances, the lady was legally married and was already expensive enough.

Stollenberg ordered more schnapps.

They were double again.

"I ordered plain ones."

"We only have double ones," said the waiter.

"It's all right with me," said Teichmann.

Stollenberg drank bottoms up.

"I guess the drink will make it easier," said Teichmann.

A pretty girl came past their table and smiled at them, but she was grabbed by a middle-aged guest who had been waiting longer.

"She'd do the trick," said Stollenberg.

"The smile was for me," said Teichmann, who had meanwhile downed his schnapps.

"You must have a parallax in your eye."

"There come the regulars. . . ."

The reinforcements appeared. One had an ungainly, spongelike body, enormous legs, and pointed knees.

Her associate was all skin and bones. "I'll take the blond one," she said, and sat down on Stollenberg's lap.

It's the bottom of the barrel, thought Teichmann, and couldn't help laughing at Stollenberg's face. Stollenberg sat motionless in his chair.

"I guess you haven't had anybody in a long time," said Teichmann.

"Is that how you greet a lady?" asked The Sponge.

"It's an outrage—an outrage," a man shouted. "I was here before those fellas."

"Eugene, don't shout so loud," said The Sponge, "you'll have trouble with Moonface."

From behind the bar there appeared a giant with an enormous belly, a bald head, and tiny protuding ears that looked like pot handles.

"Hiya, Moonface. Don't hurt him, he's boiled," said The Sponge.

"Mister," said Moonface, "this is a respectable house, we've never had any complaints here and I must request you to change your behavior."

"Shaddup," shouted Eugene, "you ass with ears."

"That remark," said Moonface, "I choose to ignore."

"Eugene, behave," said The Sponge, and to Moonface, "Eugene will apologize to you later."

Moonface vanished behind the bar. Eugene repeated that it was an outrage.

"Calm down, Eugene. We'll be finished with these boys in a minute, and then it'll be your turn," said the skinny one.

They demanded ten marks.

"You're out of your minds," said Teichmann.

"Big rush tonight. Special prices."

"We haven't got all that money," said Stollenberg.

"Well, as a special favor, nine."

"Five and not a pfennig more," said Teichmann.

"We don't do it so cheap."

"Five marks is a pile of money."

"Oh, all right. They're nice boys. It'll be a good beginning. What do you say, Marian?"

"That's got to cover the schnapps too," said Teichmann.

"Man! Pretty soon we'll be paying them to come upstairs with us," said the skinny one and began to scream.

"Girls, don't make a stink. They're recruits, they ain't got much dough," said an older man, a seaman from the merchant marine.

"We're in a minesweeper flotilla," said Teichmann.

"That's fine, boys. Well, there's a war on, don't give yourselves airs, take what you can get. I'll pay for your drinks. Now you're all set."

Teichmann said, "Thanks, pal. We're not exactly rolling in wealth. We haven't been . . ."

"Forget it."

Teichmann and Stollenberg stood up. Teichmann thought he'd be better off without baggage on this kind of expedition and tried to stow the professor's little package in his pocket.

"What's that stuff you got there?"

"We'll make you a present," said Stollenberg, who was sick of carrying the things around. The packages were unwrapped.

"Say, what is this? 'Light and strength for the days!' Ha, ha!"

"Looks like you've come straight from Sunday school."

"You can pipe down."

"They're perverts," Eugene shouted, "taking Bibles to the whorehouse."

A moment later he lay under the table; Teichmann had given him a poke on the chin.

Moonface came out from behind the bar with incredible speed. Teichmann thought, I can knock him out cold if I can get him in the right place. While he's out we'll beat it. He gave Moonface a knee in the hip. Moonface let out a yell and went down. Another chap whom Teichmann had never before set eyes on got a hook to the chin and lay down beside Moonface. Then just in time Teichmann saw the waiter coming up from behind with his dirty napkin ready to throw around Stollenberg's neck. Teichmann gave him a kick where it hurts most. The waiter clutched his anatomy, leaning

21

slightly forward; his chin was free, and Teichmann had time to get set for a solid swing to the jaw, which put the waiter out of commission. Moonface came to and flung a bottle at Stollenberg, who ducked, and the bottle struck a customer who was just coming in. The customer toppled over and Moonface got the side of Stollenberg's hand in the neck and went down again. Stollenberg pulled Teichmann toward the exit. "This is great!" said Teichmann. "Let's stick around." He tucked his tie in his shirt and put his wrist watch in his pocket. He lobbed a few chairs into the middle of the room and finished off with a little table. Stollenberg wielded a table leg indiscriminately at all who came near. Suddenly Teichmann saw the pretty girl who had cast the encouraging glances round her coming down the stairs, wearing only a short jacket and clogs, and he heard her shouting, "Cops!" The other didn't seem to hear her.

Teichmann and Stollenberg departed. Outside, a police car stopped and the cops swarmed out. Teichmann called out to them to take a look at the mess inside.

When Teichmann and Stollenberg had turned the nearest corner, they ran a few hundred yards and then ambled on toward the harbor. It was raining, but they didn't mind.

Next morning Stollenberg thrust his blond head over the edge of his bunk. "Rested well, I hope."

"Thank you," said Teichmann.

"I slept first-rate. Must have been the wine and schnapps, and that fight did me good. Say, those were nice people last night."

"Mighty nice."

"Those girls weren't anything special, were they?"

"I guess not."

"They weren't my type. That Eugene really had a disgusting mug."

"I doubt if it's improved any since."

"No. You really pasted him. Well, he won't be troubled with toothaches. Come to think of it, everybody got pasted but us. Great night, wasn't it?"

"It's all in how you take it," said Teichmann.

Heyne came in. "Morning, gentlemen. I trust you read

22

your Scriptures before you went to bed. Well, that's the way he is; hands out Bibles the way other people do flowers. It's a tic with him."

"There are worse things people can do," said Teichmann.

"Yes. For instance, the old man won't give me a recommendation. I was just in to see him. He'll write one for you but not for me, because of my dirty mouth, he says, and because I insulted Dora."

"Don't worry," said Teichmann, "I'll straighten that out."

"She isn't staying here any more."

"I know, but she's coming aboard for lunch. I'll talk to her."

"Don't crawl on your belly. I don't need his recommendation that bad. To tell you the truth, I'm still glad I told her what I thought of her."

"You're just browned off because you pulled a blank with her."

"I can get along fine without her."

"But once upon a time you felt like it and she for a change didn't."

"Old stuff. Anyway I gave her a piece of my mind."

Heyne had done more. He had taken a hammer and mounted on top of the captain's cabin. Straight over Dora's bunk, he had chipped paint where there wasn't any until Dora came running out of the cabin and told him to stop the racket. Then he had said, "The mate told me to chip paint." "I can't sleep with that noise." "You don't want to sleep." "Oh yes, I do." "Afterwards, maybe." "After what?" "After that." One word had led to another. In the end the old man had had to tell him to stop the noise. Heyne called this his shock therapy for Dora's sexual anomaly, and he had tried it several times.

Shortly before twelve Teichmann went to the pier. He bought a newspaper and sat down on a bollard. When he read that a general had swum across the Vistula, he thought it was a theater write-up, but it was the Polish campaign. Then he studied the sports page.

When he saw Dora, he folded his paper and slid off the bollard. She gave him her hand.

"Hiya, little one."

"You're looking pretty sharp."

"Little overhaul job."

"Looks like it."

"Yeah, I got a new one. He owns a café, classy joint, and we're getting married next week. But that don't mean you have to stand way over there."

"How old is he?"

"Oh, he's a little older than you. Sixty-two. But he looks like fifty."

"You'll finish him off pretty quick."

"Don't get fresh."

"And you'll be boss over the whole place?"

"I'll say. Real nice place. Two side rooms, all done over, four girls . . ."

"You got red wallpaper?"

"Why? Well, yes, it is kind of reddish."

"And the girls sleep in the house?"

"It's more convenient."

"Then it's all perfectly clear to me."

"It's not what you think."

"If it isn't now it soon will be."

"Well anyway, it'll be high-class. If you'd like to come in sometime, you'll be welcome. You know the ropes, I guess."

"Don't worry about me. But here's what I wanted to say: You won't be seeing the old man any more?"

"Today's the last time. We're parting on the best of terms. But what's that to you?"

"Right. I wanted to speak to you about my friend, Gerd Heyne. The old man won't give him a recommendation."

"He don't deserve one, either."

"Maybe you could put in a good word with the old man."

"You want me to be extra nice to him today, is that it?"

"I thought you might manage it just like that, without . . ."

"You can't do a thing in this world 'without,' and don't forget it. You never get nothing for free. But I'm not that way. For you I'd even do something for free, ha-ha. If it'll be

24

doing you a good turn, then by all means Heyne must have his recommendation."

"Thank you very much."

"It's nothing at all. Ta-ta, little one. And don't get drowned on that battle cruiser."

She went into the captain's cabin. When she was gone, Heyne appeared. He had been watching while Teichmann was talking to her.

"Well, will she fix it?"

"She'll fix it."

"Wouldn't have thought so."

"Sometimes you think wrong."

"But I won't thank her."

"She didn't ask you to."

"So my recommendation depends on whether the old man is satisfied with her today."

"Wouldn't say that."

"You seem to have a crush on that bag."

"Not true. But she's not a bad sort."

"That's one way of looking at it."

There were pork chops with beans and potatoes. Teichmann took three ladles full and two chops belonging to men on liberty. Then he lay down in his bunk and decided that so far the war was endurable. Stollenberg and Heyne also lay down in their bunks but they couldn't sleep; the older seamen drank schnapps and bellowed. When the schnapps from the canteen was drunk up, they went ashore and got more. The quality was poorer, but if you drank enough of it you got tight just the same.

"Medical examination tomorrow at eleven o'clock," shouted Boatswain Schwalber. "We shove off at ten. Some big-shot Navy doctor is in charge. So wash your necks."

"To hell with that!" shouted Pitt. "What's the Navy to us? I've been going to sea for twenty years and I'm not going to dress up for any of your white-collar sailors. I'm going to that examination in these here rags, and I'm going to show them my bare behind."

"You'll have to anyway," said Stüwe. "They'll want to see if you've got hammeroids."

25

"They'll see more than that," Pitt roared. His schnapps bottle was empty. Meckel was tight too; he pounded the table so hard with his fist that the bottles danced, and Hinsch cried out, "We thank our Führer." After he'd said it twice, they poured him into his bunk. Then he began to sing the "International." They threw a blanket over his face, but muffled cries of "Heil" could still be heard.

"The recommendations," said Heyne, and came in with three envelopes.

"Did the old man give them to you?"

"No, Dora. She typed them out on the machine; the old man only contributed his signature."

They read them.

"Why, they're first-rate," said Stollenberg. "Not a single mistake in spelling. My compliments."

In his envelope Teichmann found a visiting card with an address and, underneath, the words "Beginning next week my name will be Frau Holm." It's no skin off my ass, he thought.

They took little slips of paper and wrote on them, "Completion of application," and pinned them to the recommendations. They addressed the envelope to the Inspector of the Naval Training Academy in Kiel. Heyne took them ashore to mail.

Next morning it was announced that the medical inspection had been postponed for forty-eight hours, and likewise the issuing of uniforms that had been set for the afternoon. The drydocking of the ship was postponed for the fourth time. They realized that they were in the Navy.

After lunch they played rummy, for a tenth of a pfennig. After Heyne had played the jack of clubs three times in one game, they stopped. The others drank or put on cockroach races, but only a few of the roaches reached the finish line; most of them stopped by the wayside. When they didn't run fast enough, they were helped along with lighted matches, which was more than most of them could stand.

"Teichmann, get up here, you've got a visitor," cried Schmutzler, the cook.

On the pier stood Dora.

"Hiya, little one. Have you got a moment? Good. Now listen. In three days at the latest I've got to have eleven hundred marks; if I don't my place will be seized. So far I've collected six hundred. The rest is still missing."

"I haven't got any money right now, Dora; maybe sixty marks, no more."

"I thought maybe you knew somebody that had a little money."

"Except for a hymn-singing professor, I don't know a soul in Hamburg, and you could hardly expect him to finance your—your café."

"I'd make out a regular I.O.U."

"I believe you."

"Then there's nothing you could do?"

"No. Is it bad?"

"What do you mean bad? I just won't be married."

"And you absolutely want to."

"Yes, and for reasons that are none of your beeswax. But never mind, I'll manage. Ta-ta, little one."

"Good-by."

"Say, I wouldn't want you to think I was asking you for money on account of those recommendations. . . . I'm not like that. Honest."

"I assure you I had no such thought. And thanks for the recommendation."

"Are you satisfied?"

"Sure thing. So are Heyne and Stollenberg."

"I know. Heyne told me so when he thanked me, before I went ashore. He didn't tell me if you were satisfied. Well, good-by."

Heyne was lying in his bunk reading a newspaper.

"Greetings from Dora," said Teichmann.

"What's that bag want?"

"She wanted to know if I was satisfied with my recommendation, and why I didn't thank her like you."

"Bilge. And what else did she want?"

"Five hundred marks."

"Mighty expensive recommendations," said Heyne.

27

"It has nothing to do with that. If she hasn't got the money in three days her place will be seized."

"Five hundred M's ain't hay."

Boatswain Schwalber truck his head in: "Medical examination tomorrow morning at nine. Fall in at eight. I'll check to see if you've washed properly."

"Shut up," cried Stüwe. "If I'm not clean enough for their Lordships, they can . . ."

"Don't get excited, Stüwe. I meant the youngsters."

"You like to see them washing, eh? Well, one day they're going to beat the . . ."

"Stüwe, you're blond and simple. That's all anybody can say about you," said Schwalber.

"And you're a fruity blockhead," Heyne called after the boatswain.

Teichmann and Stollenberg went ashore. Teichmann bought a pack of tax-free cigarettes; Stollenberg purchased a pipe with "Guaranteed Genuine Briar" inscribed on it, and three packs of tobacco. They drank a few beers and then went back on board.

"They're having a bit of a brawl down below," said Boatswain Schwalber as they came up the gangplank. "Want to come aft?"

"We don't mind a little boozing," said Teichmann.

"Do what you like. We fall in at eight A.M. I say no more."

"Guess we can remember that."

Pitt, Löbbermann, whom they called Jellyfish, Stüwe, and Osterbuhr were treating the crew. "Ah, the babies! Have a drink, it's all on us," they said to Teichmann and Stollenberg. The older men had a long head start and before the two of them were tight, Pitt, Löbbermann, and Stüwe lay under the table. Toward midnight Teichmann slipped under the table. Stollenberg sat down beside him. Later Stollenberg and Osterbuhr carried Teichmann to his bunk. Then Osterbuhr filled up Teichmann's shoes. It stinks something terrible, I've got to pour it out, that's the least I can do, thought Stollenberg after he had lain down. But he felt as if he were on a merry-go-round, except that you couldn't get off because it didn't stop, and no one was collecting any money.

Teichmann's roaring woke him up. Teichmann had one shoe on; the other had run over when he tried to put his foot in. "Who was that? I want to know who it was." "Osterbuhr," said Stollenberg, not realizing what he was starting. Teichmann went to Osterbuhr's bunk and clouted his face so hard that the bones crunched. Osterbuhr cried for help and after a while just lay there moaning. Osterbuhr had an upper bunk; Teichmann hit his fist on the overhead as he was swinging, and that added to his fury.

"Hey, Hans, stop, you'll kill him," called Stollenberg, and got up out of his bunk.

"He's had enough," said Teichmann, and poured the contents of his shoe in Osterbuhr's face. Osterbuhr choked, but said nothing. He didn't seem to be conscious. If I could only throw up, thought Teichmann, I'd fill Osterbuhr's shoes.

Teichmann was unpredictable when he had been drinking. He was not one of those fortunate souls who only have to stick a finger down their throats to get rid of the alcohol. He had little experience in drinking; he hadn't started until after leaving school. He'd only had a bit of champagne at family festivities at home, and that had never affected him. But he had got good and drunk at his first class jamboree; in this condition he and Stollenberg had rung the doorbell of their most detested teacher, thrown a sack over his head, and beat the stuffings out of him. A hole had developed in the sack, the teacher had recognized them, and two days later they had been expelled from school. At Teichmann's suggestion they had signed up for the deep-sea fishery.

"If the boot was full up, it couldn't have been just Osterbuhr," said Stollenberg.

"Name the others and I'll knock them for a loop."

"Let's wash out that boot, Hans."

They took a string and slipped it through the loop in the boot top and hung the boot over the side. When they had given it a good rinse, Stollenberg went back to the crew's quarters. Teichmann stayed on deck. But he couldn't manage to throw up. He leaned over the side, but the best he could do was to gag a bit. Now and then he spat, and the whole time he shivered. Finally he drew a deep breath and held it, remembering how it stank of schnapps and cigarette butts down below. Then he slid down the hatch to the crew's quarters, dropped into his bunk, and drew the curtain. Then the schnapps came up. He pressed his mouth tight, but it came out through his nose.

It was seven o'clock when Heyne turned up on his bicycle. Under his arm he carried a cake tin containing four ampoules packed in excelsior. He leaned his bicycle against a bollard, then carried the can carefully on board and put it behind the winch. Then he went to the crew's quarters and awakened Pitt, Löbermann, Stüwe, and Meckel.

They went up on deck and Heyne gave them the ampoules. Each one paid him a hundred marks. They weren't real ampoules, just glass tubes in which Havana cigars had been packed. Heyne had taken them from his father's cigar cabinet.

"Do you think it'll work?" asked Meckel.

"Absolutely," said Heyne. "My uncle has enough sugar in his urine to open a candy shop. The Medical Board will turn you down as diabetics. Even though he's a general, my uncle was discharged from the Army for diabetes."

"You've just come from Nienstedten?"

"Yes. I told you my uncle gets up early in the morning. I greased his maid's palm, went into his bedroom, and emptied his chamberpot while he was taking his morning walk. You've got to shake the ampoules a little before you pour them into the test tubes they give you. And don't get caught."

"Don't worry about that. So that's the deal."

"A hundred M's isn't very much for a service like this."

"It's what we agreed on," said Pitt.

"Then I'll just have to get another couple of guys to cover my costs."

"No, you won't," said Löbbermann. "If there's too many of us, it'll look fishy."

"O.K., Jellyfish. Let's each give him another ten marks. It won't make no difference to us now."

"Twenty," said Heyne.

"All right. But there it stops."

Now, thought Heyne with pleasure, I won't have to fork over my own hundred; as a precaution he had asked his father for a hundred marks. Then he went ashore, straddled his bicycle, and was off.

Shortly before it was time to fall in for the medical examination, he was back. On the march to the recruiting station he told Teichmann and Stollenberg that Dora had her five hundred marks, and how he'd got the money. They didn't believe a word of it. "It's the gospel truth," said Heyne. "I've got an uncle, my father's brother. He's a general and he was discharged from the Army for diabetes; he lives in Nein-stedten . . ."

"And he obligingly loaned you some of his urine?"

"Well, no, that's the only hitch in the story. He just provided the inspiration. Of course I wasn't out in Nienstedten. Good God, it never even entered my head to pedal all the way out there. I generously contributed my own urine."

"Amazing what you do for that whore," said Teichmann.

"I didn't do it for her. Just for the hell of it. For the fun of crossing up those clunks."

"They'll clunk *you* if they get wise."

"I'll be far, far away by that time. Last night I phoned our undersecretary friend in Kiel, and he said the thing could be fixed. He'll call up again this afternoon."

Teichmann reflected that a fight was due anyway on account of Osterbuhr, so it was all the same. Osterbuhr couldn't go to the examination. His nose and lower jaw were broken, most of his teeth were missing, and his eyes were closed. The mate had sent him to the hospital after Boatswain Schwalber had washed his face. "That's no way to treat a shipmate," Schwalber had said, "That's going too far."

It was three hours before their turn came. Then it went quickly. The examination was friendly and superficial. Only one of the doctors tried to be conscientious. He was a young fellow; maybe that was why he shouted, or maybe because his work didn't satisfy him. The men had to lean forward, thrusting out their bare behinds and parting the cheeks with their hands, so the doctor could look in as far as possible.

Three men came up at once. Ostensibly because the mate and Löbbermann didn't hold out their cheeks far enough, the doctor roared, "I'll tear you open to the larynx, you lugheads." In reply the mate emitted such a blast of wind that Teichmann, who was in the room with them, thought the walls were shaking. Before the doctor had recovered from the explosion, Löbbermann answered in the same terms. The blast was not quite so powerful, but it was adequate.

For a moment the doctor was speechless. Then he rushed into the next room where the head physician was at work and described the incident. Their behavior had been bestial, he reported; they must be punished, what should he do?

"Open the window," said his superior, adding that when nature demanded its rights nothing could be done.

"But they did it intentionally," screamed the doctor. "What's more, they did it in unison."

"In that case," said the head physician, "they are artists. You've got to hand it to them."

Next they went to the room where the urine was examined. Pitt and Stüwe were standing outside, waiting for Heyne. They announced their intention of killing him. But Heyne kept out of sight. Stollenberg had told him in the ear-nose-throat room what was in the offing. Heyne said his examination had long since been completed and he was going home.

Next morning as they were washing down the deck, Molly appeared with greetings from Herr Heyne. Herren Teichmann and Stollenberg, she said, must come to Blankenese at once; the gentleman from Kiel had telephoned, and if Herr Heyne's bicycle was still there, they should kindly bring it with them.

2

The check-in in Kiel was interesting.

First there was a medical examination; then they had to write a theme on the topic "What would happen if the moon were made of cheese?" Next each of them had to make a speech. Teichmann spoke about natural philosophy. Heyne had given him Haeckel's *Riddle of the Universe* to read, and on the way to Kiel Teichmann had copied out a number of unusual foreign words. In the first sentences of his lecture he managed to drag them in—in addition to some others that he'd known before. That was enough for the examining commission.

Heyne, who came up last, spoke about the history of naval warfare. Alone of all the speakers, he folded his arms across his chest; the others had modestly held their hands behind their backs.

"What is the purpose of that posture?" asked the chairman of the commission sharply.

"It seemed to me that it would be tedious if all the speakers were to stand in the same way. Besides, this was Napoleon's favorite posture, and he wasn't a bad speaker."

The chairman took the monocle out of his eye and said, "You don't seem to have an inferiority complex."

"If I had, I wouldn't have picked the Navy," said Heyne.

The gentlemen of the examining commission made sour faces, but they listened attentively to his speech, and Heyne spoke like a professor. Stollenberg wasn't in the same group. He had refused to prepare any speech, although Heyne had suggested a dozen or more subjects.

"What did you talk about?" Heyne asked when they met in the dining room of the *Milwaukee,* a former luxury liner.

"About herring fishing."

33

"I can see already that you're cut out to be an admiral."

"If I hadn't known that I wouldn't have exposed myself to all this misery."

On the second day of the examination a tall gawky fellow came to their table and introduced himself: "Count Bülow." They sat down, and before they had even begun to eat, the newcomer said, "Let me buy you a round of drinks. I need a strong drink; I flunked the exam."

They drank a round of Korn. When the glasses were empty Teichmann ordered another round. "If we keep on like this," said Stollenberg, "I take a dim view of the psychological test this afternoon."

"Couldn't be too dim," said Bülow. "I've had it and they threw me out. But I'll be glad to tell you how they do it. Everyone doesn't get the psychological, you know. You've still got a chance of missing it."

"Better be on the safe side," said Heyne. "Go ahead, tell us."

"Well, first there's a character who rattles off a list of numbers fast as he can. Every time he said an even number I was supposed to raise my right arm; when it was an uneven number, I was to raise my left arm. If a number was divisible by three, I was supposed to stamp my right foot. When a prime number came up, I was supposed to wag my head. No joking, gentlemen, it was like the bughouse. I asked the psychologist what it was good for; he said it showed whether you knew which way was up. Then I had to talk on all sorts of subjects, and they interrupt you right in the middle with trick questions to get you balled up. One of them wanted to know what color underwear my girl-friend wore. I told them that when I was with my girl-friend she usually didn't wear any underwear, and anyway we always put the light out because she was kind of bashful. The psychologists grinned and seemed satisfied. I thought, Well, if that's what they like, I can give them plenty more of the same. Then some dried-out old psychologist asked me what I'd do if I weren't taken in the Navy. I said I'd go to the Air Force. And supposing they don't take you in the Air Force? Then I'll settle for the Army. Very well, and what would you do if they rejected you, too?

34

I'd try the Waffen-SS. But it's possible that the SS won't take you either. Then what will you do? Well, I said, then I'll buy me a wooden head and get to be a Navy psychologist. I was just good and sick of their stupid questions. At this point they threw me out. As I said, I can only hope that you miss the bughouse. Your health."

When the drinks were finished, Bülow handed out coffee beans. "Chew them slowly and your alcohol barometer will go way down. If you chew them very slowly, you'll have real fair weather. And now much luck."

They assembled outside the building that Bülow had called the bughouse. An officer appeared and said that the names he was going to call out had passed the examination and didn't have to take the psychological. Those who so desired could stay in Kiel and go to Stralsund next day where the training school was. But in one week at the latest all had to be in Stralsund.

"Count von Bülow" was the first name. A little later "Stollenberg" was called out, and shortly afterward "Heyne." Heyne went aboard the *Milwaukee* to notify Bülow.

The remaining candidates were divided into groups of four for the psychological test. Teichmann's name was not called. He had to report to a middle-aged officer, a lieutenant commander, who inquired about the certificate of paternal approval that was necessary for voluntary enlistment since Teichmann had not yet reached the minimum age.

Teichmann said that he would be seventeen on September 29, and that his father was dead. The officer wanted to know what his mother thought of his enlistment. Teichmann told him that his mother had remarried and was in Switzerland. The officer asked if she knew he had volunteered. Teichmann said his mother knew very little about him altogether since her remarriage. The officer still couldn't make head or tail of the story; Teichmann was embarrassed and said that since his father's death, he had scarcely heard from her and that he wouldn't be missed. The officer thought it over for a while and finally said Teichmann could go to Stralsund too.

They sat drinking in the bar of the *Milwaukee*. Everyone drank everyone else's health. They drank everything available in no particular order. They forgot to go for supper. Later they drank brotherhood, and from then on it was bottoms up.

At ten o'clock Heyne was full up; Teichmann had to take him to the station. Heyne had decided to take the last train to Hamburg and return to Kiel next day. They had to run for the train and that cleared Heyne's head a bit. Teichmann sat him down in a first-class compartment and just barely had time to get off the train before it started.

On the way back he sauntered along the harbor and watched the boats bringing the workers to the wharves for the night shift. The city was completely blacked out. Only the moon wasn't blacked out and looked like a butterball. Then suddenly the moon was gone. There were no clouds in the sky; Teichmann couldn't see what had happened to the moon. He felt like asking one of the couples sitting on the benches, but they were too busy with themselves to worry about the moon. He went on his way and then the moon was back in place again. Teichmann saw that it had hidden behind a barrage balloon. Then he noticed a number of balloons and had the impression that they were going up. He had only taken a few steps more when the sirens began to scream and outside in the bay the torpedo boats began to wail too. Searchlights played over the city. Teichmann heard a few people running. Then the planes were there. The heavy AA opened fire. It made such a racket that Teichmann at first thought it was bombs, but it was only 88-millimeter AA.

The planes circled the city but remained out of range of the AA fire. Only two or three attempted to fly high through the AA barrier and attack the docks. They dropped their bombs too soon and turned away. The bombs fell in the water. For the first time Teichmann heard the sound that falling bombs make. The screaming of the bombs grew shorter, the pitch became lower; he saw columns of water springing up in the harbor basin and coming toward him; he was knocked down, and he felt the back of his head striking something hard.

He pulled himself to his feet. He didn't know what had happened. Something must have happened, he thought, and for a moment he felt funny. He heard someone shouting "Gertrude." There was a roaring in his ears as though a waterfall were passing over him. Intermittently he heard the cry "Gertrude." Now he saw the man who was shouting. The man stood a few yards away from him, screaming "Gertrude" and again "Gertrude." It was more like a howl: "Gertru-u-de." That was all the man did. The woman was lying on the ground.

"It don't hurt," she said. "It don't hurt at all."

Another man ran over to her. Teichmann went too.

"She got some of it," said the other man and snapped on a flashlight, holding one hand in front of it to dim it. The woman was bleeding. The wound was in the right knee. The leg was twisted a hundred and eighty degrees, the heel of the right foot lay beside the toe of the left, and the two feet were parallel. The man who belonged to her stood by, crying "Gertru-u-ude." The woman sat up and saw everything. "It don't hurt," she said, and then she called out to the man, "Stop your screaming. It's awful."

The man with the flashlight laid the woman down on her back. Teichmann was holding her leg in his hands. A bomb splinter had pierced her bone; the metal was still hot. Teichmann had wanted to turn the leg back into its normal position; he had apparently turned it the wrong way, and at that very moment the man had laid the woman down. Now Teichmann had the leg in his hand.

The woman was carrying a handbag with a shoulder strap. Teichmann tore off the strap and tried to tie up the leg stump with it. When he pulled the strap tight, it tore.

"I'll go get a car," said the man with the flashlight.

"Gertru-ude," screamed the other.

"Make it quick," said Teichmann.

The man dropped his flashlight and ran. Teichmann took the woman's leg in his hands and squeezed. The blood stopped gushing from the stump and merely dripped to the ground. He pressed the leg tight till his hands hurt, and because he was tired he laid his head on the woman's stomach. The woman lay perfectly still.

"Douse that light," someone cried. Teichmann kicked the flashlight out with his heels. He felt as if he were deaf; he knew that the man beside him was still shouting the woman's name, but he no longer heard it. There was a beating in his ears, as though someone were pounding a membrane with an enormous drumstick and trying to burst it.

When two men came and took the woman away, he was frightened at first and then happy. He didn't know how long he had knelt over her. The men laid her on a stretcher after briefly busying themselves with her leg, and shoved the stretcher into an ambulance. Then they slammed the doors, got into the front seat, and drove off. As the door slammed, Teichmann's hearing returned.

Beside him the man who had been screaming "Gertrude" lay on the ground, staring at the leg; the ambulance men had forgotten it. Teichmann gave the leg a kick and it fell in the water. When it splashed, the man stood up, said his name, which Teichmann didn't catch, and held out his hand.

Teichmann wanted to wipe his bloody hand on his pants, but the man said, "I don't mind, it's my own blood."

"Oh," said Teichmann and could think of nothing else to say.

"It was my daughter," said the man. "I only had this one child, do you see?"

It occurred to Teichmann only later that the man had spoken of his daughter in the past tense. While he was wondering whether or not the woman was bound to die—and he didn't think so—a passenger car drove up. A man in uniform got out. "Has something happened here?" he asked.

Teichmann nodded. The question struck him as so absurd that he wanted to rub his bloody hands on the man's face.

"Oh, there's blood," said the man in uniform and frowned. "Quite a lot of blood, isn't it?"

Too bad, thought Teichmann, that the leg isn't lying there any more.

"Was it bad? I mean was somebody killed?"

The man to whom the flashlight belonged was back again.

"Where's my flashlight?"

It was lying in the pool of blood. The man picked it up.

"There's her shoe."

Teichmann picked up the shoe and stuck it in his coat pocket.

"I wish to know if someone has been killed," said the man in uniform briskly.

"That's her father over there," said Teichmann.

The man in uniform stepped back into the car. The driver started the motor, but then the man in uniform got out again and said, "We've got to grit our teeth, comrades, we . . ."

"I beg your pardon?" asked Teichmann, who had not understood.

"Turn off the motor. We've got to save gas," said the man in uniform to his driver. And to Teichmann, "We have a war on our hands and we've got to grit our teeth. But we will be victorious."

The man in uniform went back to his car. When the engine was running again and he was sitting beside the driver, he cried out, "God punish England!"

The man with the flashlight cried, "Heil Hitler," and to Teichmann he said, "Now there's an official who takes an interest in his national comrades."

"Yes, I suppose he does," said Teichmann. "But he would have saved more gas if he'd left the engine running. It takes more gas to start up than to let the motor idle a while."

"Man, I envy you your nerves."

"Why?"

"Oh, I mean . . . well, Heil Hitler."

On the *Milwaukee,* Teichmann asked the night steward if he could take a bath. "Certainly, sir, of course," said the steward.

They went up to A deck, where the first-class cabins with baths were. The steward said, "Maybe you'd better leave your clothes out here. I'll send up a Chinese to clean them while you're bathing."

"Good idea," said Teichmann. "You can tell him to take his time, I'll be in that water for at least an hour."

Teichmann let the warm water run. The tub was made of green tile; the whole bathroom was green, and he found it very pleasant. First he washed the blood off his hands, then he undressed and laid out his clothes in the cabin.

He lay for half an hour in the hot water. He loved this bath. It was like a new experience—beads of sweat came to his forehead, and the clear hot water brought him strength and peace. The perfumed soap gave off the scent of an exotic flower, and he squeezed it in his fist like modeling clay. Then he soaped himself until his whole body was covered with thick, flaky foam and lay back in the water. After a while he pulled the stopper. As he was about to shower off, he discovered a package of bath salts. He filled the tub again, shook in the bath salts, and lay again in the water for a while. Then he let it out and showered hot and cold by turns. At the end he spent several minutes under the cold shower.

When he opened the door to the cabin, he saw a Chinese setting down a lady's shoe beside his own freshly polished boots. The Chinese was grinning shamelessly. Before Teichmann could say anything, the yellow face vanished. He opened the porthole and threw the lady's shoe overboard.

His clothes were clean, and there was a crease in his pants when he put them on. He laid ten marks on the table, joined the others in the bar, and proceeded to get drunk.

The alcohol did him good. He drank with the awareness that he had lived through something and come out alive. That's the only way to take things, he philosophized into the void. With that state of mind you can get through the war. Then he lit a cigar, and even though he felt sick he smoked it to the end.

"Man!" somebody said to him. "What are you sniffling about? You homesick for Mamma so soon?"

"No—it's the smoke."

The reception in Stralsund wasn't exactly cordial.

At the gate they were taken in hand by some noncoms who formed them into a marching column. They marched through the city in step, with their luggage on their backs. The heat was crushing. When Heyne wanted to take a taxi, a sergeant forbade it with the remark that this was the Navy and not the Salvation Army. Heyne invited the sergeant to ride along in the cab but it didn't do any good. They all had to walk. Now all we need, thought Teichmann, is for them to make us sing, but this was not done; the noncoms only insisted that the civilians should keep step. Meanwhile it

40

had got around that the barracks weren't in Stralsund but in Dänholm.

Dänholm is an island containing barracks, a mess hall, several gymnasiums, an armory, a few trees and bushes, an abundance of grass and sand, and absolutely nothing else. In the morning a few women wearing woolen stockings or none at all came over to work in the kitchen, and in the afternoon they went back to their families in Stralsund. The boots soon found out that they were all happily married.

The first weeks, while the companies were still forming, were pretty soft. The recruits were not permitted to leave the island, but they were allowed to go swimming and to sail the cutters that lay in the harbor.

On the fourth day Teichmann caused a little mishap. First his cutter made a turn that he hadn't counted on and was driven into a fish net; then it was almost rammed by a yawl. "Why don't you play sailor in your bathtub, you jugheads!" Teichmann shouted at the occupants of the yawl. He was furious over so much hard luck at once. The yawl should have given way, since she was in the port tack.

Next day the boots were forbidden to sail the cutters. Teichmann was called up to the battalion adjutant, who informed him that the yawl had been handled by the wife of the harbor commander, who had remembered the number of the cutter and taken umbrage at the word "jughead." She demanded a written apology from Teichmann. Teichmann declared that he hadn't known the occupants of the yawl were ladies. Even his argument that the ladies must have been flat-chested to be indistinguishable from men in their sailing clothes didn't help him any. The adjutant insisted that Teichmann apologize. Heyne helped him with his letter of apology, which included the words "and so I fell a victim to your boyish build."

When the four boot companies were full strength, training began. Teichmann, Stollenberg, and Bülow were in the first platoon of the second company, Heyne in the fourth platoon. It was thanks to their early arrival in Dänholm that they got into the same company.

Heyne was the first in the company to "attract notice." The

clothing-issue corporal threw him a jacket that was much too tight, a pair of pants that were much too long, and a frayed sweater, crying at each throw, "Fits." Heyne threw the articles back one at a time, saying at each throw, "Doesn't fit." He spoke these words with benign calm, as though it was the most natural thing in the world. The corporal roared. He was a staff corporal; compared to him, Heyne was so much dirt, and this justified the corporal in all his shouting. Heyne said, "You don't have to work up a tantrum. Give me something that fits or keep your nasty rags." The corporal called Heyne a snot-nose brat. "I'll smash your face in if you don't shut up," said Heyne. The threat sounded eloquent, but it was out of place, especially as it was so loud that the clothing sergeant heard it. "Give me your name," he said to Heyne. "I'm putting you on report."

That Saturday morning at ten o'clock Heyne reported to the company commander.

Saturday morning was general cleanup. The recruits wore fatigues, canvas shoes, and sailor caps, and thus attired Heyne appeared punctually at ten o'clock in the orderly room. When his corporal saw him, he asked, "What are you doing here?"

"Reporting to the company commander."

"Are you the joker that was bitching in clothing issue? And you report to the company commander in that rig? Man, you must be off your rocker." The corporal took a deep breath. "If you know what's good for you, you'll get out of here quick and get into regulation uniform. On the double."

Heyne ran to his barracks and soon reappeared in field gray, steel helmet on his head, and bearing his rifle.

"Christ Almighty," cried the corporal. "What are you doing with that shooting iron?"

"I thought it was part of . . ."

"You will leave the thinking to the horses, they've got bigger heads. Leave the smoke pole outside."

The corporal went into the orderly room. Heyne heard him saying to the topkick, "Here comes the man who keeps the company commander waiting."

Heyne lengthened the sling and hung his rifle on the hook affixed to the orderly room door.

Then he knocked and cautiously opened the door. Inside the room he saw his corporal, the first sergeant, his platoon leader, and an officer with two stars on his shoulder straps. That must be the company commander, he thought. The company commander had only come back from leave on Friday night; the recruits had not yet set eyes on him.

Heyne took off his steel helmet as if it were a top hat, made a slight bow in the direction of the CO, and said, "If you please, Heyne, Hamburg."

After this introduction a dense silence fell. Heyne looked at the other men and saw that the corporal had averted his eyes, emitting a soft moan. The topkick was staring grimly into a corner of the room; the platoon leader was squinting timidly toward the company commander, shifting from one foot to another.

The company commander grinned.

Then he said to Heyne in the same tone, "I too should like to introduce myself: Lieutenant Wegener, your company commander."

"I'm delighted to meet you," said Heyne.

The company commander said, "The pleasure is all mine. In all my military career I have never met so complete a civilian as you."

Heyne became uncertain. "I am sorry if I have behaved awkwardly."

"Not at all," said the company commander. "Your behavior hasn't been awkward in the least, just a little bit unmilitary. Didn't they tell you what it is to go on report?"

"No, sir."

"Very well, I'll let you off this time; but if you should be put on report again, we will not just make conversation. Do you understand?"

"Yes, sir."

Heyne put on his helmet, raised his arm in what was supposed to be a salute, and left the room with a right-face. In his joy at having got off so easily he closed the door a bit violently, and the butt of his rifle thudded against the door.

He was about to run off in a panic when the company commander stepped out into the corridor. "Don't you know that the rifle is the soldier's bride? Were you going to run off and leave your bride in the lurch?"

Heyne hesitated for a moment; then he said, "My bride isn't in a bad spot, sir."

The company commander couldn't help laughing. Below the hook where Heyne's rifle was hanging, a sign had been tacked up: "For the Company Commander only."

"My dear boy, with me you can permit yourself such remarks. But with other superiors I urgently advise you to keep your mouth in check or I predict some very rough going."

The prophecy was only too sound. The platoon leader and the corporal had it in for him. They were not quick to forget his manner of introducing himself to the company commander, and above all they did not forget that he had conversed with the CO over their heads, so to speak, as though noncoms were air. They made life hard for him whenever possible, and that was often. Heyne didn't mind, although he spent more time crawling than walking. He knew that what they had against him was his intelligence, and that gave him no little satisfaction.

Hard times began for his friend Teichmann as well. He was the second tallest in the company, and that was no joke when it came to gymnastics. It took him longer than the little fellows to lie down and stand up. "We'll soon cut that beanpole down to size," shouted Reimann, corporal of the first squad, and made Teichmann march around the drill ground by himself, with shouldered rifle. When his tongue hung out after a dozen rounds, Reimann asked him, "Do you feel that you're being treated unjustly? Or do you think we're riding you?"

"Right, Corporal," said Teichmann with a grin. He never turned off that grin, although it raised Reimann to white heat.

"You're mistaken, friend. Very much mistaken. The purpose of all this is training, understand, just training."

Purely for the sake of training they drove the boots over the scaling wall and made them crawl on their elbows and chased them cross country for hours in gas masks. Anyone caught loosening the filter on his gas mask to keep from

44

smothering in his own sweat got three days in the guard-house. Just for training they made the squad run down a steep hill with fixed bayonets, and at the steepest place the squad leader shouted, "Lie down." In this exercise a few of the men regularly received bayonet cuts. While the injured were taken to the infirmary, Master Sergeant Semmler, leader of the first platoon, delivered his traditional speech about the virtues of the German military in general and of the Navy man in particular, and the word "toughness" occurred at least twice in every sentence. He stood out in front of his platoon, put on an innocent look, and said in the tones of a kindly, sympathetic soul, "Comrades, I want you to get me straight. I've got three months to teach you what they take a year to learn in the Army. Infantry drill is a serious business; it's the soldier's ABC, his alphabet you might say. Anybody that thinks he's going to have it soft in the Navy has another think coming. And so now let's get ahead with our work. I assume that as officer candidates you have enough gray matter to understand infantry training. When I get through with you cadets, you're going to be model infantry-men, virtuosos I might say. You can rely on that. So will you please not make things hard for me with your sloppy ways."

After this little talk he ordered gas masks on and fix bay-onets, and Semmler's circus continued.

After two more hours of double-timing, they were all in fine shape. Then Semmler had his platoon march around the drill ground singing, "It's wonderful to be a soldier . . ." and be-cause Teichmann couldn't stop grinning he was made to trot around the marching platoon in circles like a sheepdog. At the end of this exercise he was still grinning. Semmler made him run around the drill ground three more times, while the platoon had to wait for him. Teichmann ran as fast as he could. When he had completed his third circuit and saw his comrades' faces, he grinned no more. Pleased with this pedagogic success, Master Sergeant Semmler dismissed the platoon.

Afterwards Heyne said, "What did you expect? They get

45

their two hundred and fifty marks a month and that's the end of it. You can't expect any better for that money. . . ."

"But they're sadists," said Stollenberg.

"Oh no," said Heyne. "They're just dumb. To be a real sadist you've got to have a head on your shoulders. These fellows are village idiots. For that trade—and it is a trade—you need village idiots. They have no complexes. The main thing to remember is this: the whole business is completely senseless. It's even senseless to think about it, let alone get excited. Thinking is the worst thing you can do. The lighter your pack the better you march, and that goes for intellectual baggage too. That's what you've got to remember. When you think, you show the corporals your weak spot, and that's the spot they step on with their regulation boots. And you're the losers."

Heyne was pleased with himself for having sized up the situation, but he was none too happy about it.

Teichmann's cleanup detail was the noncoms' recreation hall. This was a place that no noncom ever set foot in. When they had nothing to do, they lay in their bunks and slept. They spent evenings and week ends in town. Morning, noon, and night Teichmann had to dust for fifteen minutes. One of the principal articles of furniture was a glass-fronted case full of books. There was no key to the case and no one missed it. Out of boredom Teichmann learned the titles by heart from left to right.

On Saturday there was general cleanup. At least three buckets of water were supposed to be used in every room, and the noncoms saw to it that the men took their quota of water. Teichmann drew his three buckets and poured them out of the window onto the lawn in front of the rec hall. Then he sprinkled the floor with the help of an old tin can and wiped the splashes away with the swab. This made the floor look as if it had been wet and wiped dry. The whole operation took no more than ten minutes; it was safe because the duty sergeant didn't get around to the rec hall until the tail end of his inspection. On the third Saturday the company commander turned up unexpectedly at the noncoms' rec hall; barely an hour had elapsed since the beginning of the cleaning period; three hours were allotted to the task.

"You're the only man in the whole company who knows how to swab a floor dry. Already finished, eh?"

"Yes, sir."

"Your name?"

"Teichmann, seaman second-class."

"Very well, I'll remember that in case there's something to be done in my quarters. You seem to work quickly."

The company commander was well liked. After this encounter Teichmann didn't feel too comfortable. Why, that's a common swindle I'm pulling, he thought, but on the other hand the CO might devote a little more time to his company. But he had married recently. The recruits had heard it from his own lips in the course of a lecture informing them among other things that nowadays officers' wives were no longer addressed by their husbands' titles. Several of the boots had greeted his wife as *Frau Kapitän-leutnant*. His wife was highly regarded in the company, if only because she was the only woman living in Dänholm. But so far only a few members of the company had seen her. Bülow said she was a cute little doll. And Stollenberg had replied that it would be better if she were a little less cute and would leave her husband more time for his company. For when the CO appeared on the drill ground, the noncoms grew perceptibly milder.

One day a near-miracle happened: Corporal Reimann of the first squad became almost amiable. Up till that time, whenever Reimann had spent the night in Stralsund, his men were in for trouble next day. He was no Apollo, and it seemed that female company was a great financial drain on him. Or perhaps the drain was more than financial. In any case he was always in a horrible humor next day. Nobody could please him: the portly Sümmermacher was a "stuffed pig" and the slender Rehberg was "too lazy to eat." But when the bottle took the place of women as the companion of his evening in town, he allowed his squad to take full cover in the brush next day, and no company commander and no platoon leader could find Reimann's men. The first squad of the second company slept in the brush until training time was over. Unfortunately, Reimann's friendship with alcohol was only intermittent.

It was Stollenberg who decided to help Reimann organize his free time. He asked his father to send him a case of wine. When the case arrived, he asked the corporal where he could store it, because the boots were forbidden to keep liquor in the barracks. "Maybe we could store the wine in your quarters, sir. I'd be very grateful to you. To pay the storage, I'd be very glad, sir, to offer you a bottle a day for your own use."

"A bottle a day? Did you say 'a bottle a day,' Stollenberg?"

"Yes, sir."

"Man, the case won't last long at that rate."

"We can get another, sir."

"Who's 'we?' "

"My father and me, sir. My father's a wine dealer."

"Request granted."

It was one of Reimann's habits, when he returned home at night from his devotions to Venus, to come into the barrack rooms shouting, "Everybody up. Forward march, sing us a song." Whereupon the recruits had to sing, "From heaven on high I come . . ." Then he commanded, "Under the beds, march, march—a song," and from under the beds resounded the chorale, "In deep distress, I cry to thee, O Lord, hear my entreaty . . ." The one who sang loudest was the first permitted to go back to sleep.

Now there was an end to such sport. Instead, Reimann would stagger into Stollenberg's room at about midnight and say, "Ah, to hell with the broads, eh, boy? What I want is another drink. O.K. Stollenberg?"

"I'm flattered that you find the wine to your taste, sir," came Stollenberg's voice from his bunk. And next day Reimann's squad took to the bushes.

Two days before induction one man was bilged. It was a little innocent-looking fellow from the third platoon, by the name of Premaier. He received a written notice to the effect that he did not possess the characteristic qualities of a cadet. Instead of scouring pots in the kitchen, he had reached under the skirts of one of the cooks, and had had the bad luck to hit on a happily married one.

Premaier's career as a cadet was ended. He assured his comrades that he was innocent; he had only picked up the wrong skirt; there was one of the cooks who liked this kind of thing, but he was a gentleman and hadn't mentioned the lady when he reported to the CO.

After this incident there was still more saltpeter in the food, and the training was made still stiffer. The result was that next day three men of the first platoon went on sick call. The first was Teichmann. The man ahead of him, Sümmermacher, son of a Westphalian landowner, over six feet tall and weighing two hundred and twenty pounds, the biggest and heaviest man in the company, had accidentally stepped on his hand when the squad was lying on the ground and Reimann ordered them to get up. At the infirmary the medics treated Teichmann's hand with iodine and bandaged it. When they had finished, Bülow reported. He had a bayonet wound in the thigh administered by the man beside him. An hour later three men carried Heyne in. He was unconscious. That morning he had fainted while getting a shot. The medics had been pumping impressive quantities of serum into the men's chests with the tenderness of butchers sticking pigs. "I'll bet you get a medal for that," Heyne had said. Their answer had been to double his dose of serum. He had had to be carried out. Although the right side of his chest developed a swelling that would have done honor to a farmer's daughter, he had to take part in training. According to the three men who brought him in, he had suddenly keeled over in rifle drill. A doctor ordered two hours of bed rest. The same morning still another boot turned up at the infirmary; his name was Vorhölzer, he came from Munich, and he was simulating sunstroke.

For lunch there was soup; it tasted of saltpeter as usual and was officially called vanilla soup. Then there was cauliflower with potatoes and worms and an indefinable sauce. Teichmann got the biggest worm; it was three inches long, the company record. He wanted to turn in his plate for a new helping, but they wouldn't let him into the kitchen. Since the recent incident, the mess sergeant told him, recruits weren't allowed in the kitchen. Teichmann collected a few more worms from his comrades and garnished his cauliflower with some dead flies. Then he picked up his plate and went to the orderly room. At the door he set the plate down, because he could only use one hand, took off his cap, and knocked.

"Yes," came the call from within.

"Seaman Second-class Teichmann asks permission to enter."

"Come in."

Teichmann opened the door, took his plate and set it on the floor of the orderly room, closed the door, picked up the plate, clicked his heels and said, "Seaman Second-class Teichmann requests permission to make a statement."

"What's up?" asked the first sergeant. Opposite him sat Master Sergeant Semmler; the two of them were drinking coffee and smoking.

"I beg permission to announce that I'm not getting enough to eat."

"Hell, man, why don't you eat what's on your plate?"

"There are worms in the cauliflower, sir."

"That's the best part of it," said Semmler.

"A soldier can't get too much meat."

"I beg permission to show the plate to the company commander."

"Let's have a look," said the topkick, and examined the plate. "Say, that's the Loch Ness monster," he said to Semmler, showing him the biggest worm. Semmler admired the beast at length and said, "Why, he's even alive. That's a good sign. That means he can't be very old. There's nothing unappetizing about a good fresh worm. On the contrary, it picks up my appetite. In the old days, Teichmann, we wouldn't have wasted words over a little worm like that."

"It's not the only one," said Teichmann.

"We can see that," said the topkick. "Leave the plate here. You go over into the mess hall and get another helping. I'll give them a ring."

That afternoon there was cleanup for the swearing-in ceremony next day. The company commander himself took over the arrangements. Teichmann was exempted from heavy duty;

when the company fell in, he was placed off to one side. The most he could have been expected to do was dusting. "Come to my office afterwards," the company commander said to him.

Teichmann waited outside the office until the topkick came out with the men's paybooks for the CO to sign. Then he was called in.

"I have a special detail for you. You are the only man in the company who will be permitted to go to town before the swearing-in. You will escort my wife. I have no time, I have to attend a meeting of company commanders. My wife has some shopping to do; after that you will go to the movies with her. The tickets have been reserved at the box office. Now remember, you are going to town on duty, not for pleasure."

Teichmann grinned. "Yes, sir."

"Don't laugh too soon, wait till you know my wife. And now put on your blue dress uniform and get the first sergeant to issue you a pass or they won't let you through the gate. And here's your paybook. At three o'clock you will be outside my house. Have you any questions?"

"No, sir."

"It's pretty goofy," said Stollenberg as he was helping Teichmann to dress.

"It's perfectly simple," said Bülow. "An officer's wife isn't supposed to go out without an escort."

"But, man, we're not in the Orient," said Stollenberg.

"That doesn't make any difference," said Bülow. "It's tradition. In the Navy everything is tradition. Actually it's not so unreasonable in ports and garrison towns. If a woman looks like anything at all everybody tries to pick her up, and I don't mind telling you that the company commander's wife is quite a dish."

"You must call her ma'am and walk on the left side of her, and avoid the language of the gutter. . . ."

"And don't hesitate," said Bülow, "to tell her that the training's kind of rough and she should give her divine husband leave more often, or they'll really run us ragged. Ah, it's too bad I'm not going out with her, maybe I could put some sense in her. No, it's got to be the youngest man in the company. They only picked you because you look so harmless."

At five minutes to three Teichmann stood outside the CO's house. At three-thirty he was still standing there. Shortly thereafter a young girl came down the steps.

"Are you waiting for me?"

"No, I'm waiting for Frau Wegener."

"That's me," said the girl, and held out her hand. "Good afternoon."

"Good afternoon, ma'am," said Teichmann, stuttering with embarrassment, for the girl seemed implausibly beautiful.

"That was pretty hard for you, wasn't it?"

"It's a long time since I've had a chance to say 'ma'am' to anybody."

"Oh, that's it. I thought you took me for a child. I'll be of age next year, though. You know, you could have given some sign of life. I would have come out sooner."

She surveyed him from head to foot. Then she said, "Let's go."

At the camp gate the sergeant on guard greeted Frau Wegener with extreme politeness, and she nodded to him. Then he took Teichmann in hand. Meanwhile Frau Wegener stood outside the gate and waited. The sergeant studied Teichmann's pass and paybook. Teichmann had time to look at the wife of his company commander. She was blonde, slender, graceful, and a good head shorter than himself. Maybe her legs are a bit too long, but, he reflected, she looks good that way. She has skin like a goldfish with the sun shining on it and she smells delicious and she has lovely, almost fragile hands, and altogether she . . .

"Password?"

"I don't know."

"What? You call yourself a sailor and you don't even know the password?"

"Nobody told me anything about a password."

"That's your own fault. The password for today is 'Bulkhead.' "

"Yes, sir," said Teichmann.

"Can you remember that till you get back?"

"Yes, sir," said Teichmann.

"Repeat the password."

"Bulkhead," said Teichmann, and looked toward Frau Wegener. She had turned her back and was fooling with the twigs on a hedge. It was a dog-rose bush with the flowers gone.

"Remove your cap."

Teichmann removed his cap. The sergeant checked his haircut.

"Replace cap."

Teichmann put his cap back on again.

"Fingernails."

Teichmann held out his bandaged hand; no fingernails were visible.

"The other hand."

Teichmann held out the other hand.

"The nails could be cleaner."

"How can I clean my nails with a bandaged hand?"

"Shut up and don't talk back," said the sergeant. And then he cried out, "When you go out with a lady, your appearance has to be perfect. Do you understand?"

"Yes, sir," said Teichmann.

The sergeant began leafing through the paybook again. Frau Wegener turned around and addressed him. "Can't you read?"

"How am I to take that question, ma'am?"

"Literally. You don't seem to be able to read very well. I could have read through that paybook three times while you've been studying it."

"I must also examine the man's appearance, ma'am."

"I have already done that. May *we* go now?"

"Yes," said the sergeant, and then, "ma'am."

"Funny fellow, that sergeant. Acts like a detective looking for an escaped convict."

"Yes, ma'am," said Teichmann.

"You don't really have to call me 'ma'am.' It's all right with me if you just call me by my name."

Teichmann was furious. He had not fully recovered from

53

the interview with the sergeant. First the sergeant lays me out, and now this kitten puts in her two cents' worth. And he wondered how he could pay her back.

"My husband was in some doubt about sending a sailor along with me; according to regulations, a sailor can't leave the post before taking the oath. Because if you were to run out on me now, you couldn't be convicted of desertion."

Aha, thought Teichmann, now she expects me to say, Oh no, ma'am, I wouldn't run out on you. I might even go so far as to say, I don't think any man would run out on you. But then he heard himself saying, "Duty is duty."

"That's just what I think. Maybe you could take my shopping bag. It would look better."

She gave him the bag. It was empty and light as a feather; he felt as if he had nothing in his hand. The handle was still warm from the girl's hand; that seems to be the only warmth she's got, he thought.

"There wouldn't be any sense in my going over the hill; I'd be recognized first thing by my bandage," he said, hoping she would ask him why his hand was bandaged. But she didn't even nibble; the bait didn't seem to interest her one bit. What do I care if she's miffed, he thought, beginning to feel nervous.

"Please don't swing my bag through the air; my purse is in it."

He could think of no answer to this, and he felt his blood rushing to his head just as when the sergeant was looking him over. He glanced in her direction and saw that her eyes were laughing. "You see, I'm trusting you with my whole fortune," she said.

He tried to make up an answer, such as There can't be much in your purse, it's so light. But then she might say, Thousand-mark notes aren't very heavy, and he'd be the fool again.

"It's not much of a fortune, I must admit. You wouldn't get very far with it. But I'm sure you wouldn't want to either. And now tell me what your friends said when they heard you had to escort me."

"They envied me, of course," said Teichmann.

54

"When you come back this evening you'll tell them there was no call for that."

She said these words very matter-of-factly. But Teichmann had a feeling that she didn't mean them.

"We'll have to walk a little faster, or we'll be late. I'd like to see the newsreel. Or are you tired? You had shots this morning, didn't you?"

"Yes, ma'am. But I'm not tired. The shot didn't bother me."

She asked him various questons, and suddenly he was talking about the food. He didn't mention the saltpeter, but he did speak of the worms. The food wasn't bad, he said, only kind of tasteless; the portions were plentiful at lunch, but there was scarcely time to eat, and the training made you hungry.

She was horrified about the worms and said she would speak to her husband. Teichmann said it wasn't necessary, he didn't want her to think that was why he had spoken about them.

"I know. But you and your buddies ought to get something out of this little excursion."

Outside the movies she gave him money to pick up the tickets while she went shopping. As he approached the box office, an officer ordered him to the end of the line. Teichmann could have told him that he was just calling for tickets reserved by his company commander, but some strange feeling made him reflect that if he didn't have the tickets when she came back, she would have to get them, and for some reason this pleased him.

When she returned, he was still standing in line. She went to the box office and got the tickets. They were for loge seats. The usher didn't want to let Teichmann into the loge; there were only two loges and they were reserved for officers. Frau Wegener sent for the manager. While she was speaking with him Teichmann saw that she had green eyes like a cat's.

When they were seated, she gave him a bag of little buns. "But eat them quietly."

They sat at the left end of the left-hand loge, and when

Teichmann held his head as though he were looking at the picture and squinted to the right he could see her profile. It was a funny picture, and the people laughed. She laughed too in certain places, and then she looked at Teichmann, and Teichmann looked at the screen and laughed, and when she looked back at the screen, he stopped looking at the screen.

Then the film was over.

"It was a nice picture," she said, "but not nice enough to keep you from eating a single bite."

Teichmann had an idea, a brilliant idea it seemed to him. "May I take the rolls back to my room?" he asked.

"You want to share them with your buddies?"

"Yes," said Teichmann, glad that she wasn't looking at him.

On the way home they didn't talk much. The sailors they passed obviously wondered how Teichmann came by such a woman, and the noncoms wondered how a lady could go out with an enlisted man.

The guard at the gate let Teichmann pass without objection and took notice only of Frau Wegener. It was not until they were fifty yards off that he called, "Password?"

"For heaven's sake say 'Bulkhead,'" said Frau Wegener.

Teichmann turned round and called, "Bulkhead."

As he was starting off again, he saw that Frau Wegener stood frozen to the spot. Her eyes flashed at him, and they were very green.

"What's the matter, ma'am?"

"Oh, nothing. Only I have good ears. Would you mind shouting, 'Why don't you play sailor in your bathtub, you jugheads?'"

It was a moment before Teichmann saw what he had got himself into. Then he said, "But you're not the harbor master's wife."

"No, but the harbor master's wife is a good friend of mine, and I was in her boat when you chose to call us jugheads."

He began to explain that the yawl should have given way, and he gave the exact reasons; he recited half the rules of the road. She listened to his lecture without interrupting,

56

and when he could think of no further argument she said, "Is that all you have to say?"

A light went on in Teichmann's mind. It may have been glimmering there for some time, but he hadn't wanted to take notice of it. "I regret the incident and beg your pardon, ma'am."

"You might have said that in the first place. Then you could have dispensed with the lecture. It would be a pity if you knew only the rules of the road and not the rules of courtesy. But here the matter ends. Frankly, I didn't take offense; I wouldn't have made you apologize in writing."

"It was very hard for me."

"A good many things seem to be very hard for you. Incidentally, that so-called letter of apology was sheer insolence. I suppose you know that."

"Yes."

"My friend showed me your letter. I'll tell you the truth. If I hadn't dissuaded her, she would have shown her husband that letter, and it would have cost you dearly. But don't get any ideas on that account; I didn't know you yet."

"Thank you just the same."

"Forget it. Anyway, there's one good thing about that letter —now at least I know your name, Herr Teichmann. Oh yes, I have a memory for names. You know, you really should have introduced yourself at the beginning of our acquaintance. Then I should have known whom I was dealing with."

"I beg your pardon."

"Don't mention it. I must say that you've changed for the better since then. Today I really wouldn't expect such language from you. But perhaps I'm a poor judge."

"I don't think so."

"What else could you say?"

They both laughed. She held out her hand. "Good-by, Herr Teichmann, and when I want to know something about sailing, I'll come to you."

"Fine, and many thanks."

"What for? Except for the movies, you haven't had much fun."

Teichmann was already a few steps away when she called after him, "Hey, your buns."

He turned back and took the buns from her shopping bag.

"You almost forgot the most important thing," she said.

Teichmann wanted to say that they were not the most important thing, but he didn't. He said, "May I carry your bag upstairs?"

"Thank you, it's not necessary. My husband's coming."

"Well, everything go all right?" asked the company commander.

"Yes, sir," said Teichmann. He saw the CO kiss his wife's hand and take her bag; they went upstairs side by side, and then Teichmann saw the window being closed on the second floor.

That night he ate the buns. He ate them all by himself, slowly and quietly, so that no one would notice, and so the night passed.

Heyne spent six days in the infirmary. One day was necessary; the other five he malingered. In the morning his thermometer read 100 and at night 101. He rubbed it on his woolen socks until he got the desired temperature, and when the doctor came he coughed in his face. On the morning of the seventh day he reported back to the company orderly room. He had recovered so well that that same afternoon he was able to report for the first distribution of passes, and on Sunday he was able to participate in the final match of the battalion handball championship.

Heyne wanted to go to Stralsund with Teichmann and Stollenberg. At two o'clock in the afternoon the first pass inspection took place, and only Heyne came through. Teichmann, Stollenberg, Bülow, and Sümmermacher were sent back for improper dress. The trouble was with their bow ties, and Teichmann's scarf was out of order too. Heyne had ordered a rubber tie from the city. You didn't have to twine it round the scarf half a dozen times before you made the knot; all you had to do was tie it ready-made to the scarf, all very simple. The drawback was that it got you three days in the guardhouse if the duty sergeant happened to notice it.

Heyne decided to wait for his friends and go after the next inspection; he went to Teichmann's room, where they sat with their feet on the table, smoking and batting the breeze about their chances in next day's handball game. Then Heyne wanted to hear about the swearing-in ceremony.

"You didn't miss a thing," said Teichmann. "Not in the morning anyway. But they could have used you in the afternoon, in the game with the fourth."

"But you won."

"Sure, but ten to eight isn't very good," said Sümmermacher.

"Yes, but Teichmann and Bülow couldn't play."

"We'll win tomorrow. The swearing-in ceremony was nothing," said Teichmann. "At eight we were called out for church. The Protestants by themselves and the Catholics by themselves, but you didn't have to go if you didn't want to."

"If we play as badly as we did against the fourth, we'll lose, I'll take bets on that," said Sümmermacher.

"The Catholics were led by the commander of the first company, the Protestants by our CO. We all fell out for church, even the boys from Napolas.* There was only a Viennese who was brought up by the Jesuits, said he was godless and wouldn't go. . . ."

"I take my hat off to him," said Heyne.

"While we were in church he had to sweep the street outside the barracks, and carry the potted laurels and other greenery out onto the drill ground, to make it pretty for the ceremony."

"He's a good goalkeeper, though," said Sümmermacher.

"So we marched to the Nikolai-Kirche—not a bad-looking church—and first listened to the organ."

"The organ's always nice," said Bülow, "no matter what they play on it."

"The pastor put on quite a show," said Teichmann. "He made great big gestures and pursed his lips; only for my taste he spoke a little too loud. Anyway, it didn't make me any more pious."

"He couldn't very well whisper," said Stollenberg. "It's not a small church."

* National Political Association.

59

"Emil the Magnanimous. There he goes defending something again," said Heyne.

"Im not defending anything, I'm just saying how it was," said Stollenberg with a slight blush.

"Let's talk about the lineup of the team for tomorrow," said Sümmermacher.

"The pastor told us something about a young man who was a banner bearer, and he wrote his mother about it; in fact he wrote her three times, and asked her to love him. Whether she should love him because he carried the banner or just on general principles, you couldn't tell from the sermon."

"The story is from Rilke," said Stollenberg.

"You never forget a thing," said Heyne.

"I didn't know that Rilke was such a good soldier," said Teichmann.

"He wasn't, he was just good at rhyming," said Heyne.

"Anyway, the story was out of place, because there are no banner-bearers in the Navy," said Sümmermacher. "And now let's talk about handball. It's better."

"After that," said Teichmann, "there was more organ music, and then the pastor said a prayer, and that was a washout for us because nobody knew if we should stand up or not."

"That must have been a sight for the gods," said Heyne.

"I'm afraid we're going to lose after all . . . "

"In the Hitler Youth nobody taught us when you're supposed to get up and when you're not," said Teichmann.

"We're sure to lose tomorrow if you don't put a little zip into your game."

"The company commander made us a sign to get up."

"So we did."

"Then there was a hymn, but there was no uplift to it, because nobody knew the words, but it didn't last long. The ceremony in Dänholm was nothing but a military exercise. The company was drawn up in an open square; in the middle there was a platform with greenery on the left and greenery on the right. The CO climbed up on the platform and delivered a speech in the old style; one man out of every company stepped into the middle and held on to the flag;

60

then we had to repeat the oath and, what was worse, stand at attention. In the end a band played, and that was the best part of the whole business."

"Marches are always nice," said Heyne.

"And organ music," said Bülow.

Just as Sümmermacher was starting in on handball again, the duty sergeant blew the whistle for the second pass inspection.

Teichmann, Stollenberg, Bülow, and Sümmermacher were sent back.

At three o'clock the same thing. In addition to his other failings, Teichmann's hat band was badly tied.

"There's no use my going any more," said Teichmann. Half an hour later Stollenberg, Bülow, and Sümmermacher tried again and got through. When they received their passes, the duty sergeant made it known that the company commander still needed a few men to crew the yacht. Teichmann, Stollenberg, and Bülow volunteered. The duty sergeant said to Teichmann, "Your'e eliminated. If you can't even dress properly, you don't need to go sailing."

He ordered the others to get into sailing gear, to get their bathing suits, and report at the dock. Teichmann thought he might as well watch and went to the dock with them.

Nine men were making the boat ready and getting in one another's way. An old sailor who ran the boatyard knew how to bend on the sail; the others couldn't agree and left the work to him.

Two officers and two ladies appeared.

"Which one belongs to the CO?" asked Stollenberg.

"The one on the right."

"The beanpole," said Bülow.

"Hans, for safety's sake you'd better clear out; the fellow with the four stripes is the harbor master, so I guess the one beside him is his wife."

"I certainly will not."

He had no need to hide; the ladies were not looking in his direction.

Stollenberg, Bülow, and Sümmermacher went on board. A motor launch took the yacht in tow. Teichmann watched from the end of the mole as the sails were set and the yacht steered a course for Hiddensee.

At ten o'clock they came back and told about their afternoon. Heyne was sorry he had gone. Teichmann pretended to be asleep.

The camp commander with his wife and children and the company commanders and their wives were present on Sunday afternoon when the whistle was blown for the handball game between the first and second companies. It was a rough game; the presence of the ladies in the audience did not subdue the animal spirits of the players. Even so, the referee seldom blew his whistle, and then usually at the wrong times. It was more like a battle than a handball game; the players knocked each other's teeth out and broke each other's ribs and the audience applauded.

The score was 16 to 10 in favor of the Second. As a reward Lieutenant Wegener invited his company's team—with the exception of Sümmermacher, who had been sent off the field for unsportsmanlike playing—to his wife's birthday party that was to take place in three weeks in Hiddensee.

3

You're the guy I like best to drink with, Teichmann, ha-ha, it's a lie, a whopping lie, but it sounds good. Prost. Take to the bottle, Hans, that's what the mate said— Maybe he was a pig, in fact there's no doubt about it, but what's to prevent a pig from being right some of the time? You're another, Teichmann, granted, but the biggest pig of all is lying out in Hiddensee, in the ladies' tent. Yes, there you lie, and all I have here is your sweater and your shoes. I've got them, I can touch them, I can throw them away, get them again, throw them away, get them again—and that's the hell of it; I have to get them again, they won't come to me of their own accord; nobody ever came to me of her own accord. You're not even happy in the ladies' tent; probably you're counting the hours and thinking, Just on my birthday I can't have him, it's too silly. Just because he promised those boys that they could all celebrate my birthday together in Hiddensee, from Saturday noon to Sunday evening, with a picnic and tents and all the trimmings. Yes, that's what you're thinking about, and nothing else. Or maybe your tent-mate, your girl-friend with the boyish figure, is telling you how boring it is to have the same man all the time. I'm faithful to him, you say. So far, says the other. It's not hard for me, you say. Because you've never had anything else, says the other. He does everything the way I want it, you say. I'm perfectly satisfied. Tell me about it, says the other. Oh no, I'm tired, you say. You're lying, but what else can you say? You must have opportunities with men, says the other. Plenty of them, you say, but they don't mean a thing to me. And the other says, Really? Listen, dearest, you know, they don't mean a thing to me either, anyway not much, do you see what I mean? And then you say, There was a little boot

63

that got a crush on me, but I gave him a kick and sent him sprawling. And that's the truth. It was a good hit, maybe the hit was even better than the aim. But the kick wasn't the end of it. When you saw that you'd hit the mark and that he was lying on the ground, you trampled him. But you don't tell your fine girl-friend that. You trampled him with your shoes, yes—Teichmann, you've had some dealings with ladies' shoes before. How did that business end? Don't remember. But I remember how it began. Drink, Teichmann. You're far from being drunk, anyway you're not drunk enough, and you've got a good memory, it'll take a while to kill it. Too bad you can't turn it off like a water tap. The damn thing goes on dripping, no matter how hard you turn the faucet; it keeps right on, maybe it'll keep on forever, maybe as long as you live. So drink and drown your memory. Drown your memory, your good memory. It began with my hand. That was the only reason why they let me escort you to town that time and take you to the movies. You know that, don't you? And the second time, too, it was none of my doing. The company commander gave the boots permission to wear long hat bands when they went out on Sundays. I didn't buy one; I never got to town anyway because of the strict pass inspection. Sunday morning all the boys in the company put on their long hat bands. At one o'clock Monday morning the topkick pulled a surprise locker inspection. All the men but me still had the long bands on their hats, although it had been Monday for the past hour and the long bands could only be worn on Sunday. There was extra drill next day and I was the only one who didn't have to take part. Result: the CO picked me to take his laundry to town. I told you all about it as I was pulling the cart with the laundry and you walked beside me on the right-hand walk. You teased me because I was always logged at pass inspection and because this was just what had got me permission to leave the post for once. And now, you said, they won't even let you go out by yourself. And you laughed. In the automatic laundry they told you the washing would take three hours; there was more than usual. You said, It doesn't matter, we'll wait. Then you slipped some cake coupons into my hand and told me the name of the café where I should wait. In among the coupons there was a folded twenty-mark bill. I wasn't sure whether you'd given it to me on purpose or whether it had got in with the coupons by accident. But I thought it was on purpose, and it probably was, because you said then, Order coffee and cake or whatever else you want. When you saw my face—I'm a poor actor —you said, And order some pastry for me while you're at it, maybe a tart with sour cherries if they still have any. I'm going to the hairdresser's, I'll be at the café in half a hour. Before I could say a word, you were gone. I left the cart in the laundry and went to the café. I ordered a bottle of mineral water and paid for it out of my own money. When you came back from the hairdresser's at the end of an hour, you were very beautiful and made green eyes because I hadn't ordered anything besides the water. You put some cake on my plate, and the same people who had looked me up and down when I came into the café, clearly giving me to understand that this was no place for enlisted men, craned their necks and looked as if their eyes would pop out. We had a wonderful time. It seemed so to me anyway. I was happy to be near you and to hear your voice, that sensuous voice with the slight ironic undertone. Your perfume was spicy and intoxicating, and your mouth and your hands, and— You're nothing but an adolescent, Teichmann, that's the long and the short of it, haha. But when you drink too much, you quickly graduate from that age. Prost, adolescent! You told me about your childhood and your school years, how you wrote algebraic formulas on a slip of paper and when the teacher caught you copying them you stuck them into your dress and pulled up the zipper. How the teacher said he was sorry he wasn't a lady, so he could take out the slip of paper, and you answered, If you weren't a man, I'm sure you would have no desire to open my zipper. And the whole class laughed and the teacher blushed and said, I am a gentleman. And you said, In that case my calculations were right. That's just the way you told the story. I have a good memory, even if this is the fourth bottle. We talked about music, the only art that I could discuss at all. You noticed that very quickly and dropped literature and painting. You didn't want me to have to bluff or make an ass of myself. You can be very tactful. Our conversation became more intimate. Maybe that seemed perfectly natural to you. Not to me. I wasn't used to such conversations. I had never been able to talk that way with a woman. And for that hour you were a woman and not a girl any more. And when it was time to get the laundry, you asked me if I wasn't still hungry and if I wanted to take some more buns home for my buddies. Then I told the truth. I didn't want to lie to you again, perhaps only because you are so beautiful; beauty fills me with a kind of awe—and veneration. Or perhaps because you had been good to me, treating me, a mere lad of seventeen, as an equal, though I was only an enlisted man. Maybe I just imagined all that about your being good to me, maybe that was just your way with young men. Don't kid yourself, Teichmann, don't lie now. *All these explanations you're giving now that it's over are lies. You* wanted *to tell her and you had a little spark of hope. That was the lousy part of it, Teichmann, you— Wash it down. Wash it down and drown it. I told you that it wasn't because I'd been interested in the movie or because I wanted to take them to my buddies that I hadn't eaten the buns, but because I had been looking at you all through the picture. That was the truth. The moment I had said it, I knew I shouldn't have, and you must have seen that I knew. But you just raised your eyebrows, those damnably lovely arches over your eyes, and said in the most indifferent tone in the world, with a nonchalance that completely paralyzed me, and that would have sent anything I could have said bouncing back like pebbles hitting a wall, It's time to go. And to the waitress, The gentleman wishes to pay. I paid. Maybe my eyes had said more than my mouth. That occurred to me on the way back, when it was too late. I pulled the cart. You walked on the left-hand sidewalk. In between us there were cars and people. You walked quickly. When I was stopped at crossings, I had to hurry to catch up with you. Later I purposely let you get ahead a little. You didn't turn around a single time. Some drunks came out of a tavern and gaped at you. That's all they did. I would have given a lot if one of them had spoken to you or tried to paw you. Then I could have slugged him. I would have given him a terrible* beating. I would have knocked him dead if you had wished it. Then you might have had to say thank you. But none of the drunks laid a finger on you; they only looked after you just the same as I did, except that I was sober. In Dänholm you took the narrow path; that was a shortcut for you. I had to take the road. In order to reach your house at the same time as you I ran, pretending that it was fun for me to run with the cart. We passed by the drill ground. To avoid looking at me, you gazed off to the right, and as you rounded a corner, you started with fright when suddenly a soldier stood in front of you, shouting across the drill ground, "I neglected my bride by not cleaning her." It was my friend Vorhölzer. He was giving a solo performance. He was goosestepping around the drill ground with shouldered rifle; behind him marched a non-com, and after every tenth step Vorhölzer stood still and said his piece. He said it loud and clear; the noncom saw to that. The soldiers moved back from the barracks windows when Vorhölzer came by; they didn't want to laugh. You pretended you couldn't help laughing. It was the first time I saw you not quite bringing something off. When the CO summoned the noncom to the orderly room next day, his harangue could be heard out in the hall, and every member of the company knew whom the noncom had to thank for that. You went into your house and asked the janitor to carry up the wash. I put away the cart and gave the janitor the change from the twenty marks, adding as much of my own money as I had spent of your money on myself; I couldn't replace the cake coupons. That ended matters between us, I thought. But there I was mistaken. Twice the company commander ordered me to sail you and your girl-friend to Hiddensee, because the wind was too strong for Sunday sailors at that time of year. Anyway that showed you hadn't complained about me, and I hoped that your reaction to my clumsy . . . no—why not admit it?—my unwarranted behavior, was just a mood. Twice I made sail and took your boat out to the harbor mouth. Both times you sent me back. But you can wait for us, you added both times. I waited at the end of the mole till you came back, and then went out in the launch to tow you in. It wasn't my fault that you had to take me along the third time, because

67

your husband was on the dock to say good-by to you. Your girl-friend was going to spend a few days in Hiddensee and I thought you were going to keep her company. On the way over I didn't say a word. Your friend, the harbor master's wife, who had every reason for not talking to me, tried a number of times to draw me into the conversation, but you blocked her with remarkable ingenuity. You'll have to admit that I didn't make it hard for you. In Hiddensee you said, Wait. I was surprised, because I thought you were going to stay on the island with your friend. Four hours later you came back, stepped into the boat, and told me to cast off. We were alone for the first time since the scene in the café. I wanted to apologize to you, I wanted to ask you to forget what I had done, and when I said, Ma'am, you interrupted me, saying, Have you something to say to me in your capacity as boatman? I said no. You said, Then be quiet. You have official orders to sail me to Hiddensee and back. You have no orders to entertain me. That's exactly what you said. Off the heights of Prohn I jibed. It had breezed up, and we came over from the starboard tack to the port with a sudden jerk. You lost your balance and you might—I won't say for certain—you might have fallen overboard. At any rate I had good reason for holding you. I had no intention of touching your breasts. If you touch me again, I shall report you to your company commander. Right then it wouldn't have taken much for me to throw you overboard. You sensed it, and I think for the first time you were afraid of me. At the same moment I knew that you would never forgive me for making you afraid. We would have had no further dealings if the CO hadn't ordered me to take some more washing to town; after all, he said, I knew where the laundry was. When I stood outside your door, you showed no surprise. You had handled your little play very smoothly till then, and this was your first slip. Because now I knew that you had asked for me by name. I saw your bedroom, and what was worse, I saw your bathroom. You had me put the wash into a laundry bag, your dirty wash. When one of your shoulder straps slipped, you reached inside your dress and pulled it up again. Previously you would have turned around. You can be very tactful. You turned around the first time we went out, when the sergeant was bawling me out. You had done more than turn around. Now you were shamelessly teasing. And that wasn't all. While I was in the bathroom putting the wash into the bag, you went into the bedroom and came back in a wrapper and threw me the soiled underclothes that you'd just been wearing next to your skin. Then you went out of the bathroom to give me time . . . And what happened then was nothing new, really nothing new at all, just a variation on an old theme. Now that's over, and I feel like a fool to have fallen for it. Maybe my age accounts for it — Gotta have a drink first, if you don't mind, otherwise I'll never get the whole story together. Hell, why do I think so much, what's the good of finding excuses for myself, of finding excuses for her, the God-damned bitch that just doesn't happen to look like one. Once I've emptied this bottle, maybe things will be better. They're sure to be better. Little by little I'll get to hate you. To hell with the sweater, and to hell with the shoes. To hell with the whole business. I'm getting the whole thing out of my system. Once and for all. And never again will I fall for your pretty puss. No matter how alluring you make it. Even if you make it as alluring as the day before your birthday when you were suddenly friendly to me again. And because you were friendly to me I thought you'd finished punishing me and that you would forget what had happened between us. Perhaps, I thought, you were being friendly because I had taken all your shameless behavior in silence. How could I know that the whole thing was a put-up job? I took it seriously. Otherwise I'd sooner have reported sick than go on that junket to Hiddensee. In the morning the company commander took me with him to Hiddensee in the motor launch. We found good places for the tents and staked them off where the grass was thick and soft. Your tent was going to be at the edge of the pine woods. Maybe, said the captain to me, the rustling of the branches will make the ladies sleep better; what do you think? Maybe they'll be frightened, I said. Not mine, he said, and the other is a seaman's wife too. Then, sir, I said, the rustling of the trees won't make them sleep any better. What makes you say that? Well, if the ladies aren't afraid, they have no romantic feel-

ing. Maybe you've got something there. I never have noticed any romantic feeling in my wife. I'd say that such things leave her cold. You seem to understand women. Now I see why my wife always wants to sail with you, ha-ha. Then we went back to Dänholm. The CO ordered me to make sail and give the yacht a tryout, so that everything would go smoothly later on. At three in the afternoon I came back from the tryout. We were to start at four. When you came on board, you greeted every member of the crew and shook hands with them. Meanwhile I tinkered with the main halyard; I too can be tactful, I thought. You came over to me, held out your hand, and said, You don't take any notice of me? Your tone was so friendly that it sounded like a joke. Shortly before we cast off you said to your husband, It's warmer than I thought, I'd rather not take my sweater, and I don't really need my street shoes either; I'll put on my sneakers right away, they'll do for Hiddensee. Then you went below. You came back with the sweater and the shoes under your arm. Let the big fellow there take the things ashore. He can run fast, even with a cart, isn't that right, Herr Teichmann? Your husband said, Good, take the things to the boathouse, but hurry. And as I was leaving, you came close to me and said with your most seductive smile, Won't you please take the things to my house. I wouldn't want them lying around the boathouse, it wouldn't be good for your comrades who are going in and out. You don't have to hurry, we'll wait. The boathouse is a hundred yards from the pier, your house about eight hundred. The more I ran, the plainer it became to me that you'd made a fool of me. I ran more slowly. In the end I walked. I came to the first company barracks. I went up the stairs to the third floor, where I knew I'd have a clear view of the sea. The yacht was already a good way from shore. You must have put off in a great hurry. Presumably your husband didn't know that a member of the crew was missing. He had no way of knowing if you didn't tell him. He was below deck when I ran off. That's the whole story. It's nothing much, nothing special, a lot of nonsense, when you come to think of it, just nonsense. But the kind of nonsense that can hurt like hell. For a while you think

*you can't stand it. But you can stand anything, Teichmann,
everything, even that, and you're nothing but a soft, senti-
mental fool, and when you've been drinking you're as talka-
tive as an old washerwoman. Go hang yourself. No, you bitch,
I won't. Your division came out even. But I had a re-
mainder. At seventeen a fellow doesn't reckon so well. But
now I'm going to draw a line under my reckoning, yes,
that I can do at seventeen. But first I'm going to have a little
more to drink. There. And now get this: I hate you. That,
too, can be done at seventeen. I'm not drunk. Don't come
around afterwards and say I was drunk. I am seventeen, and
you have turned twenty-one today. When you are twenty, I'll
be twenty-four—no. When I am twenty you will be twenty-
four. And when I'm twenty-four, you will be twenty-eight.
Make a note of that. And when I am twenty-eight, you
will be thirty-two and a worn-out old hag. I've kept a careful
watch, I know your routine. You shouldn't turn on the light
at night, not even for a short while when you live across the
way from a barracks full of young soldiers. And first you
close the windows. Yes, you're willing to spare that much
time. Mighty decent of you. You've got such a damned easy
way of taking life and acting as if God blessed your marital
relations. With you everything works fine. If you don't want
children, you don't get any. You may have to lend a helping
hand now and then, but you're healthy and unscrupulous
enough so it doesn't matter. I've seen your bathroom. And
it doesn't even mar your beauty. Yes, beautiful you are. But
that's all. Aside from your beauty, I see nothing else in you,
nothing— But that was enough for you, Teichmann. You've
never had a girl, that's the whole trouble. And you, you bitch,
you saw that, didn't you? But to make up for it, you can't
drink as much as I can. You can't drink half as much as I
can. So don't go supposing I was drunk. I know exactly what
I'm doing. Now I take your sweater and your shoes and I
spread out the sweater in front of your house door, and I
put the shoes inside the sweater exactly where your breasts
belong, and all I want is for as many men as possible to pass
by your door tomorrow, and for you to find the sweater and
the shoes tomorrow evening exactly as I am laying them*

down. I'm laying them down very carefully so you'll see I wasn't drunk and so you'll see what I had in mind— And now I'm going to bed, and believe me, I'm going to sleep like a log.

4

They rode back the same way they had come. Half of the second company had been assigned to minesweepers. The whole first platoon had been assigned to the 52nd minesweeper flotilla, Lieutenant Commander Wegener commanding. Embarkation point: Hamburg.

Teichmann, Stollenberg, Heyne, Bülow, Vorhölzer, and Vögele sat together in a third-class compartment. Vögele had belonged to the third platoon of the company. He was a Swabian.

Nobody spoke. They sat dozing, assimilating the alcohol they had imbibed at the farewell party. When the compartment seemed too crowded, they hoisted little Vögele up into the baggage net. But the change of air didn't agree with him. He had scarcely been up there a moment when he shouted "vatch out" and dropped the contents of his stomach down Bülow's neck.

"You pig!" roared Bülow as the soup trickled down his back.

"I told you vatch out," said Vögele. "I gouldn't hold it no more."

"If you can't drink you should leave the stuff alone," said Bülow.

"I drink fine, I choost can't fomit so good like you," said Vögele.

"Shut your trap, you sawed-off Polack," shouted Bülow.

"I shut my drap ven I feel like, and I ain't no Bolack, I'm from Böblingen. Anyway, you can kiss my . . ."

Vögele was sent flying down from his net, and landed in the corridor on the piled-up sea bags. That was all Bülow did to him. Soon they could hear Vögele snoring. Bülow had to change his clothes.

They were all lodged in Professor Heyne's house.

"You'll just have to put up with the official part of the Christmas celebration in God's name," said Heyne. "There's nothing I can do about it. I had to argue for hours to get us out of going to church."

"We'll bear it like men," said Bülow. "Ve don't mind," said Vögele. "Anyway," said Vorhölzer, "it's better than the Nazi solstice festivals. At least we don't get cold feet."

When they entered the large living room on the second floor, Heyne's relatives were all there waiting for the presents to be given out. Teichmann and Stollenberg greeted the Diebolds, who were there with their daughter.

The company spoke in subdued tones; even the younger ladies were singularly quiet. The older ladies seemed to be looking inward, and one had the impression that their dress betokened more hardship than necessary.

It was quite some time before the sliding door leading to the Christmas tree opened. The wait would have been embarrassing except for the eager questions of the children. An elderly gentleman with a full beard hit on the idea of singing a carol. "Oh, merry, merry," they sang, but it didn't sound very merry—more like a dirge. The old man who gave the keynote began too low; the little children couldn't sing in that pitch, and didn't know what to do. The grownups too were soon stumped; they didn't know the words. Only Vögele attempted to sing all the verses; he pronounced the words in Swabian and sang so out of tune that Heyne whispered to him, "You won't get to heaven with that singing." But Vögele went right on. "Man," said Bülow with a gentle poke in the ribs. But Vögele was imperturbable, he went on singing louder than before, but no more in tune. Only when Bülow gave him a poke that almost knocked him over did he stop. The song was almost over anyway, but Vögele was deeply offended.

The sliding door opened and the professor with a wan smile invited them in. The light in the dining room went out. In the other room stood a Christmas tree with electric candles. To the left and right of it were tables bearing the gifts. Right in front of the tree stood General Heyne, retired,

Professor Heyne's eldest brother, in an ill-fitting black suit that further detracted from the little man's stature. In his hands he held a thick old family Bible. His unmarried sister Luise stood one step behind him and a little to the left.

They all sang "Silent Night." Only the general did not join in. He pressed his thin lips together as though holding back the hiccups.

The general quickly opened the Bible, wedged his monocle, which hung by a thin ribbon, into his right eye, and began to read the Christmas gospel in clipped military tones, giving his voice a pastoral sound in the passages that struck him as significant.

". . . And suddenly there was with the angel a multitude of the heavenly host praising God, and saying, Glory to God in the highest, and on earth peace, good will toward men. Amen." And the general slammed his Bible shut.

Then the hymn was sung: "Glory to God in the highest and peace on earth."

"And now, if you please, the presents," said the general to his sister. Luise nodded and began handing them out. The children came first. They received tin soldiers, helmets, swords, and guns, and those who could read, war books. The children were delighted, and so were the parents. When a little boy handled his gun clumsily, the general couldn't resist showing him the proper position. "No, little man, that's not the way. Look here. Press the butt to your shoulder, your right hand here, your left hand farther forward, like this, and now you line up your sights, and then you press the trigger."

Two other children were arguing about what part of the body to aim at. The general came over and enlightened them: "No. One does not aim at the head. One aims at the chest or belly."

"But then he won't be dead right away."

"That does not matter. The important thing is to put him out of commission."

"Yes," said the bigger of the two children.

" 'Yes, sir,' is what you must say."

"Ye-es, sir," said the child.

"No, you mustn't drawl. In replying to a superior officer you

75

must speak briskly." The child was utterly intimidated and suddenly began to cry.

The general was horrified. "Heavens, does a soldier cry over nothing?"

The child took this as an invitation really to bawl. The general, completely at a loss, just left the child standing there. Then the older of the two children who had been listening in silence had an idea: perhaps Uncle deserved a reward for his efforts, and not tears. He ran after the general, held out his tiny hand, and said, "Merry Christmas." The general was quite taken aback. Then he laughed and said, "Yes, of course, of course, my boy."

The lights on the tree were turned off. The men spoke about business, the ladies about children's clothes, and it was generally observed that these were hard times. A few of the gentlemen cherished the feeble hope that this would be the last wartime Christmas. "God willing," said the ladies. The General said he hoped there would be no large-scale military engagement with the West, or who knows how many brave German soldiers would meet their death? "We are living in an age of technology," he said with a droop of the mouth. "Unfortunately, personal bravery is not enough." Then he spoke of the Maginot Line. "The Führer must know what he's doing," said a gentleman dressed as if he were about to be confirmed. "So far he hasn't made any mistakes." "God willing," said a lady in the background. "I only hope that the leaders study the situation carefully before they act," said the general. "The bow must not be drawn too tight." "We will trust in God," said his sister Luise. the name of God passed over their lips like butter. "God willing, we shall have a mild winter." "God only knows what the English had in mind when they declared war on us." "God reward you," when Stollenberg picked up a lady's handbag. "God will always help us," they said.

An unfortunate incident occurred when Teichmann tried to promote an exchange of presents. They had each received a bottle of cognac, three boxes of cigarettes, and a leather-bound book full of blank pages, entitled "My Diary." Teichmann took Vögele aside and tried to interest him in a proposition. In return for Vögele's bottle of cognac and his cigarettes, Teichmann would be glad to give him his diary. "You dake me for a dumbhead," Vögele replied, tapping his forehead with his forefinger. Bülow came over, and Teichmann repeated the offer, with the difference that now he asked only for the cognac *or* the cigarettes. "You're bats," said Bülow. "Even Vögele isn't that dumb." "Pülow," said Vögele furiously and quite loud, "you're a stupid pastard." Bülow laughed uproariously; Fräulein Luise blanched, went over to her nephew Gerd, and spoke to him very emphatically. Thereupon Heyne told Vögele as tactfully as possible that he would have to withdraw to his room; Aunt Luise insisted on it, otherwise she would report the incident to the general.

"Did she say 'rebort?' "

"Yes, that was how she put it."

"Den I go. She don't got to make no rebort from agount of me."

Heyne promised to bring him up something to drink soon. "If Vögele goes, I go too," said Bülow, and the two of them went upstairs together. Half an hour later their comrades followed.

Tired and suffering from hangover, they trotted back and forth on the pier in the rain. There was absolutely no shelter. With them waited forty men of the former first platoon of the second company. An administrative officer had told them that the flotilla was on its way from Bremerhaven to Hamburg and would reach Hamburg at about ten o'clock.

The flotilla arrived late that afternoon. It consisted of nine remodeled fishing boats. The sixth to dock was the *Albatross*. Five men were assigned to each ship. Teichmann, Stollenberg, Heyne, Bülow, and Vögele were assigned to the *Albatross*. This was the doing of the mate, who was now chief quartermaster, and who supposed that he was doing the former *Albatross* hands a favor.

As they went aboard, they received an appropriate welcome. "There come our future admirals," cried Pitt. "You ninety-day wonders. You're going to get your asses kicked till the sauce runs out in front," shouted Osterbuhr. He had false teeth that rattled slightly when he opened his mouth, his lower jaw no longer had its original form, and in general he had not changed for the better. "Where's my money?" cried Löbbermann. "You just come below, you dirty crook. You can milk your grandmother, but not me," roared Stüwe, and Heyne paled.

"Nice people," said Bülow.

"Looks as if we've got a fight on our hands," said Teichmann.

"Vot's dis?" asked Vögele.

"You'll see soon enough."

They dumped their sea bags on deck and went off to report to the captain. The captain was an ensign named Wagner. The executive officer was named Pauli; he too was an ensign, but a reservist. The captain shook each man's hand and told them they should toe the mark. No one knew exactly what he was talking about.

In the crew's quarters there were many new faces, signalmen, radiomen, quartermasters, all young fellows between eighteen and twenty-five. They had their bunks on the port side, where the five newcomers also made up theirs after they had received oilskins and life jackets. The original crew slept on the starboard side; Pitt was now master-at-arms.

The crew was summoned to topside, where the exec announced that the captain had been promoted to lieutenant j.g. and the chief machinist's mate to ensign. When the captain appeared, the exec reported and congratulated him in the name of the crew. The captain thanked the crew, and so did the ensign, who was already tight. The captain donated three cases of beer, containing sixty-two bottles each, to the deck force. The black gang got two cases.

"We won't get out of this mess," said Bülow when they were back in their quarters. "We'd better not drink too much," said Stollenberg. Heyne wondered if it wouldn't be more prudent to spend the evening ashore. He still had a holy dread for brawls. He did his best to cover up his fright, but it oozed out of his eyes. He was powerfully enough built, but he couldn't overcome his ingrained fear of being struck in the face; even his stint with the fishing fleet had done no good.

He fancied that his head was made of glass and would smash at the slightest touch. The result was that he joined a fight only when the others had done the main work.

"We've got to stay here," said Stollenberg. "It's a point of honor. After all, we did screw them out of five hundred marks."

"It was only for Dora," said Heyne with a glance at Teichmann. Teichmann behaved as though the whole affair had nothing to do with him. With infuriating calm he cracked his second egg on the edge of his plate, smeared a mountain of salted Danish butter on a slice of bread, and topped it with a chunk of ham.

Pitt assigned Bülow and Vögele to mess duty.

"O.K." said Teichmann, "but they'll only wait on the port table."

"Oh no, they'll wait on the starboard table too," said Pitt.

"And I say that any of us that does mess duty will only wait on our table," said Teichmann.

"I suppose your fancy-pants is too good to wash our dishes, eh?" shouted Pitt.

Teichmann reflected that the fight really needn't have started so soon and put his wrist watch in his pants pocket. As he was doing so, a clap rang out. Pitt stood there rubbing his left cheek. Bülow had slapped him.

That slap in the face had produced a beautiful sound, and intrinsically there was nothing to be said against it. But it was an absolutely new and unheard-of way of starting a fight among sailors. Pitt was somewhat taken aback. Nothing like that had ever happened to him in all his long years at sea. A slap in the face belongs in a girls' boarding school, not on a ship; it was an insult to a seaman. This Bülow did not suspect. And another thing he didn't know was that you must put your adversary out of commission as quickly as possible if you don't want to be put out of commission yourself. Pitt proceeded to show him how this is done, by kicking him in the groin, remarking. "*He* won't get it up very soon." A moment later Pitt lay beside Bülow. Teichmann's sea boot had sailed into his stomach, and he had folded like a jackknife. The starboard side sprang to the attack. The sailors on the port side jumped up, but at first assumed a waiting attitude, feeling no eagerness to be the next victims. Only Vögele remained seated. He made big baby eyes and stared as though hypnotized at Bülow, who was rolling on the floor groaning.

Löbbermann flung himself on Stollenberg. He's harmless, thought Teichmann; Emil can take care of him. He saw Osterbuhr removing his false teeth. Then Teichmann ducked as he saw Stüwe about to smash a full beer bottle on his head. The bottle struck Teichmann in the spine and hurt like hell. Teichmann seized Stüwe by the hair, pulled his head down, and rammed his knee into the tip of his chin. Stüwe was out for a long while.

Meckel approached Teichmann like a moving mountain of muscle, slow but self-confident. He knew that he was the strongest man on board. He got hold of Teichmann's left arm and tried to twist it out of its socket. Teichmann went down on his knees. With his right fist he struck Meckel full in the face, but not hard enough. Meckel showed no effects. Maybe it's even improved his health, Teichmann thought. Meckel had strange impulses from time to time. Once when he was roughhousing with Lauer, a puny little fellow, he let himself·be shellacked without resistance. But for the moment the masochistic vein was plugged. Teichmann had an·idea that Meckel was out to break his arm. With the utmost exertion he could barely stay up on his knees. And now Osterbuhr struck. Teichmann felt the edge of the iron ring that Osterbuhr wore on his left hand—he was left-handed—split his eyebrow and drive in to the bone. The blood ran into his eye and down his nose to his mouth. Instinctively he was going to lick the blood off with his tongue, but it occurred to him just in time that this would cost him his tongue if Osterbuhr caught him on the chin. He could no longer see out of his right eye. If he gets me once more in the same place, my eye is done for, he said to himself. There was nothing he could do about is; his arm was caught in a vise, and Meckel was pressing with all his might. Teichmann waited for the next blow. Osterbuhr took his time. He's taking his measurements, thought Teichmann; if he only didn't have that damn ring . . .

Osterbuhr struck again. Not the same spot, a little lower down, under the eye, but again with the ring. Teichmann felt the skin burst under his right eye and he felt the ring digging into his flesh. They're going to slaughter me, he thought. He pressed his chin against his chest, pulled in his head, pushed up from the floor, and let himself roll forward. This set his left arm free. Meckel was not a quick thinker. In the midst of his roll Teichmann saw Vögele standing on the starboard table, smashing a beer bottle on Osterbuhr's skull. Vögele has seen the light, he thought. Vögele saw that Osterbuhr had enough, and still standing on the table gave Meckel a kick in the face. "That's the stuff, Vögele," cried Teichmann. "Finish him." But then he had to turn his attention to Hinsch, who was moving in.

Vögele was a plucky little fellow but he wasn't a practiced brawler. After kicking Meckel, he stood irresolute on the table, a little frightened at his own heroic deed. He seemed to think that Meckel was finished if not dead. But Meckel could take more than a kick. He picked up Vögele and flung him out into space. Vögele crashed against the wooden edge of the port-side bunks.

Teichmann had meanwhile knocked Hinsch groggy with two shorts hooks to the chin and laid him out cold with a swing. He gave Schmutzler the cook the side of his hand, and then devoted himself to Meckel. With his right foot he kicked him in the shin as hard as he could. Meckel bellowed with pain and reached for his shin. This brought his head close to the table edge. With the cool rationality that never left him on such occasions, Teichmann saw at once what had to be done to put Meckel out of commission without incurring any risk himself: quick as a flash he seized him by the hair and twice banged his head against the table edge. Meckle was visibly stunned. He raised his head and before Teichmann could give him the *coup de grâce* Vögele, once more standing on the table gave him another mighty kick in the face. But Meckel was far from finished. He was just a little confused. Teichmann took a punch in the stomach that made him gasp for air, and he saw Vögele flying through the air once again and landing on the port side. Then Teichmann managed to get in a one-two. Meckel's weakness was his slow reactions. Before he knew what was going on, Teichmann followed up with a left that landed squarely between chin and jugular vein. Suddenly Meckel had enough and sank down ingloriously beneath the starboard table.

Lauer attacked Teichmann from behind and hammered his head with his little fists. Teichmann's skull was hard; Lauer's knocking merely annoyed him. But he had no need to act; Lauer stopped of his own accord when his knuckles hurt.

Teichmann had time to draw a deep breath and survey the situation. It was a gratifying sight. He saw Heyne in action, which meant that to all intents and purposes the battle was won. All those on the port side were now participating. A signalman, whom they called Harry, was getting in some fine punches; he seemed to have a sound knowledge of the art, as Teichmann noted with satisfaction. Vögele too was magnificent. It was amazing how quickly he had recovered from his journeys through the air. Again he was standing on the table, shattering full beer bottles on the heads of the starboard host. When none remained, he shouted, "Pring dem ofer, I finish dem off."

But there were no more candidates. The battlefield was a chaos of broken dishes, shattered beer bottles, remains of food, and teeth; not to mention the wounded. Meckel was the worst sight. His face looked like raw hamburger. But otherwise there was nothing wrong with him. His eyes were intact and he could even speak. Löbbermann, on the other hand, had lost his front teeth. That was Stollenberg's doing; a tooth was still embedded in the back of his hand. Stollenberg pulled it out with Heyne's nail scissors and extended it to Löbbermann. Osterbuhr had no further use for his false teeth; his lower jaw had shifted again, and the plate wouldn't go in. "Maybe the Jellyfish could use your teeth," said Heyne.

"Better no teeth than his," said Löbbermann, "too many broads have been holding them." Ever since his teeth had fallen out at an inopportune moment, Osterbuhr had been in the habit of giving them to his companion of the hour for safekeeping. In addition he had a small gash in his head from Vögele's beer bottles. Bülow was in great pain. They laid him in his bunk and made him cold compresses. There was blood in his urine. Stollenberg was almost undamaged; he merely had a cauliflower ear and a swollen eyelid, and his right fist was cut open. Schmutzler had lost his sense of balance and didn't get it back for some time.

Then the chief quartermaster appeared in the crew's quarters. Pitt as master-at-arms gave the regulation report. The chief explained his appearance by saying one of the firemen had said the crew were killing each other. "That's a damn stinking lie," said Pitt, "as you can see with your own eyes." "It don't look pretty in here," said the chief. It was absolutely nothing, said Pitt, they had just settled a little difference of opinion. "I request the name of that fireman." By way of emphasis, Pitt lined up his hands on his trouser seams. So he stood, asking his superior for information, buoyed up by the feeling that he was speaking for his comrades and convinced that the fireman's betrayal had been a great injustice to them.

"I don't know his name," said the chief.

"What did he look like?"

The chief looked at Pitt and then at the sailors; then he shook his head, turned around, and mounted the ladder to the top deck. Halfway up he stopped, shook his head once more, and said with a laugh, "I hand it to you."

"What does he mean by that?" said Pitt when the chief had gone.

Teichmann, Meckel, and Osterbuhr went to the petty officer's quarters and had themselves doctored by a petty officer who had once taken a quick medical course. What little knowledge he had acquired he must have forgotten, thought Teichmann when he saw what he was doing to Meckel. But the man was happy at his work. In sewing the cut in Teichmann's eyebrow, he took a good many unnecessary stitches, and sometimes stuck his needle in the wrong place. Whenever this happened, he said "Hoppla." Teichmann suffered in silence until he saw that the petty officer had no thread in his needle. Then the whole business began all over again. The man was pretty well boiled, and Teichmann was glad that the cut under his eye didn't have to be sewed up.

After this the evening meal was resumed. There was still plenty of beer in spite of Vögele's battle action. The beer had grown no cooler, but warm beer had never tasted so good. Osterbuhr, who couldn't quite manage to drink out of the bottle because of his wobbly jaw, drank out of a cup; there were no glasses on board. Meckel, too, had trouble getting at his beer. They had wrapped up his head in bandages and only left a small opening for his mouth. Heyne enlarged it with his scissors, and after that Meckel was able to drink properly. The injured received two additional bottles. At Meckel's suggestion Vögele was given three extra bottles for valiant conduct in his first brawl. Vögele wasn't keen on beer and soon withdrew to his bunk. Pitt paid Bülow a polite call and promised to see to it that he got his cold compresses all night. "Man," said Bülow, "the first day I can walk I'm going ashore. Got to find out if the thing still works. You stinkers gum up the only fun that a sailor has left. Why, life would be . . ."

"Hell," said Pitt. "It'll work all right. It ain't going to lie down and die for a little nothing. Mine has lived through worse. We'll go out together, and I'll get you a broad that'll make it work, guaranteed."

"I'm glad to hear it," said Bülow.

Pitt returned to the table. His little chat with Bülow had done him a world of good; it wasn't every day that he had a chance to talk with a real count. Reconciled with God and the world, he devoted himself to his beer. "Go get your groanbox, Benno," he said. Hinsch went to his locker and took out his accordion. He was a little embarrassed as he sounded the first chords. They sang "The Four-Master out of Hamburg," "Thirteen Men on a Dead Man's Chest," and a few chanteys.

At midnight they were still singing. The chief quartermaster came and sat down at the end of the starboard table. He didn't join in the singing, he just listened, taking a swig now and then from a bottle he had brought with him. At the end they sang "Rolling Home."

In the night Stollenberg heard a soft moaning. He got up, switched on the light, and went to Bülow's bunk.

"How's it going?"

"Awful."

"Did you groan?"

"No. Have a look at Vögele."

Stollenberg made Bülow a fresh compress.

"Next time, between you and me, you're going to see some action. I'm going to make Pitt go around looking like a knocked-up virgin."

"You won't do it with a slap in the face."

"I know that. But just let him touch me again, that piss-pot."

"All right. All right. Go to sleep now."

"O.K."

Stollenberg turned out the light and groped his way to the next bunk. "You were wonderful," he said. "You made a big hit. You're tops with us from now on. No kidding. It's a fact. You were great."

"Do it happen much?" asked Vögele.

"No, that is, it's bound to happen now and then, but not . . ."

"Nefer I live through it again."

"Sure you will. You'll learn."

"No, I nefer learn. I don't vant to neither."

"I had to."

"I ain't no yellowpelly, Emil."

"I know."

"Even in school I hated poxing. But I didn't choost let dem smack me."

"Oh, boxing is just sport."

"Yes, and shports got rules."

"We have rules too. If you go down and stay down, nobody touches you. Except for that one kick, Bülow didn't get touched. Once you've socked or been socked that's the end of it. Even Teichmann was a bit shaken up the first time, and for him that's something. And Heyne's still scared when a fight starts. But in time you get used to it; you've just got to choose between socking or getting socked or being yellow. I know, it's harder to do the socking, in the beginning anyway, because you've got to force yourself to act like a brute. That's how it was with me. I couldn't hit anybody in the face until I had my own face smashed; after that it came easy. You learned pretty quick yourself."

"Yeh, but I'm sorry vot I done to Meckel."

"No call to be sorry. He didn't handle you with kid gloves."

"I'm sorry choost the same."

"It passes, Vögele. Go to sleep now."

"O.K."

They plowed their sector as a peasant plows his field, furrow by furrow—except that they reaped what they hadn't sown, a harvest that could mean death if they weren't careful. And even if they were careful, it could mean their death: it was a matter of luck, like almost everything in war. At first the luck was bad.

The sweepers advanced abreast. Behind them came the buoy ship, laying buoys on the swept strips. On the way back it retrieved the buoys and then marked the next swept strip with them. The *Albatross* was buoy ship, and when, two hours after the beginning of operations, the first mine surfaced, the order was semaphored from the flotilla leader to deactivate it and bring it aboard intact.

Four men paddled off. The *Albatross* lay motionless. The sailors looked on from a safe distance while the four disarmed the mine. After a quarter of an hour the watching grew tedious and the sailors went below. Teichmann poured out what was left of the breakfast coffee and was putting in some canned milk when his cup slanted toward the port side and the milk missed it. A second later he heard a short hard report and then a sound such as the stream of a fountain makes when the fountain is turned off and it collapses into itself. Then all was quiet. The *Albatross* rolled from side to side. The sailors ran up on deck.

Off to starboard the sea looked as if a giant had hurled an iceberg into the water. A minute later it looked perfectly normal.

From the flotilla leader came a semaphore message: "C to K: Put out boat and search."

For ten minutes the *Albatross*'s starboard boat crisscrossed over the scene of the detonation. It came back with a load of dead fish whose gills had been stove in. They had seen parts of the raft, reported Becker, the coxswain, but it hadn't seemed worth while to take them aboard.

Harry Meisel, signalman on the *Albatross,* semaphored back: "K to C: Search unsuccessful. Discontinued."

The fish were welcome to the cook; they made a tasty addition to the noonday meal, and each man had two for the first course. After lunch Stollenberg said to Teichmann, "Is that what naval warfare is like?"

That afternoon a second mine floated up scarcely fifty yards ahead of the *Albatross.* The ship passed it to port and stopped when it was three hundred yards astern. From the flotilla leader came the message: "C to K: Send out mine-disposal team."

"Volunteers only," called the captain from the bridge.

The seamen who happened to be on deck spoke up.

"No petty officers," said the captain. "I need four men."

"Let the five midshipmen throw for it," said the exec.

Bülow won.

The spare rubber raft was lowered. Teichmann, Stollenberg, Heyne, and Vögele tied on their life jackets and jumped in.

The sea was smooth as glass, a rarity at this time of year, and it was beginning to snow. Visibility was poor. They paddled along mechanically with their eyes glued to the mine, wondering why the first one had exploded. Suddenly the raft was lifted up in the air, tipped over, and driven under water. Teichmann dived under the raft, rose to the surface, gasped for breath, and saw a vertical wall of water coming at him. The little snowflakes stood out clearly against the gray-green wall. They looked white now and not dirty gray as before. Then the wall collapsed and fell down over him like a waterfall, pressed him under water, and lifted him back on the surface.

Slightly stunned, he lay on the water, surprised that it should be lukewarm. Once he realized that he was staying up even without swimming movements, he ran his fingers over his scalp. His head hurt. He felt drilling, circling pains, and it seemed to him that someone had nailed a board to his skull and that he absolutely had to tear it off. But when he felt his head there was no board but only hair. He could not see the *Albatross*. He simply began to swim at random. It went surprisingly well. His arms and legs were in order, only his boots were dragging his feet down. He turned over on his back, but then he felt dizzy; he had a feeling that his brain was spinning all by itself and bumping into his skull. When he turned back on his stomach, his brain stopped spinning, and aside from the shooting pains over his eye sockets, there seemed to be nothing wrong with him. Only when he moved his head he had a feeling that there was a swarm of hornets inside that wanted to get out but couldn't.

He saw no sign of his shipmates. A few yards ahead of him a paddle was floating about. He grabbed it. When he touched the wood, he suddenly felt how icy the water was, and the cold cut into his flesh.

Then he saw the *Albatross*. He made sure that none of his comrades was near by and swam for the ship. He swam slowly; he was beginning to feel very weary. His arms and legs grew as heavy as lead. The salt water burned his eyes; he closed them and thought, They'll come and get me. From time to time he opened his eyes for fear of losing his direction.

He saw that the *Albatross* wasn't budging and had apparently forgotten Seaman Second-Class Teichmann. But he was too tired to care. Then he saw an object ahead of him. He thought it was one of his comrades. The object did not move. The snow was falling more heavily. When he looked up again, the snow had swallowed up the *Albatross*. He could see nothing but water and snow. He began to be frightened.

Ahead of him lay the object, and he now saw that it was the rubber raft. He was glad it was the raft. "Hans," he heard someone calling. He heard it indistinctly and could not tell from what direction the sound came. He shook his head, supposing that if he could get the water out of his ears he might hear better. He gripped the line that ran along the outside of the raft. The line was taut. He worked his way along it to the other side of the raft. When he had reached the stern and could see around the corner, he saw his comrades. They were holding on to the line; their lips were blue and they were shivering. The *Albatross* was in sight too; the raft had been exactly in line with it and had concealed it from view.

"What are you swimming around in circles for?" asked Stollenberg through his chattering teeth.

"We've been yelling ourselves hoarse," said Heyne, "and you just swim around as if you're competing for some free-style certificate." Heyne was trying to talk himself into a rage, but he was too cold.

"Didn't hear a thing," said Teichmann.

"You never did have much of an ear for music," said Heyne.

"Don't talk so much," said Vögele. "Ve got to right dis raft. Cheesus. I'm cold."

They all climbed up on one side and pressed the raft under water; Teichmann reached over, seized the line on the other side and pulled till the bottom hit the water.

Meanwhile the *Albatross* had come close. The CPO pulled the raft alongside with a boat hook; the four men were hoisted aboard, and the raft after them.

"How are the young admirals feeling now?" asked Pitt.

"Thank you," said Heyne, "the fever has gone down."

"The old man is giving you each a bottle of schnapps to keep you from getting sunstroke," said Pitt. "You haven't done anything to earn that schnapps; the least you can do is share it with your rescuers."

"Admirals drink their schnapps themselves," said Heyne.

Half an hour later they were back on deck tossing buoys into the water. When it began to grow dark and the visibility got still worse, the buoys were retrieved, inspected, hauled to the port side, and made ready to stream. The men worked in silence. At most, one of them would let out a curse when an anchor weight fell on his foot. They worked evenly and reliably like machines, but their hands were not made of iron. The salt water ate into their skin and dug deep sores; the cold turned their fingers bluish-red like fresh blood sausages. But that didn't bother them much; the cold stopped the flow of blood and there wasn't much feeling left in their hands.

For a week nothing of importance happened, except that from time to time the sea was rough and Vögele was seasick and wanted to die, but changed his mind on the fifth day when the weather improved.

The *Albatross* was running abreast of the other minesweepers when a twin-engine plane appeared on the horizon. The alarm was sounded. Teichmann, Bülow, and Vögele had their battle stations at the 20-millimeter guns, referred to on board as machine guns. Heyne was at the engine-room telegraph on the bridge; Stollenberg was No. 4 man on the 55-millimeter gun in the bow. This last was known by the crew as the night watchman, because it always fired too late. There was nothing its crew of five could do about it. It was of First World War manufacture; its breech mechanism was worn and hard to work, and its sight was antiquated. To be assigned to the night watchman was regarded as a punishment. As a result its crew treated it none too tenderly, which didn't improve its fire power any. The plane was heading for the flotilla.

"Hope he's not a German," said Stüwe, who was manning the 20-millimeter; Teichmann was ammunition passer.

"Fire a burst in front of him," said Teichmann, "then you'll find out." As he pressed the metal surface of the magazine, the inside of his hands felt moist and ants were crawling up and down his back.

"Don't tell an old hand what to do," said Stüwe. "Can't fire without permission." Teichmann felt a surge of irritation.

The plane veered to the left. The flotilla leader had fired a burst ahead of it to make it identify itself. When the plane banked in turning, they recognized the English markings on the wings, and suddenly the plane, flying low, came in for the attack. Its method was very simple and effective. Because of their gear, minesweepers must run abreast. The plane came in directly from the beam, with the result that only the boat on the port end of the formation was able to use its guns; the others had no free field of fire, and the buoy ship was too far astern to take a hand.

It flew over the *Albatross* last. At this very moment the 20-millimeter in the bow had loading trouble and the crew of the stern gun was blinded by the smoke from the stack. Only Stüwe fired. He hit the plane in the right wing. The right-hand motor began to smoke. Leaving a trail of smoke, it skimmed low over the waves, out of "machine-gun" range. Now only the 55-millimeter in the bow could have scored a hit. *Boom!* went the night watchman, firing exactly where the plane had been half a minute before. As it fired a second time, the plane vanished below the horizon.

"You blockheads," the exec bellowed at the gun crew, "do you think this is a circus?" "Lord Almighty, men," fumed the captain, "this isn't a pleasure cruise." Then a message came from the flotilla leader: "C to all units: That was a catastrophe."

Osterbuhr was the whipping boy; he was in charge of the gun, and he came in for most of the cussing.

As they were eating lunch, a mine was cut adrift. The *Albatross,* again the buoy ship, stopped.

"God damn it, where's that mine-disposal team?" shouted the exec.

"Send out different ones this time," said the captain.

"I think the midshipmen are the most suitable, sir," said the exec quickly, putting his hand to his cap.

"Only volunteers in any case," said the captain.

Since the sea was rough, the starboard boat was prepared.

"Boat ready to be lowered," said the exec to the captain.

"Lower away," said the captain.

"Lower away," repeated the exec. Then he roared at the four volunteers, "I ordered you to lower away. Have you got dirt in your ears?"

"We thought, sir," said Heyne, "that you were only repeating the captain's order and we were waiting for your own personal command."

"Don't talk back," said the exec.

"Aw, leave him be," said Vögele to Heyne, "he's *plemplem.*"

"What's that man's name?" roared the exec.

"Vögele, Seaman Second-Class."

"I'm going to have you put on report."

"Fine," said Vögele, "but you vait blease till I come back." And then to his comrades, "Let's go."

91

"I'll get back to my machine gun and give you cover in case the Tommy comes back," said Stüwe as the boat was being lowered.

"Very kind of you," said Heyne.

The captain leaned over the rail. "That thing moves a good deal faster than the raft. Nothing can go wrong if you just head full speed for the mine. But turn your motor off in time so you don't ram it. Row the last few yards. Good luck."

They made good speed. The outboard motor worked like a charm. A hundred yards from the mine it stalled. They took the oars and pulled. Heyne kept calling the distance to the mine, a useless activity, but there was no oar for him and it gave him something to do. A few yards from the mine they stopped rowing and lay on their oars. The boat drifted slowly toward the mine. The mine rose and fell in the waves like a buoy. Cautiously, to avoid touching the lead horns, Heyne propped his arm against the mine and Teichmann held it fast with the boat hook. Stollenberg made a big bight in the line and threw it over the mine. Then he pulled in the line until a piece of the mine's anchor chain rose to the surface. Heyne took the line and passed it through a link in the chain. Then they passed him the wrench and he began to unscrew the horns. After a few turns he was able to remove them and hand them to Vögele in the boat, who laid them on the canvas under a thwart. As he was about to start on the last horn, Heyne shook his hands; they were frozen stiff. Teichmann told him to hurry, no use getting blown to kingdom come on account of one last horn. "Somebody else unscrew it," said Hayne. "I haven't got any feeling in my fingers, any more." Teichmann and Heyne changed places. Teichmann gave Vögele the boat hook. For a moment Vögele let go the mine. "Watch out!" said Heyne. The boat broached, buffeted by the wind, and its stem touched the lead horn of the mine. Teichmann didn't know what had happened until he saw the look on Heyne's face. He was white.

Glass tube, acid, fuse, cap. Boom. The words were burned into Teichmann's brain; they repeated themselves over and over—they were still repeating themselves when he saw Stollenberg, who was closest to the mine, applying the wrench to the bent horn, slowly unscrewing it and tossing it into the water.

"You didn't have to throw it in the water," Teichmann heard himself saying.

"Safe is safe."

"It would have been interesting to find out why the thing didn't go off."

"Must have been some dopey factory hand in England that forgot to fill the tube with acid."

"Maybe he was a secret friend of Germany. I've been told such things exist."

"Whoever told you that was a liar."

"Chumping Cheesus," said Vögele, "ain't you got nutting else better to do but shoot the breeze?"

They pulled off with the mine in tow. Teichmann reflected that according to admiralty law mines should deactivate themselves when they part their cable; maybe this was the exceptional mine that observed the law.

Color had returned to their faces. Heyne, sitting in the stern, splashed a handful of sea water over his face. "Pull a little more to port, that's it," he said. And then, "A little more to starboard, that's it." A blind man couldn't have failed to see the *Albatross*—and Heyne himself had the tiller. Laughter was shaking Teichmann inside and he had to fight to hold back, but he said nothing to Heyne.

"Has that mine been rendered safe?" the exec shouted. When the boat was alongside, he said, "You seem to have taken your time. You held up the whole flotilla with your pussyfooting. It took you damn near half an hour to disarm that thing. Why, we used to carry those things on our watch chains, what say, Schwalber?"

"Right you are, sir," said Schwalber, who for some mysterious reason had been advanced to the rank of coxswain.

The mine was hoisted aboard and stowed on deck.

"What made you stop before unscrewing the last horn?" asked the captain.

"We had to wait, sir, because the feeling was gone out of our fingers," said Heyne.

"I watched you through the binoculars, and I couldn't make head or tail out of it."

"One of the horns fell in the water, sir," said Stollenberg.

"To hell with that."

They went to the crew's quarters and ate their lunch cold. Then they lay down in their bunks; they were off watch.

"Get up out of there, you lazy lubbers, the war's still on," said Schwalber, and shook them awake. "We've got to arm the depth charges. An English sub has been sighted; we're a subchaser now."

"Who saw that sub?"

"I don't know. Came in over the radio."

"Who's got the watch?"

"Pauli."

"He's always got his pants full, that ass-h . . ."

"I didn't catch it this time, Stüwe, but if I hear that word once more, you're ripe for . . ."

"Sure," said Stüwe, "because you're one too."

"All right, boys, get up now."

"*Boys,* he says, did you hear that?" said Stüwe.

"He's going to need a little lesson," said Heyne.

"You just show your face in here once more," said Stüwe, "and we'll show you that boys will be boys."

While they were arming and setting the depth charges aft, the captain appeared and watched them at their work.

"You've been put on report, Vögele," he said. "The story is that you were disrespectful to the executive officer. Now, what did you have in mind?"

"Nutting, sir. I got nutting in mind."

"And what did you say to the exec?"

"I said he vas *plemplem.*"

"What? Why, man, you're out of your mind! How can you say such things to an officer?"

No answer.

"Have you nothing to say in self-defense?"

"No, sir."

"Did you wittingly tell the exec he was . . . you know what."

"Yes, sir."

"I mean, perhaps you didn't mean to say that to the exec but to one of your comrades?"

"No, sir, my gomrades are O.K."

I could give him a good kick in the rear end, thought Teichmann, and the others had the same thought as they listened to this dialogue.

"Perhaps you were a little excited. Is that it?"

"Me, egcited? Not vun pit, sir. The exec vas egcited. He vas running around like a pillycoat."

"Vögele, my boy, you certainly have an odd way of expressing yourself. You'd better learn to talk differently. You'll never get to be an officer with that lingo."

Vögele, turned a bright red. He couldn't bear to hear his pronunciation criticized. When he was angry he lost all control over his tongue and then, like most people who have no gift of eloquence, he became gross.

"Seaman Second-Class Heyne requests permission to make a remark."

"Fire away."

"Sir, in South Germany *plemplem* just means excited, nervous, upset, and that is what Vögele wished to say."

"Is that right, Vögele?"

"Yes, sir, but I vasn't egcited, the exec vas egcited."

"Good. Good. But really you're not supposed to express opinions about such matters. In any case you didn't wish to insult the executive officer?"

"No, not exactly, sir."

"I'll have another talk with the exec before I put you in the brig."

No sooner was the captain gone that Vögele said to Heyne, "Do you subbose I like people butting in ven I'm having a gonversation?"

"You are a rare blockhead, Vögele. The Swabian bluntness of yours is beginning to smell to . . ."

"Planes!" came the cry from the bridge.

They dashed to their battle stations.

Six planes were attacking the flotilla. They approached from the port side.

The engine-room telegraph jumped to "full speed." "Fire at will," cried the captain. The helmsman spun the wheel hard astarboard. The *Albatross* heeled heavily to port and her bow veered sharply to starboard. Then the bullets from the planes were buzzing about the sailors' ears.

Stüwe fired but didn't hit anything.

The planes leapt over the *Albatross* like water skiers. Teichmann shoved in the second magazine. Stüwe swung his gun around 180 degrees, fired on the vanishing planes, and hit one in the fuselage. It fell with a splash. A second climbed vertically as if preparing to loop the loop, and began to burn; like a glowing red mass it darted through the blue sky and then burst like a rocket. A parachute opened and stood out against the sky like a little white mushroom. As it descended, there was a black something under it, swinging back and forth like the pendulum of a clock.

"Say, I've fixed him," said Stüwe, and gave Teichmann a thump on the shoulder that made him fear for his collarbone.

"Don't waste your time bragging. Get that gun ready."

"Maybe they'll attack again. Man, what a party that would be. . . ."

"Might be. Anyway, I'll put in a new magazine and fill the old one."

"Yes, do that. Hey, look over there. What's the matter with him?"

The sweeper with the tactical number 6 was sinking. She was paired with the *Albatross* to make the third team in the sweep formation. Her stern was already awash and settling quickly. The crew had collected in the bow and seemed to be looking on calmly. The captain, on the bridge, could be recognized by his white cap. Through the megaphone he shouted something to his men in the bow. They ran to the rigging and unlashed the wooden rafts. The lifeboats were lowered aft. The starboard boat fall jammed and the cook, still wearing his white pastry hat, scrambled up the davits and cut the line with his long carving knife. The boat dropped heavily

96

into the water. A few men jumped in. The coxswain waited till all his men were on board and then shoved off.

The stern was now under water as far as the captain's cabin. The rail of the after battle station was just barely visible. Except for the captain and a signalman, the crew had left ship. The signalman stepped to the edge of the bridge and semaphored in a calm, even rhythm, "K to K: Please pick up my men. Caution, I have armed depth charges on board."

The signalman waited until the *Albatross* signaled back, "Message understood." Then he rolled his flags together, stuck them in his belt, and jumped overboard. After him the captain jumped. No one was left on board.

The ship was settling aft; she had taken a bomb hit in the stern. The water reached the stack, which began to smoke more and more violently. Thick, gray-black smoke spread over the ship. The bow shot bolt upright and stood there for a few seconds. Then the ship went under.

Eddies formed as over the drainpipe of a bathtub. Two of the wooden rafts were caught and spun around in a circle. A third raft that was already quite far off was carried back by the suction. And then the sea burst. Thundering and roaring, it leapt high—as if a volcano had erupted under the water. A mountain of white foam rose up and collapsed with a crash. The *Albatross* listed to starboard as if she were going to capsize, but then righted herself and rocked back and forth.

"Put out boats," cried the exec.

The port boat swung in the davits, was lowered, and landed hard in the water. Meckel jumped in, with Teichmann close behind him. Teichmann turned over the outboard motor. They started off with the starboard boat in their wake. Then the motor skipped and a moment later stalled completely. Teichmann had to turn it over twice. He pulled the starter cord with one hand and held the tiller with the other.

The boat zigzagged.

"Hold the damn thing on course," cried Meckel.

The motor stalled again. Seems to be water or dirt in the carburetor, thought Teichmann, and cried out to Meckel, "Come here and hold the tiller."

Meckel was looking straight ahead, searching the sea for survivors.

"Come back here and give me a hand," cried Teichmann, furious because the starboard boat was catching up with him.

"I can't. Get going, will you?"

"*You* stupid idiot, I've only got two hands."

"Hey, there's a man swimming up ahead. Get moving, damn it."

"You get moving."

Finally Meckel came back and took the tiller. Teichmann could now devote himself to the motor. When it stalled, he pulled the cord immediately, and that way they managed to get ahead.

They heard a voice crying "Mother" and headed for it. The man lay on his belly. He turned his head sideways like a crawl swimmer breathing, and cried out "Mother." Then his face fell back into the water. Meckel stuck the boat hook into his life jacket. Teichmann seized the left arm, where the rating badge was sewed on—the right arm was gone—and pulled the man aboard. He was a chief quartermaster. They laid him out over the two forward thwarts. Because he was heavier on one side, he rolled over. His left arm dangled loose and touched the floorboards. His right arm must have been torn off. A deep wound ran from behind his left ear to his shoulder. Meckel took bandages from the medical kit and stuffed them into the wound. They vanished, and the blood, which refused to be stanched, dripped down over the seat. Meckel tore open one pack of bandages after another and stuffed them into the hole.

"Cut that out," cried Teichmann. "You're nuts."

The bandages now emerged from the dead man's mouth and swung back and forth with the movements of the boat.

They cruised a while over the site of the sinking and found more corpses. From far off they could see the white guts floating on the water like the tentacles of an octopus, and when they approached they saw that the bodies were slit open lengthwise like gutted herrings. There were also pieces of wood, torn life jackets, and a quantity of dead fish floating about.

"Jesus Christ Almighty," said Meckel. And suddenly he began to bellow. "The lousy rotten shit! Jesus, Jesus, Jesus!"

It didn't sound like swearing, but more like groaning. Meckel's whole body was trembling. His head wagged back and forth like an old man's, his walrus tusks chattered, the skin of his face kept shifting about as though he were trying convulsively to make faces, and little streams of moisture ran down over his flabby cheeks. Teichmann couldn't make out if it was sweat or sea water. Meckel covered his wet face with his bloody hands, as if to draw a curtain over what he had seen, and when he removed his hands, he looked like an Indian in war paint. He didn't know what to do with his hands; his thick sausage fingers vibrated as if he were playing a trill on the piano. "Jesus Christ Almighty! Is that what it's going to be like? Your buddies getting it right in front of your nose!"

The mountain of muscle was a bundle of misery. His muscles seemed to have developed at the expense of his nerves, said Teichmann to himself as a defense against Meckel's jitters.

"It's the depth charges. They didn't have time to disarm them, and they all went off at once. There's nothing you can do about it."

"Oh hell! It's our buddies. Just like that. Conked out. Feeding the fishes. Jeeze."

"Quit it. You won't bring them back to life by cursing."

"It does me good." Not knowing what to do with his trembling hands, he stroked the dead man's hair as though trying to make a part.

There were four corpses on the deck of the *Albatross*. The captain had been hit in the head; they had covered it with a Turkish towel and he could be recognized only by the stripes on his sleeve. To the left of him lay the pilot who had parachuted, a young fellow; blood flowed from his ear, and Stollenberg had hit on the idea of stuffing a wad of cotton in his ear. To either side of them lay the boatswain whom Teichmann and Meckel had fished out of the water, and a midshipman who had belonged to Heyne's squad in Dänholm. There had been nine fatalities on other ships. The corpses were sewn up in sailcloth. Their faces were expressionless, except for the captain's, which wasn't there at all. When they took off the towel Vögele had to look away.

At dusk the flotilla stopped. On the *Albatross* the port raft was unlashed, the bodies were laid on it, and an anchor weight was attached to their feet. Four men of the off watch took their places at the head of the raft. At a signal from the flotilla leader the battle flag was lowered to half-mast. While a CPO blew taps, the raft was set on the rail and tipped so that the corpses slid into the water. The battle flag was raised, and the vessels started off again.

For supper there was fried liver with rice. Meckel gave Teichmann his portion of liver, then went to the galley and brought back sugar, cinnamon, and a little can of milk. "We ought to begin weaning you one of these days," said Stüwe. "You act like a suckling babe," said Pitt. "Pretty soon we'll having to wipe your ass." They let him be only when they saw little drops of water falling into his rice along with the sugar and cinnamon. Then they began to praise the qualities of their fallen captain. Osterbuhr said, "If Pauli takes his place, I'll volunteer to jump overboard."

"All right," said Heyne, "but don't get the idea that he'll put on any man-overboard maneuvers on your account. He'll just give her full speed ahead."

Pauli was no longer exec. Now he was captain, but only in name; in civilian life he manufactured brassières. Halber-nagel, who stuck his nose into everything and found a way to be servile and insolent both at once, had ferreted that out. In his capacity as captain's orderly he had poked around in Pauli's papers and come across a · letter from the brassière firm. It was a Christmas circular. The firm, it said, was proud to announce that for some months its junior execu-tive had been performing "hard, heroic service" in a suicide detail—more could not be said for security reasons; it was almost a miracle that he was still alive. The firm and its employees hoped to welcome Herr Pauli home on leave in the very near future. Meanwhile they wished him the best of everything, Merry Christmas and Heil Hitler.

Halbernagel had brought the letter up to the crew's quarters and read it aloud. For the general edification of the men he wanted to post it on the bread locker. But the sailors didn't want it in their living quarters; in fact, they wanted as little as possible of Herr Pauli. In the end Halbernagel had to take it back aft. It was too bad, Heyne said, that the Führer wasn't absolutely consistent, for if the German woman doesn't smoke and the German woman doesn't paint her face, he could perfectly well have added that the German woman is well shaped by nature and doesn't need a brassière. Then Pauli would have gone broke.

Heyne made similar speeches on the bridge and consequently landed in the stokehole; Pauli had overheard him and this was his "punitive assignment." It was news to the black gang that the stokehole was a penal establishment. And then they began to fight over which watch Heyne should be assigned to. Pauli thought up a solution worthy of King Solomon. "You're big and strong enough to shovel coal, and you gave me a sloppy salute this morning," he said to Teichmann, and sent him down too.

Two older men shared Teichmann's watch. They had stoked for several years in the deep-sea fishing fleet, and they had given up overworking. After every third shovelful they stopped for a break, and Teichmann let them alone as long as the *Albatross* did not have to run more than half speed. At that pace he could feed the boilers by himself; the two others lay in the coal and slept.

At midnight Schmutzler brought down a pot of coffee.

"Should I give them some too?"

"This is the fifth night you've brought down that coffee, and every time you ask the same stupid question."

"I just meant . . ."

"If I do all the work myself, I've got a right to all the coffee. Can't you get that through your head?"

"Yes, but suppose they report me to the authorities?"

"The authorities?"

"Yes, to Pauli."

"You're just too dumb, Schmutzler. There's no use talking to you," said Teichmann—and suddenly he was hurled against

101

the wall of the coal bunker. Now he could see nothing. Everything was dark. He couldn't breathe, and he thought the coal dust would smother him. Somebody was gripping his right arm. When he tried to wrench himself free, the darkness danced before his eyes and he felt as though he were riding by turns on a seesaw and a merry-go-round.

"Let's get out of here!" he shouted. And then he had to cough.

"Help!" roared Schumutzler.

It was a short tussle; Teichmann spun round in a circle and shook Schmutzler off. Then he groped his way to the bulkhead separating the stokehole from the engine room. It's usually closed, he thought, but I know how to open a watertight door; there's a dog on the top and another on the bottom—wait a minute, do you turn the top one up or down? Up, of course. He turned it up. Good, and now the bottom one goes up too. There you are, it's all perfectly simple.

The door wouldn't open.

In my excitement I must have turned the dogs the wrong way. Wrenching both dogs down, he threw his weight against the door.

The door refused to open.

Now he was perfectly calm. Schmutzler pressed against him. He felt Schmutzler's breath coming in gasps and tickling him around the nipples.

He flung himself with all his strength against the watertight door. But it would not give.

Then he heard voices in the engine room. Now! he thought. And with the strength of despair he once more threw himself against the door. He felt as though all his bones were breaking. But the door didn't give. Then he hammered on the iron with his fists. He retreated a few steps, took a run, and flung himself again at the door.

"The bastards have locked us in. They're going to let us drown. . . ."

"Help!" Schmutzler roared.

"There's nothing we can do. Absolutely nothing."

"Help me," Schmutzler whispered. His voice trembled so that Teichmann could hardly understand him.

Teichmann sat down on the deck and leaned against the bulkhead. I've got to think, he said to himself and closed his eyes. He wiped his nose with his fingers and passed his tongue over his teeth and tasted the coal dust and spat it out. But he didn't think a thing.

Water was pouring into the stokehole. He opened his eyes, because then the sound wasn't so loud.

Soon the water was up to their waists. Each of them waited for the other to stand up. They knew there was no sense in standing up; it doesn't make any difference whether you drown sitting or standing.

Then Schmutzler stood up. He's smaller than I am, he was bound to get the idea first, thought Teichmann.

The water kept rising.

Teichmann stood up. Now it's Schmutzler's turn, he thought, and fear kept him from thinking any more. He had suddenly realized that he would have to die two deaths, Schmutzler's and his own. If I had some cyanide, I'd take it.

Schmutzler began to scream and pressed against Teichmann. This is the beginning, Teichmann said to himself. The idea came to him of strangling Schmutzler first. But then he would be alone. . . .

The water had risen to the level of the fire door. Fire and water mixed with a gurgle and a sharp hiss. For a moment he could hear the sound of the water pouring in.

Teichmann leaned against the bulkhead and breathed in the steam. His brain was still working a litle. He would have given a good deal if it hadn't been there or if it had been unable to work, and swiftly, like a racing film, but clearly, memories sped by: how as a child he sprinkled water on the red-hot stove . . . how the maid licked her finger and quickly touched it to the iron . . . how the lead molds were set in water . . . how at school he put a lighted candle under the inkwell and the boiling ink ran over. . . how Siegfried cooled his sword in the water, that was in Bayreuth in 1939, Lorenz sang Siegfried. . . .

It had grown light. The door of the fire hole had sprung open. The rising water had pressed it from below. The glowing coals lit up the room and through the steam Teichmann saw the ladder. He examined it very carefully. When the fire went out and it was dark again, he knew that there on the port side, three yards away from him, there was a ladder and that this ladder had been there the whole time; he had only forgotten it.

As he moved toward the ladder, which was no longer visible, he couldn't dispel the nightmarish thought that it might meanwhile have vanished. When he set his foot on the first rung, Schmutzler, as though they had rehearsed the act a hundred times, threw his arms around his neck and twined his legs around his thigh. They couldn't have closed the hatch cover, he said to himself, and at the same moment it occurred to him that of course they had closed it. At the order "Close watertight doors," they had to close it.

The thought paralyzed him. He knew that he had six feet at most to climb up to the hatch cover, but he couldn't make it. He had no strength left. He felt Schmutzler getting heavier and heavier. He was overcome with a dizzy feeling that drew him downward, but suddenly it stopped because fresh air was coming down from above; he felt a kick in the head, someone was standing on his hand, and he yelled. His hand was free.

"Hans?"

It was Stollenberg's voice. Teichmann climbed up; arms drew him through the entrance hole, and he lost consciousness.

"Haile Selassie was a piker," said Pitt as they laid Teichmann and Schmutzler down on the top deck and turned their flashlights on them. "Ain't nothing wrong with them. They're just black," said Halbernagel. After a mouthful of schnapps Teichmann came to.

"Listen, Negus," said Löbbermann, "and we'll tell you what kind of a captain we've got."

"Not so loud, Jellyfish," said Pitt.

"You can kiss my ass; I'm going to have Pauli courtmartialed. Anybody can hear what I have to say. The flotilla leader sends out a light signal: three shorts. And now pay attention, Teichmann. Are you listening?"

"Yes."

"Good. So Pauli turns around to me and asks, What does that mean? Can you believe it? The captain asks me what three shorts means."

"We've always known Pauli was an ass," said Bülow.

"An ass? He's a common criminal."

"Not so loud, Jellyfish," said Pitt.

"I'll say that to anybody who wants to listen."

"No, Jellyfish, he's a brassière manufacturer," said Heyne.

"He's a criminal, I say. You can't trust a ship to a guy like that. But the best is still to come. I say to him, Sir, that means British MTB boats. But Pauli don't even change his course. I say, We've got to turn toward them. I don't see any, says Pauli. There they are, I say, come right thirty degrees. No, we're going to pull away, says Pauli, and orders the wheel turned hard to port. Half a minute later, bing! If he'd only turned thirty degrees to starboard, our bow would have pointed straight into those PT boats and we wouldn't have been hit, the torpedo would have passed us on the port side. But just because he was scared to get any closer to the enemy, Pauli pulls away."

The cold drove the men below. When Teichmann lay in his bunk with a piece of canvas under him, Stollenberg said, "Do you know, it's not just that Pauli hasn't the slightest idea of handling a ship. He's a swine too. Right after he gave the order to close all watertight doors, Gerd comes up on the bridge and reports that the firemen are knocking on the bulkhead. He asks him if they can't open the door quick, there can't be much water in the stokehole yet. Pauli shouts that he'll kill anybody that opens a watertight door, the safety of his ship comes first, he can't concern himself with individuals. But Gerd didn't give in. . . ."

"Or you either?"

"Two more times we got on Pauli's tail about that watertight door. In the end he chased us off the bridge. Gerd said you could climb down into the stokehole from the entrance hatch, so he tied a line under my arms and let me down. I guess I stepped on your paws."

"Might be."

"It was lucky that it was the coal bunker that was hit, otherwise more water would have got in. But without Wegener we would have sunk just the same."

"How so?"

"He brought his ship right alongside. Then he and No. 2 ship passed a line under us. That was seamanship."

"And what did Pauli do while it was going on?"

"Nothing. Just drove everybody nuts with his shouting."

"If that bastard is still captain on our next mission, I'm going to toss him overboard."

"I'm with you," said Stollenberg.

5

Pauli gave Teichmann and Stollenberg three days in the brig. They had come aboard at 0111. Pauli put them down as AWOL for eleven minutes. They had actually stayed too late at Dora's, but they would have got back on time if they hadn't taken the wrong wharf entrance on the way back. The *Albatross* had been taken into drydock that morning, and that had slipped their minds.

Before the drydocking they had helped to remove the remaining coal from the bunker. The bodies of the two firemen who had shared the watch with Teichmann came to light. The air pressure from the explosion had slapped them against the top of the bunker. Pauli insisted that the bunker be left clean as a whistle; the drydock workers, and especially the engineers, he said, wouldn't like the sight of blood and crushed bones.

They went off duty at 1600. Then the crew had to muster on deck in dress uniform and look on as the Iron Cross Second Class was conferred on Reserve Ensign Pauli. The same decoration was given to the fallen captain and to Stüwe for the plane he had shot down. The flotilla commander commended the crew for their conduct in bringing in their heavily damaged vessel and spoke a few words in memory of the fallen captain and the two firemen. In conclusion he announced that an ensign named Paschen had been appointed executive officer.

"Attention. Eyes right," cried Pauli. The flotilla commander thanked them.

"Carry on."

Heyne poked Löbbermann in the ribs. "I like the way you got Pauli court-martialed."

107

"Wegener shouldn't have given him that Iron Cross," said Bülow.

"He had to, or Stüwe wouldn't have got his," said Stollenberg.

The flotilla commander saluted his former trainees, shook hands with them, and chatted with them for a few minutes. "Well, how's it going?" he asked Teichmann. "What do you . . . ?" He broke off, smiled a little uncertainly, and clapped him on the shoulder. "It'll all come out in the wash."

"Have you any idea what he was talking about?" Teichmann asked Heyne.

"To hell with it," said Heyne. "Let's go see Dora."

On their way ashore, they passed two ladies. One, dressed in black, was the widow of the fallen captain; the other was the wife of the flotilla commander. All the men saluted, and even Pitt took pains to give a proper salute. Teichmann saluted the widow of his fallen captain.

"I wouldn't mind shacking up with that one," said Pitt, smacking his lips. "You'll always be a pig," said Stollenberg and blushed. "Say, whom are you talking about?" asked Heyne with unusual sharpness. "About Madame Wegener, if you don't mind," said Osterbuhr. "Just go ask if she'll let you," said Teichmann with a laugh that sounded as if he had swallowed the wrong way and had to cough. The ladies drove past them in the flotilla commander's car. Bülow and Vögele went to the barber's. Teichmann, Stollenberg, and Heyne had some shopping to do. It took them a while to find something suitable. Finally they bought a scarf of bright printed silk; a friendly salesgirl let them have it for twice the normal price without clothing coupons. They met Vögele and Bülow at the barber's.

When all five of them were freshly shorn, they went to Dora's.

"To tell you the truth, I'd rather go to a bar and drink something decent."

"Don't talk rot, Hans," said Stollenberg forcefully. "You're coming along."

When they entered, the place was almost empty. It was a cross between a café and a beer hall, and you had to look twice before you suspected that the waitresses did more than wait on table.

They sat down at a corner table near the bar and sent Vögele to reconnoiter. He proceeded to ask for a pack of cigarettes "without coupons."

"Sorry can't do," said the girl behind the bar. She was a peroxide blonde and of all the girls seemed the one most likely to do a little business on the second floor.

"I'd like to see the boss."

"She's very busy right now. I'm sorry."

"Vit who?"

"I beg your pardon?"

"Vot I mean iss who's she laying now?"

"I wouldn't advise you to get fresh around here."

"Anyway, I pring her recards."

"From who?"

"From the *Albatross*."

"Who's that—a man?"

"A whole bile of 'em."

"I don't get you. Would you mind speaking more plainly?"

"The *Albatross* iss a ship. It's got men on it. See?"

"I'm sure that won't be of any interest to the boss."

"You choost tell her."

The girl made a face and disappeared. "Some hunk of meat," said Vögele, tapping a coin on the bar. "Hey . . ."

The hunk of meat came back instantly with Dora. Dora was dressed like a lady, and in so far as features can change, hers had become more ladylike.

"Who do I see!" she cried and greeted Teichmann, Stollenberg, and Heyne as if she hadn't set eyes on them for twenty years.

They gave her the scarf and the books.

"It's a lovely scarf. And three diaries all at once . . ."

"Maybe you can use them for your bookkeeping," said Heyne. "It's good paper."

"You shouldn't have gone to such expense."

She left them for a moment and came back with five hundred marks. Heyne said he didn't want the money back, they'd had a good fight and that was the end of the matter. But Dora insisted.

"Then we'll drink it up on the premises," said Teichmann.

"That's out of the question. From you I don't take money."

Stollenberg suggested that they return the money to its rightful owners, but his proposal was unanimously rejected. Then the whole fight would have been for the birds, said Heyne. They finally agreed to accept the money but to leave it with Dora for safekeeping. "Now, what would you like to eat?"

"Not a thing, Dora. We've been doing all right in that line."

"Well, what *can* I do for you then? Something for the heart?"

"This is our first time ashore," said Bülow with a grin.

"Take your pick, my heroes."

"Dot's a dream," said Vôgele. "I take the one dot wouldn't give me no cigarettes."

To the girls she said, "The gentlemen are my guests. Treat them accordingly." And to Teichmann, "Come with me, little one, I know you're an old hand at this kind of thing. Maybe I can learn something from you."

The girls had their rooms on the second floor. Dora's private apartment was on the third.

"What about your husband?"

"What's he to you?"

"Off duty today?"

"No. Pensioned him off long ago."

She showed him the living room and then the bedroom. Both were decorated with taste as far as Teichmann could tell. In the bathroom she let the hot water run. "You'll feel like a new man after a good bath. I don't want anything to remind you of your filthy work on board. You've got to leave all that behind you now. You'll just forget all about it, won't you?"

"I'm going to try very hard."

"Maybe I'll be able to help you a little."

When he emerged from the bath, she had on a velvety purple dressing gown. She smelled even better and stronger than before. She had opened up the bed, which offered plenty of room for three. Teichmann had never before seen such a piece of furniture and was a little frightened. The palms of his hands grew moist as they had been in his first aerial attack. Dora snapped out the ceiling light. She left the bedside lamp on, and it gave forth a warm, reddish-yellow glow.

"Is the bed too big for you, little one?"

"Looks like it."

"Don't worry. Once I'm in it it won't be too big."

She slipped off her dressing gown and turned off the bedside lamp, after allowing him one second's glimpse of her naked body.

For a time, perhaps only for a few moments—he did not know—he felt happy, because he managed to forget the past and the present and everything else, even Dora, and because his body was caught up in a wave that washed away everything that was unimportant and opened the gates to the one thing that a man had left when there was nothing else.

When it was over, he felt older. But very soon he began to be curious as to what happened next. Dora was happy. He could feel it, and she told him so. She told him several times, and she was very lively, and when she had no words she would utter other sounds. Teichmann was glad but secretly amused. She's a little naïve, he thought.

They didn't talk much. She asked no questions and he had nothing to say to her, but he was glad that she was with him. Once she got up and came back with a bottle of wine. She made him drink slowly.

Shortly before midnight Stollenberg knocked on the door and said he was leaving. "I'm coming," said Teichmann, and began to dress.

"You haven't got liberty for the night?"

"No. A sailor doesn't get any. And especially not with our new captain."

"It's too bad. I would have liked to sleep with you. Really sleep, I mean. I miss that terribly, you know, just to lie peacefully in bed with someone I like. You don't need to be afraid, I'm not going to talk about love. . . ."

"Love is the bunk. But it feels mighty good. That's the main thing."

"That's a sensible way of looking at it. Though you didn't have to say that word 'bunk' so loud. Just the same, I'll tell you something, but there's no call for you to get stuck up; you're exactly the kind of man that every woman wants, even if she doesn't admit it. And do you know why? Because you're not selfish. I'm telling you that because I think this was your first time. But here in Hamburg you mustn't go to anybody else, see?"

She got up and slipped into her clogs, put on her dressing gown, and walked to the house door with him. Outside, Stollenberg was waiting.

"Heyne didn't stay," he reported. "He went home; he said he was better off with Molly."

"It's up to him," said Dora.

They bade each other good-by. Dora wanted a kiss. That struck Teichmann as silly at this juncture, and he held out his mouth while Stollenberg was busy with his shoelace.

On the way back Stollenberg said, "You can say what you please, but I feel a great deal better."

"I'm not saying a word."

"Right. Besides, what else could we have done?"

"Well, we might have done something athletic."

At this the two of them laughed so loud that the few pedestrians that were still about stopped to stare at them.

Teichmann pondered this visit to Dora as he sat in the brig. Life there was far from monotonous, for the flotilla staff was lodged in the same wooden shack. The flotilla staff consisted of an administrative officer with the rank of ensign, a chief yeoman, a few subordinate yeomen, and two female typists. The officer in charge was a reserve lieutenant named Loewe. What Loewe did in the daytime, no one had the faintest idea. What he did at night was pretty well known to the whole flotilla and was not unrelated to the two typists. For his activities he required two rooms: in one he usually sat alone at his desk, cleaning his nails with a pair of paper shears; in the other he reclined on the couch after dark, no longer alone. As a sideline he commanded the flotilla when Lieutenant Commander Wegener was on leave. The flotilla commander had gone to Berlin for a few days; he no longer made his home in Dänholm. As long as Lieutenant Loewe was in command, the flotilla did not put to sea.

The end room in the shack served as brig. It was divided into two little cells, so that two prisoners could do their time at once. Each cell had a little window, up high, less than two feet from the ceiling. Outside the window there were gratings that looked to Teichmann as though they were made of wire. In any case the iron was pliable, as he determined in the first few minutes of his sojourn; the little bars had no practical value and were no doubt conceived more as a symbol. Although the cell was not heated, it seemed advisable to leave this window open even in winter, because the latrine was right next to the cell. The shack was none too solidly built, the walls were thin, and the wall separating the brig from the latrine had knotholes in it. The wall between the two cells was also thin and full of knotholes, and Teichmann and Stollenberg were able to converse quite easily. But from the other direction Teichmann had to put up with smells and sounds that did not contribute to his happiness. Once when the behavior of the latrine guest seemed particularly uncontrolled, he called out, "Here's looking at you!" After a pause for reflection the reply came back, "Fresh guy!" A few minutes later the lieutenant appeared in Teichmann's cell and said, "One of the ladies has complained about you." "I request writing materials," said Teichmann, "I wish to send the flotilla commander a complaint in writing about those key punchers." Lieutenenat Loewe chose to press the matter no further, but he did not forget to inform Teichmann that the ladies were stenographers and not mere key punchers, and that in future he should not listen to what was going on next door. Teichmann replied that this was easier said than done; he had only two hands and could not hold his nose and ears at once. "That's enough of your insolence!" said the lieutenant and departed, banging the door behind him. Teichmann heard him in the corridor, calling for Fräulein Erika. In the next cell Stollenberg was laughing.

Teichmann's private war with Pauli went right on. When he had done his time in the brig, he was put on watch. For purposes of acclimatization, as Pauli put it; it would give him an opportunity to get used to the fresh air again.

He asked Stollenberg to tell Dora that he couldn't come. He knew she was expecting him; Vögele had told him so when bringing him his meals in the brig. Dora would give him a bang-up reception, said Vögele. He went to Dora's every night, and so did the others.

The first night Teichmann was on watch from midnight till four in the morning. At half past two Pauli came on board with a female companion. Teichmann made his report. Pauli teetered a bit and gave off a dense spirituous haze.

"Who's that?" asked Pauli's companion.

"That's the baby of my crew."

"He's big for a baby. Does he drink?"

"Big? Yes, he's big all right. Ha-ha. But he's as dumb as a baby; aren't you, Teichmann? Repeat that: I am stupid Teichmann."

Teichmann said nothing.

"Go ahead, repeat that."

Teichmann gulped.

"Make it quick, boy. Repeat that sentence, it's an order."

Teichmann was silent; a lump came into his throat and moved up and down. He was determined to spit in Pauli's face; a tremendous rage gathered inside him; it sat on his belly like a ton of bricks and weighed down his entrails. He couldn't breathe, and it cost him a great effort to keep from groaning aloud. He had spots before his eyes, and Pauli's face wobbled indistinctly back and forth. I've got to get him now while I can still see him, I've got to kill him, I've got to . . .

"Come along, sweetie, come along."

"Don't bother me. I want him to repeat that sentence."

Teichmann lowered his rifle and leaned it against the gangplank. He had himself in control again; he knew what he had to do, and now everything was simple. He took off his glove and clenched his fist. Pauli had turned up his coat collar; Teichmann waited for his chin to be free.

"Come along, sweetie, won't you?"

Teichmann took half a step back. Pauli's head was still a

bit low, his chin was still in his coat collar. Teichmann brought his fist back for a swing. He felt it graze the gangplank handrail, and he turned slightly to the side to get a better swing.

"Come along, sweetie. I want it right now."

"Don't bother me. The dog's going to repeat that sentence or . . ."

"Put your hand in here, sweetie, do you feel something?"

Inside, they were quiet for a while. Then they began to make such a ruckus that Teichmann couldn't help listening. Finally it degenerated into a brawl. They bellowed at each other and outdid one another in obscenities. Then Pauli threw her out of the cabin.

She lay on deck whimpering. Pauli threw her clothes after her.

She tried to open the door, but Pauli had pushed the bolt. She hammered on the door, and when nothing helped she urinated.

"Hey, quit that," said Teichmann. "We've got to clean it up, not him."

The porthole of the cabin opened. Pauli stuck out his head and yelled, "Teichmann!"

Teichmann approached.

"Damn it all, what do you think you're here for? See that we get some peace around here, and on the double. And get this bitch off my ship." The porthole closed.

"What did he say? What did that pig say?"

"He wants you to go ashore."

"The rotten piker didn't give me a pfennig. Not a single pfennig. He said he'd give me a brassière. A brassière—do I need a brassière? Take a look, you. Do I look as if I needed a brassière? With my figure? Feel here. It's genuine."

Next morning the petty officer on watch read in the log:

0130: Unknown lady comes on board with captain.

0218: Disturbance aft. Lady employs disreputable language and calls captain obviously insulting names.

0223: Lady leaves captain's cabin under duress.

0226: Lady relieves self outside door to captain's cabin.

0227: On captain's order lady warned to cease distur-
        bance.

0237: After settlement of 10 marks, lady leaves ship.

Otherwise nothing out of ordinary

                    (signed) Teichmann, Seaman Second-Class

The petty officer on watch was Becker. He sent for Teichmann.

"Friend," he said, "that little entry in the log can get you
into an awful lot of trouble. In half an hour I've got to bring
that book aft; maybe we could change it a bit or erase it."

"Don't bother. I just want to make a little trouble for Pauli.
He's got it in for me anyway."

"It's all right with me. But it's a dumb thing to do, mighty
dumb, that's all I can say."

"I know. Only last night Pauli himself told me I was dumb.
I really should have signed 'Stupid Teichmann' in the logbook. Too bad I didn't think of it before."

Becker didn't have to submit the logbook to the captain;
the chief quartermaster sent him to the supply depot for
some red lead. Teichmann went to his cleaning station. He
was busy scrubbing the toilet bowl when Werner, the chief
petty officer, looked in on him.

"Morning, Teichmnan."

"Morning, sir."

Pause.

"Your bearing isn't usually so military."

Teichmann went on with his work.

"On your watch last night you were a little too military. I
mean . . . " The CPO came into the head and closed the door
behind him. "What you wrote in there was absolutely right
from the military point of view. But you know, the captain's
a reserve officer. . . . "

"That's just it, sir."

"O.K. But that won't do you a damn bit of good. He can
make life mighty hard for you."

"I'm used to it. I don't mind."

"As you wish. Don't forget to scrub down the seats with
hot water."

116

"Yes, sir."

After lunch Pauli appeared in the crew's quarters. No one called "attention," as was customary when an officer came in during the noon break. Pauli screamed and yelled. It was mutiny. He'd play them a different tune from now on; never had he seen such a fouled-up crew. Then he staged a locker inspection, as a result of which half the men lost their liberty.

Teichmann's locker looked exactly like the others, but Pauli found nothing wrong. He was indulgent with Halbernagel's locker too, but its interior decoration may have had something to do with that. The locker was adorned with photographs of movie stars. They were pictures that could be bought in any store, but Halbernagel had cut off the white edge to make them look like personal photographs. They bore inscriptions such as "Your ever loving Zarah" or "With mountains of love, your faithful Marika, who will never forget you." Rather surprisingly, Halbernagel's admirers all had pretty much the same handwriting, which in turn showed a striking resemblance to that of the man they loved. Apparently Pauli took an interest in handwriting, for he examined Halbernagle's locker with the greatest thoroughness and even went down on his knees to study the nudes on the lower wall.

Again, when he left the crew's quarters, no one called "attention." This time Pauli seemed to take no notice. But perhaps he had seen the look in the men's eyes.

The men went off duty at 1700. Teichmann washed thoroughly, put on his dress uniform, and smeared his hair with pomade that made it look darker. Stollenberg had brought the pomade back from town and quietly slipped it into Teichmann's locker.

When he went up on deck for his pass, Pauli was standing by the gangplank.

"Wait outside my cabin."

Teichmann waited for twenty-eight minutes. Then Pauli arrived, went in, and ordered him to enter.

"Would you kindly report."

"Seaman Second-Class Teichmannn reporting, sir."

Pauli sat down and crossed his legs. He let Teichmann stand at attention. Carefully and deliberately he filled his pipe.

117

Teichmann had seldom seen him at such close quarters. He was a man of about fifty. With his shriveled yellow face, his green eyes and parched, wrinkled lids, his crooked, pinched, bluish lips, he looked like a poisonous goblin. His lips parted, creating a hole of remarkable roundness, and into the hole he thrust his pipe-stem. Then the hole said, "Hand me that slip of paper. Yes, the one lying on the desk."

He rolled it into a taper.

"Now will you kindly give me a light."

Teichmann took his lighter out of his pocket and held it out to him.

"No, you light it. That's it."

Pauli kindled the taper and lighted his pipe with it. "You see, I always light my pipe with a taper; I can't bear the smell of gas that lighters give off."

That was pretty smoothly done, Teichmann thought. Wonder how long he had to rehearse before he got that scene right.

"Just to teach you what is to be entered in the logbook and what is not to be entered, you will have the watch for seven days. And make a note of this for the future: Only important events are noted in the log. Im-por-tant e-vents. Dismissed."

Teichmann went to the chiefs' quarters and asked the CPO to show him the logbook. The book he held out was brand new.

"What about the old one?"

"Gone."

"Well—he doesn't do things by halves."

"No, not Pauli."

Teichmann took off his uniform and played rummy in the crew's quarters with Stollenberg and Bülow.

"Looks as if you've got the perpetual watch," said Bülow.

"Yes, I know. But I just don't like to have dogs piss on me, like the SS guards in front of Party Headquarters. I can't keep that still."

"But you could improve your rummy. That's the second time you've discarded."

Teichmann got himself a bottle of beer.

"Don't let them catch you. When you're on watch you're not allowed to drink."

The beer didn't help him much. He knew that Pauli was a pig, but it upset him to find out that he could be a shrewd pig.

Pauli came in with the new exec. No one called attention; after duty hours it wasn't required. He ordered the lockers opened. They looked exactly as before. They were clean and the uniforms and underwear were clean too. But the underwear wasn't piled edge to edge as in boot camp. To make matters worse, one man kept his underwear on the second shelf, while another used the third. Pauli worked himself into a lather and threw all the men's belongings onto the floor.

While Pauli was inspecting the lockers on the starboard side, the exec came over to Teichmann and gave him to understand that he had better get his beer bottle out of sight. Teichmann slipped it into his bunk.

Then Pauli went to Teichmann's locker and tossed just about everything out, including his toothbrush.

"Why aren't you in regulation watch uniform?"

"I haven't been assigned to the night watch, sir."

"God damn it, didn't I tell you you had the watch for seven days?"

"It is forbidden," said the exec, "to assign a seaman to the night watch for two days running, except under battle conditions."

"We're not running a sanatorium here."

"No," said the exec, "but we do belong to the Navy and we have to observe Navy regulations."

Pauli said nothing further and left the crew's quarters livid with rage. When the exec set his foot on the first step of the ladder, Osterbuhr shouted, "Attention!" It didn't sound quite right; he seemed to be having trouble with his teeth again. The exec turned around and saluted in the general direction of Osterbuhr, who blushed like a young girl on her first date with a grown-up gentleman.

"You striking for admiral?" said Pitt. "I'm master-at-arms around here. If anybody's going to call attention, it's me and not you with them choppers in your mouth."

119

"You're the one that should really have called attention," said Stollenberg to Teichmann.

And then Teichmann got ashore after all. Pauli had gone off on leave, and because a man on watch was not eligible for leave, the exec sent him ashore on official business—namely, to take a roll of films to be developed—and told him he needn't be back before midnight.

After attending to the exec's business, he went to see Dora—with mixed feelings.

Dora was not there. The peroxide blonde told him she had gone shopping. Vögele was having a regular affair with the blonde; he went so far as to maintain that she was his first and only love. He came in for quite some ribbing from Bülow, with whom he had had to share his only love at first, but who then magnanimously renounced his share. He was really in love, though, and swallowed all insults without a word. He even pretended not to hear when Bülow asked him in what language he conversed with his love, since she couldn't possibly be expected to understand his bushman's dialect. Or else Bülow would say, "Vögele, I'm sure you're not gifted in bed. She does it from pure pity. She adopted you instead of a baby, so to speak, because she's childless, poor thing, and will surely remain so as long as she's faithful to you."

Vögele always replied with the same words: "She moost like me. Or she make me pay."

Teichmann sat down at the corner table by the bar and drank beer.

When Dora came in, he stood up. He had long wondered whether to do so. But he had no other choice when he saw her done up like a fashion plate. She had driven up in the delivery truck of a shipping firm.

"At last!" she said, and gave him her hand. "I'll be right with you; I just have to watch them unload."

All sorts of wonderful things were unloaded. Schnapps, liqueurs, wines, champagne, and fancy canned goods.

"Do you always buy wholesale?"

"Of course. It's cheaper. And that way I get everything 'without.' "

"How do you manage it?"

"That's a business secret. And now dream up a menu. Whatever you want to eat and drink. You can have anything your little heart desires."

"I leave it up to you."

"Then you can add up these bills; I'm sure you can do it quicker than I could. You went to a good school."

She gave him a pile of bills, which Teichmann added up. The sum had four figures.

"Heavens, how do you do it?"

"What?"

"Add so fast. That would have taken me fifteen minutes."

She wrote out a check and gave the driver and his helper sizable tips. "Thank you, lady," said the men, lifting their caps.

Stollenberg, Heyne, Bülow, Vögele, and Signalman Meisel came in. Vögele retired at once with his only love.

"Boys, you'll have to do without my company today," said Dora. "I have all sorts of things to attend to."

"Just what I was expecting," said Heyne. "I guess our little playmate has to make up for lost time."

"Wise guy!" said Dora. "Is it any of your business?" And for the first time Teichmann discovered that Heyne too could blush. Dora repaired to her apartment with Teichmann.

"Little one, you know, I really will be busy for a little while. About an hour."

"Can I help you?"

"No, you just stay here till I come back. Look, this is my private bar. Take whatever you want. But don't drink too much, see? I've got other plans."

He had moved a stool over to the bar with the idea of trying everything. He sampled the bottles one by one. First he had a sip of Steinhäger, then a jigger each of Rémy Martin, Hennessy, calvados, armagnac, Jacobi, Martell, Dujardin. After that there was still a bottle of Scotch, and to top it off he found a Jamaica rum with a wonderful bouquet. But it was thick and sirupy, so he just sipped at it. . . .

"Your health, sir."

The man who had appeared was of medium height and

looked as if he had once been powerfully built He was totally bald and had Negroid lips that were puckered and scarred, and strikingly handsome teeth—too handsome to be real. He was wearing a suit in the latest style, freshly pressed, a garish tie, and a flower in his lapel. One of the buttons of his fly was undone, the third from the top. Dark glasses concealed his eyes. All burned out, thought Teichmann, and put his age at past sixty. And perhaps because he couldn't see his eyes, he looked at his open fly. "Don't let me disturb you," the man said. "I'm always delighted, you know, when the young fellows seem impressed by our little bar. I set it up, you know. It makes me feel that I'm contributing something, too—see what I mean?—it's about all I'm good for these days, ha-ha-ha. Good taste has its points too. If you want to do me a favor, put in a good word with my wife about my bar. And if you'll take a word of advice, try the peach brandy, it's something quite special; over there in the corner, I put it there so people won't see it right away, ha-ha. But I won't keep you any longer. My wife won't be long now. I wish you a very pleasant evening in my home, he-he-he. . . ."

The open fly was gone. Teichmann thought he had been dreaming or that he was already drunk.

He began to help himself at briefer intervals and filled his glass to the brim each time. He didn't touch the peach brandy. He hadn't had anything to eat since lunch and felt a cozy warmth in his belly. Suddenly he noticed that one of the bottles was empty. He looked around on the carpet to see if he had spilled any.

"What are you crawling around like that for? You're drunk, oh, damn it, you're drunk. . . ."

"You were gone so long . . . ."

"Nonsense. I've been much quicker than I expected. And now you're drunk. It's horrid of you. And I was so looking forward to this evening!"

"Take it easy. My sense of taste is intact. I'll appreciate your dinner."

"No, you're boiled. And you don't have to grin like that and talk so pompous; you're just boiled. Fooey. I could spank you."

"Not so loud, Your pensioner might wake up."

"Who?"

"Your pensioned husband, who's supposed to be asleep."

"Why? Was he here?"

"It so happens that he was."

"He didn't bother you, did he?"

"Oh, no. He even recommended his favorite brandy."

"Yes, he's very proud of his bar."

"I thought it was yours."

"Of course, it's mine too."

" 'Too' is good."

"You're an awful kid, Hans, really."

She closed up the bar. He remained seated on the little stool. Very cautiously, as though fearing to burn her fingers, she laid her hand on his head.

"Watch out, there's pomade on it."

She took his head and held it against her thigh.

"You're going to get spots on your dress."

She bent over and took his head between her hands and smiled at him with a kindly, knowing smile, which gave her face a surprising charm, like a sudden ray of sunlight in an autumn landscape. That was something new for Teichman. He grew embarrassed and looked away. Then she kissed him and he followed her.

"Ah! And now let's have something to eat. You're a sweet kid, even . . ."

"Quit it, for God's sake. That's all I needed."

"I know why you're that way. They're all that way afterwards. It's funny. It's something a woman will never understand. . . ."

"Oh—so they're all that way. All of them. You must know."

"Oh, don't take it to heart. It's not as bad as all that."

"What made you single me out? Am I what was missing in your collection?"

"You mustn't be jealous."

"Who's jealous? That's the bunk."

"Don't say that. I know you're jealous. And I like you, you know that."

"Well, do you think it's pleasant for me to go in where a hundred others have been before me? It's a . . ."

"What is it? Out with it."

"Never mind. Not to mention the fact that I might catch something."

"You drink beer out of glasses that other people have used before you, don't you? And if you're very thirsty you don't even look at the glass very carefully. Sometimes you even drink out of dirty glasses."

"Glasses are washed in between."

"And not me? Is that what's worrying you?"

"Some people have their own glass."

"If they can afford it and if they've found the right glass."

Teichmann turned over on his back and looked at the ceiling. He knew that she was right.

"I'm very glad you take so much interest in your health— and mine. And now let's eat something. I want you to get *something* out of your evening."

He beat her. She didn't defend herself and she didn't scream. She only said, "Why are you doing that? You're only hurting yourself." And that made him furious. He beat her out of rage and despair. In her he beat all the women he would never have, or perhaps only a single one he would never have. Then Dora began to yell; she wept and screamed, and in the end, as he was dressing himself, she just screamed. Then he drank some of the peach brandy, straight from the bottle. He would have emptied the bottle if there hadn't been knocking on the door. When he sprang up, a staff sergeant and two MP's were standing there; the sergeant laid his hand on his shoulder and said, "You're under arrest. If you attempt to escape, I will shoot." The soldiers took him between them and led him away.

They drove him to patrol headquarters and locked him in a single cell. The cell was next to the guardroom; he heard the Army men talking and playing cards, and one of them was acting very superior because he had won a grand slam. Teichmann dozed. I'm drunk, Lord Almighty, I've never been so tanked. He knew he was lying to himself again, but he kept right on mumbling into space. I really had to fill up

124

like that just once. It was absolutely necessary. It was indispensable. . . .

He came wide awake. Dora was in the room next door. He recognized her voice. He couldn't make out everything she said. But then he heard her say, "The man is innocent. He didn't do anything wrong. Please believe me. I had nothing to do with calling the police."

"But you called for help?"

"No, I can't remember doing that."

"But he was beating you?"

"That's my business. I didn't ask anybody for help."

Teichmann heard one of the soldiers say to another, "Some women are like that. They get a kick out of it."

"I don't care what you think of me. But you've got to let the sailor go. He's innocent."

"Do you want him back again?"

"No. He'll go straight back to his ship. I'll vouch for him."

"*Your* vouching for him doesn't help us much."

A chair was being moved, so Teichmann couldn't understand what Dora said. Then he heard telephoning. A little later his door was opened and a light was flashed in his face. "Hey, wake up." He was taken into the guardroom. They gave him his paybook and the sage advice to steer clear of that sort of women.

He ran up and down the street. She can't have gone very far in so short a time, he reflected. But he didn't find her; the earth had swallowed her up. Maybe she's hiding in some dark doorway, watching me running back and forth. . . .

He took the shortest route back to the harbor.

6

The flotilla went into sweeping formation. And in one of the next nights they learned—every man on the *Albatross* learned it, and so did the wounded and even those who were killed—that death was nothing compared to what you had to go through before you were dead. They found out that dying itself can be a trifle, a nothing, and that the only thing that matters in war is how you die, in what form death comes to you, and above all whether it comes quickly or takes its time and tortures its victim before taking him. They found out that death was a sadist.

No. 4 ship hit a mine. It happened at dusk, visibility seven hundred yards. The *Albatross,* which was on the port side of No. 4, stopped at once. The detonation had not been particularly impressive: a short, hard, dry pop. No. 4 hoisted a black ball as a sign that she was incapable of maneuvering. Teichmann was amazed at the routine way in which the signal was given. He heard the captain calling out commands to his men, without haste or excitement. He made out a scream or two, but that was just a few screwballs who had lost their nerve, he thought. He watched as the men unlashed the rafts and threw them into the water, and let their comrades down onto them. By this time the screaming could be heard clearly.

"Do you need help?" Pauli shouted.

He received no answer.

"I suggest we put out the lifeboats," Teichmann heard the exec say; he spoke calmly but with an undertone of urgency.

No. 4 was gone.

Teichmann, who had the watch with Stüwe, took his binoculars. He held them to his eye and saw nothing. There was nothing more to be seen of No. 4.

126

"They got the rafts off," said Stüwe, "and they're full."

"The rafts aren't big."

"Yeah, but the engine room crew must have got killed when the mine struck. Those poor bastards are always the first to get it."

"Except when it comes from the air."

"That's true."

The *Albatross* moved slowly toward the rafts.

"What are they yelling for? We see them."

"Damned if I know."

A searchlight flared up on the bridge and took in the two rafts, alternating between them. Every time the men came into the cone of light, they seemed to scream louder. Maybe it's the glare of the searchlight, Teichmann thought. All around the rafts their heads protruded from the water. As they clung to the rafts, they looked like small children sitting at a grownups' table, barely able to see over the edge; and when the waves washed over the rafts, it was as though the tables had been taken away from them.

Now there was no doubt: those men down there were howling. Not all of them, but most. At first Teichmann thought they were shouting at each other. But then he saw that there must be another reason for the howling.

The howling men were laid out on deck. But these men on the heaving deck did not lie still. They flung their bodies every which way; they banged their fists on the deck or on their comrades; they bit each other and butted their heads on the deck, and their empty trouser legs swished back and forth, right and left, left and right, swabbing the deck like wet mops. The wetness was blood. And they howled the whole while. A piercing, blood-curling howl. Each scream sounded as if it must be the last, as if it were uttered with their last, desperate, dying strength. But it wasn't the last; the howling went on and on. And those men didn't get hoarse, their voices didn't flag. There was something monstrous about those screams; it was inconceivable that men could scream like that without tearing their vocal cords.

Some of the sailors gathered round them. The petty officer

who had taken a quick medical course began to busy himself. A few other joined in and tried to help.

But there was no help. When they cut open the trouser legs, they saw that those howling men, whom two men had to hold still, had legs, but that the legs were only half length. Their feet were where the knees should have been. The force of the explosion had driven their legs up into their thighs. Shinbones lay beside thighbones.

The crew of the *Albatross* stood watching. They saw how a seaman and an ensign—the only officer among the howling men—sank their teeth into each other as the deck rolled to port, and how when it rolled back to starboard the teeth tore chunks out of their faces and the two men went on howling. They saw how a sailor bored his thumb into another one's eye and how the thumb disappeared into the eye socket and the eye ran out. They saw how one sailor's head struck the deck with full force and he still went on howling because he was not yet dead. One man slid around in a circle and his left leg emerged from his pants and lay still on the deck, while the man continued sliding, and when he came back to the place where his leg was lying he pushed it away like a piece of wood that was in his way. Another, a very young sailor, whose thighbones had been driven out of their sockets and into his guts, squeezed his head with his hands as if it were bursting.

The sea became rougher. As the rolling increased, the howling men were thrown about more and more violently. The sea drove through the scuppers and washed over the deck, and the salt water ate into their wounds.

There was something so unreal, so horrible, so obscene about the dance of these madmen with their stumps of legs, that the onlookers who still had their legs behaved like children witnessing something that no one had ever seen or heard of. They stood staring, and in their throats there was a gagging sound composed of disgust, pity, and horror.

In the end nearly all the men who still had their legs fled from the scene. Those who remained were not necessarily the best. But there was no escape from the howling. It did no good to run away. It penetrated the whole ship. It was just a little softer if you were farther away.

Stollenberg stood in the stern, leaning on the cross bar that held the lines of the paravanes. His hands gripped the bar convulsively. He bent forward, peering into the propeller wash as though he had to vomit.

Teichmann remained close to the howling men. He saw the horror, but somehow he was not horrified, or he had ceased to be, or he had forgotten. He was only amazed and a little curious. He himself was not conscious of what he was doing. But Heyne saw it.

Heyne had fled and was standing near Stollenberg, staring at Teichmann. He saw that his hands were trembling and his face twitching as though charged with electricity. But he also saw that Teichmann stood motionless and did not for a moment take his eyes off the dance. He only moved his head from time to time when his eyes followed the scene, and once he leaned forward a little, so as to see something a little more clearly.

Heyne hated him as he stood there, innocent and fearless, as if the idea of running away from the horror had never even occurred to him. Somehow he emanated a sense of power, a natural, brute power which the few poison drops of his intellect had made demonic. As he stands there now, there's something of the demon in him, there's something pathological about his strength, said Heyne inwardly as though to give himself courage. He was devoured with envy of Teichmann's vitality—envy and bitterness. "The beast! Yes, he's a beast," he muttered and gaped at Teichmann as though he were from another world, a world inaccessible to him.

They screamed for two hours, one hundred and twenty minutes. Then they subsided, one by one. Their vocal cords had ceased to function. By midnight they only moaned or whimpered. From time to time one of them cried out "Help" or "O God," and now and then one would let out a hoarse, shrill scream.

"Hans!" Teichmann heard somebody saying behind him. It wasn't Stollenberg's voice or Heyne's, and no one else called

129

him by his first name. "The exec has given permission. Hold the flashlight."

Later, much later, it made Teichmann ashamed to think back on this night; whenever it came to his mind, even if no one was near him, he felt a burning redness rise to his cheeks because he had not been a good comrade to these men who were slowly dying on deck. He had only been able to help a few; for most of them it had been too late.

They knelt down beside each man in turn. Teichmann held the flashlight. They had wound a handkerchief around it, and in the faint glow they looked for the heads. They saw the distorted, convulsed faces, ravaged with pain, faces that were no longer faces. They were soiled, scratched, torn; the lips were bitten through, and there was slimy foam around the mouth. The eyes—some were already dead, but their eyes were still staring straight ahead, as if looking into infinity—the eyes of those who were still alive had sprung out of their sockets and were ringed with blood. Gigantic cold eyes that had ceased to see and ceased to move. Cautiously, almost tenderly, as though fearing to hurt them, the chief took the head of the one who was screaming loudest, and pressed it slowly to one side, until the cheek lay flat on the deck. Teichmann held the light. With his left hand the chief held the head in this position and fired two shots in quick succession, the second shot an inch lower than the first.

They went from one to the other, knelt down, looked for the head, placed it in the right position, waited until the water had flowed off the deck and the rolling ship was approximately level. Then the chief fired.

When they came to the fourth man, the magazine was empty, and the chief had to reload. In the glow of the flashlight the man could see everything. He saw the chief opening the breach of his pistol, taking out the empty magazine, blowing into the barrel—meanwhile the carriage had slipped forward—laying the full magazine on the deck, pulling back the carriage with his free hand, picking up the full magazine, inserting it, and thrusting the empty magazine into his pocket. The man looked at the chief and thanked him with his eyes for putting him out of his misery.

From then on it was easier for Teichmann to stand by with the flashlight. They had to reload twice. And then they were finished.

Twenty-three men from No. 4 ship had been rescued. Eleven died on the deck of the *Albatross*. Three had broken legs that could be set. Nine were uninjured. The captain, one officer, two petty officers, and twelve men had been drowned.

Toward morning the wind abated a little. The flotilla had changed its course; the sea came from astern and the main deck remained dry. The stars had vanished from the sky; only the naked white light of the moon shone on the dead men. They were caked with gray salt, which gave their faces the look of plaster masks. Their arms were twisted like corkscrews and seemed elongated because the legs were missing. But all was still.

Teichmann sat on the forecastle ladder. Heyne sat beside him smoking one cigarette after another. Stollenberg was on watch.

"That lousy God-damn moon," said Heyne.

Then for a long while there was silence.

"It looks round and yellow like cake dough. I can't stand looking at it. It makes me sick the way it sits up there; it makes me want to throw up."

"I think it looks white, white with a dash of green," said Teichmann slowly, as though every word were very important. "Anyway, it's far away."

"Yes, but it looks disgusting. I couldn't drink as much as I'd like to vomit now," said Heyne. Then he cried "Ouch!" He had thrown his half-smoked cigarette overboard and misjudged the wind, which had sent it back in his face.

A radioman striker came out of the radio shack, where he had been on watch. When he saw the dead men, he screamed, "Jesus, Mary and Jo . . ." For quite some time he stood motionless. Then he lit out aft. Teichmann and Heyne roared with laughter.

"They're dead, they won't hurt you," cried Heyne, gurgling with laughter. "Look at that cry-baby, Hans, just look at him. Go on, go home to Mother, ha-ha-ha."

"Cover them up, for God's sake," sobbed the radioman. "Please, cover them up."

"If you'll lend us your handkerchief."

In the morning they were sewed up in canvas. That took an hour. Then they lay side by side, short, clumsy-looking sacks, no longer than flour sacks on a loading platform ready for shipping. Everything else that was left of them had been thrown overboard.

The *Albatross* stopped and lowered its battle pennant to half-mast. Those of the crew who were off watch fell out on deck, waiting for their captain. The exec had gone aft to report. The men stood there gazing past the sacks into the water, flexing their knees to keep from falling when the ship rolled. A cold gusty wind was blowing.

Pauli didn't appear. The exec went back again to his cabin. The men waited. Their hands crossed behind their backs, their knees swaying with the motion of the ship, they stood like a living wall, and it wasn't certain how long the wall would hold up.

Pauli was drunk. That was obvious to all as they saw him following the exec. The exec ordered the crew to attention.

Pauli said nothing. The men waited. But not one word came out of his mouth. He seemed embarrassed. The men stared at him, and their eyes became cruel. Pauli stood facing this wall of hatred and contempt; he stared at the boots of his crew and said nothing. When he belched, the exec stepped in front of him. And then the exec said a few words. It was hard for him to speak, and the words struggled painfully out of his mouth. Most of what he said was swallowed up by the wind. He stood with his legs apart, trying to keep his balance. When the ship lurched, he had to clutch the rail, but though his voice faded now and then in the wind, it remained steady. ". . . and deliver us from evil . . . and the power and the glory . . . for ever and ever." His words lost themselves in the wide sea, which gave no answer, which was cold and indifferent as the tatters of cloud that scudded across the sky. But in the presence of the young ensign the men removed their caps.

A few minutes later it was over. The bodies were gone from

132

the deck, the equipment was put out, the cooks went aft to the galley to get breakfast.

Signalman Meisel of the *Albatross* was drowned. He had been running a fever of 103, probably from pneumonia, when Pauli ordered him to go out with a boat unit in order to signal back the nature of an object flowing about in the water—it turned out to be an unopened German parachute. When Meisel, standing on the forward thwart of the boat, tried to signal, he lost his balance and fell overboard. He sank at once, no doubt from a heart attack.

In the middle of May the flotilla put into Bremerhaven. There it lay for two weeks.

The order came to be prepared to sail on June 8 at 0530. The night of June 6 the crews were allowed ashore for the last time. The *Albatross* was duty ship.

At midnight Teichmann relieved Stollenberg on the gangway watch.

"Pauli's got one in his cabin again."

"Then things haven't been too boring."

"Just a kid. A girl scout, I think, but full to the gills. I doubt if she ever had a drink before."

"Since when have you been in the Girls' Friendly Society?"

"At first it was quiet. Then she began to scream."

"They do sometimes."

"Yes, but she screamed pretty loud, Hans, and Pauli had said they were just going to have a cup of coffee."

"Is that all?"

"It's enough for me. Happy watch."

"Sleep well."

After midnight the first sailors came back from town. Heyne, Bülow, and Vögele were relatively sober.

Shortly after 0100 a port authority truck drove up; two petty officers of the shore patrol proceeded to unload sailors like sacks of coal. Teichmann awakened, Stüwe, and the two of them hauled the drunks aboard. It was rough work because some of them were positive that they could get up the gangplank on all fours. And halfway several of them began to relate in full what a beautiful time they had had.

At 0130, when Ensign Paschen, who was duty officer, inspected the watch, they were loading the last drunk aboard. Only the chief was still missing.

At 0300 Pauli emerged from his cabin and ordered Teichmann to request Lieutenant Loewe's presence on board.

Loewe was sleeping in the officers' barracks. It took Teichmann some time to find his room, which proved to be empty. He went from room to room shining his flashlight in the bunks. Most of them were empty, but finally he had the luck to find Lieutenant Loewe—not alone.

"Say, what's got into *you?*"

"I've got to speak to Lieutenant Loewe."

"But he's sound asleep."

"I'm sorry."

"Don't you dare wake him. If anybody has to wake him, I will."

The lieutenant's nostrils were held shut. That woke him up.

"Honey lamb, somebody wants you."

On the way back Teichmann met the chief. He heard him before he saw him.

"I'm full to the scuppers, Teichmann. It had to be. It was exactly ten years ago today, Hans, since I . . . Oh, hell, what would a kid like you understand?" Teichmann tried to guide him over the gangplank. "She never loved me, ha-ha," the chief bawled. "Do you know what that is, you young squirt?"

"Yes," said Teichmann, "it so happens that I do. It's King Philipp's aria from *Don Carlos.*"

"Idiot," said the chief, and mounted the gangplank alone and upright as if he hadn't touched a drop.

At 0400 Teichmann was relieved by Stüwe.

In the morning Teichmann, Stollenberg, and Stüwe drove to the supply depot in a truck for new depth charge racks. Stüwe gave the driver a pack of cigarettes and asked him to make a slight detour and stop just a moment at the Red Swan; it would hardly delay them at all, he'd be right out. The driver was reluctant, but when Stüwe told him his hard-luck story about weeks at sea and mounting watch till he could hardly see straight, he could think of no valid objection and only remarked that he himself was a married man. "There you have it," said Stüwe. "In that case you understand."

"But I won't wait more than ten minutes."

"That's plenty."

The driver parked a hundred yards from the Red Swan.

"What are you stopping here for?"

"I'm a married man. If one of the girls ever recognizes me on the street when I'm with my wife, my goose is cooked."

"Don't be silly. The girls wouldn't do that; they'd never recognize you if you were with your wife."

But the driver wouldn't move an inch.

"That must be some dragon you've got," said Stüwe, and ran for it.

Twenty minutes later there was still no sign of him. Teichmann suggested that they move up in front of the Red Swan and make a little noise with the horn. The driver still wouldn't budge.

But at the end of half an hour, he consented to park outside the Red Swan. Teichmann rested his thumb on the horn. "Good God, man," said the driver, "not so loud."

Almost instantly a number of windows opened, revealing semiclad damsels who said things that brought a blush to the driver's cheeks.

"I'm so embarrassed," said the driver, trying to look very small.

"A little embarrassment won't hurt you. But Stüwe had better step on it."

Finally he appeared. "I ain't an express train," he cried, buttoning himself up as he ran.

There was great excitement on the *Albatross* when they got back. The flotilla commander had visited every ship, asking who had brought a girl on board the night before. No one had spoken up.

"It was Pauli," said Stollenberg. "It happened on my watch."

"And I guess they got her off in mine," said Stüwe. Lieutenant Loewe had sent him away from the gangway for a few minutes to check the lines. It had struck him as fishy even at the time.

"We should have put it all down in the log," said Stollenberg.

"Sure, and got thrown in the brig for a week like Teichmann."

That afternoon the flotilla commander assembled all the crews on the pier. Beside him stood a man in the uniform of a National Socialist district chief. The district chief spoke with a man in civilian clothes who looked as pale as cheese and was holding a girl by the hand. The girl looked to be about fifteen. Behind them stood Lieutenant Loewe. These five persons passed slowly down the line of men. Three times.

When they had finished with one rank, the flotilla commander ordered the first rank eight steps forward. The second rank was inspected and then took five steps forward; then the little group passed down the third rank. The girl looked as if she might collapse at any moment. Beside her walked the flotilla commander; his face was pale and his cheekbones stood out more prominently than usual. He looked like a hungry bird of prey, waiting to pounce on its victim.

Lieutenant Loewe had reported that the crews were complete. Ensign Paschen had called his attention to the captain's absence.

"I know that. He's in his bunk sick."

"That's news to me, sir."

"If you please, Paschen. How can you mention an officer in this connection! Why, you're an officer yourself."

"I see no connection between my profession and Herr Pauli's."

"If you please, Paschen, this is no time for dialectical maneuvers."

Stollenberg said he wished to make an announcement.

"Forget it," said Teichmann. "We don't want to disgrace the flotilla. This is a little business we can settle by ourselves."

"We'll fix that swine better than any Navy Court," said Meckel. It was forbidden to speak in ranks, but on this occasion the superiors seemed to be hard of hearing. They were all ashamed.

At six next morning the flotilla put out to sea. A fresh

wind was blowing from west-southwest. The waves were greenish black, topped with whitecaps that sprang like angry dogs at the bow of the ship, their heads bursting into foam as they struck. Gulls circled low over the sea, letting out sharp screams. The clouds formed violet mountains, and where there were no clouds the sky looked like milk. In the west a thin sulphur-yellow stripe hung over the horizon.

The wind mounted and began to howl; it lashed the waves high and sent them beating against the ships. And then suddenly the storm was upon them.

Off Wangerooge the flotilla took a westward course. Now they were taking the sea head on; it pressed the bow under water, beat against the flimsy splinter shield of the forward battle station, and then flung itself with a crash against the superstructure of the ships. But they withstood the onslaught, braced themselves, and struggled painfully through the watery mass. Lifted up by the mountainous waves, they danced for a moment on the summits, before being hurled down and buried in the troughs. And then they would rise again, shake off the water like wet dogs, and climb the next mountain, only to fall once more reeling into the depths. These tough little fishing vessels might have stood the punishment indefinitely; the only danger was that the ships would lose contact with each other.

The signal "Tare George" was hoisted and lowered on the flotilla leader; the flotilla went into formation, the distance between ships was reduced, and the partners took up position side by side. But even then it was hard to keep contact. When two ships fell into troughs at once, only the trucks of their masts could be seen.

When the storm showed no sign of letting up, the flotilla put in to shore and waited two days in the mouth of the Ems.

The sea was still rough when they resumed their course. A good half of the *Albatross*'s crew went without lunch these days and contented themselves with a crust of bread. Teichmann, Stollenberg, and Heyne felt fine; the sea no longer troubled them. Bülow and Vögele, and among the old seamen Pitt, Stüwe, and Lauer, were sick. The two newcomers, Schindler and Glatzel, who had come aboard as replacements for Meisel, were utterly woebegone. They lay in their bunks, and as far as they were concerned the world had ended. The exec had to read his own messages and do his own semaphoring. The good sailors had a glorious time of it; besides their own portions of meat and sausage, they had those of their seasick comrades. Teichmann managed to wangle eight chops for himself in one day. Schmutzler was hit in the head by a flying object, and this event in turn had a good deal to do with the death of Hinsch.

Schmutzler was something of a character. Frail and sickly-looking, he had enormous popeyes and a broad mouth that made him look like a frog, except that frogs haven't got blue rings under their eyes.

On one of the stormy days Teichmann asked Heyne for his pencil, which had an eraser. When Heyne went aft with a pot of potatoes, Teichmann asked him to see that the cook didn't leave the galley for a few minutes. Heyne put the pot in the passageway outside the galley and stood there for a while batting the breeze with Schmutzler. Schmutzler was grateful for every word that anyone exchanged with him; he liked to hear himself talk and could tell hair-raising tales about things that had allegedly happened to him on shore.

As they were chatting, Teichmann busied himself with the order book that was in a glass case on the wall of the passage way between the captain's cabin and the galley. The book lay open in the case, so that everyone could read the orders for the day. The case was left unlocked, because up to this time no one except the CPO had ever thought of making entries in the book.

Schmutzler was busy opening cans of peas when Teichmann dropped the pot at his feet.

"Man, you scared me. I'm nervous today."

"You're always nervous when you haven't spent the night on shore."

"No, it's not that. It's because I haven't been able to eat anything for six days with this damned sea."

"Yeah, and I suppose it's the sea that keeps you from reading the calendar straight?"

138

"What are you talking about?"

"Since when do we have one-dish meals on Sunday?"

"Go on, it's only Saturday."

What? Will you kindly have a look at the date? The slob's got eyes like a hippopotamus and he can't even read the order book right."

"I'll bet you anything you want that today's Saturday," said Schmutzler, and went over to the glass case. "What's that? Why . . ."

"Sap!"

In the crew's quarters Teichmann told all who would listen how his mouth was watering for those pork chops and string beans, the Navy's Sunday meal. Then he entered into negotiations with the sufferers from seasickness, giving such a description of the dripping fat pork chops that their stomachs turned at the mere thought. When he had lined up eight chops, he informed Heyne and Stollenberg that he had also wangled two chops for them, but that he would have to keep Heyne's pencil for the present.

On Saturday night he erased the altered date in the order book and entered the correct one. The reasoning behind his maneuvers was that he had looked into the radio shack on Saturday morning to inquire about the weather and the report was that the wind would fall off appreciably during the night.

Which is just what happened. By Sunday noon pretty close to the whole crew were up and active. Those, especially, who had been fasting for reasons of seasickness were famished. They turned up eagerly at mess, and what should be set before them but the Saturday one-dish meal. Werner, the CPO, had informed the cook that this week could not have two Sundays in a row.

Hell broke loose. The sailors were beside themselves at the sight of the miserable, monotonous dish, composed of carrots, potatoes, peas, and an utterly tasteless synthetic sauce. They were particularly furious about the vegetables: for every pea there were ten carrots.

Such bilge on the Holy Sabbath was an outrage, said Pitt; in his capacity as master-at-arms he felt entitled to shout the loudest, and he had the full support of the men. Teichmann said, "You speak after my own heart." Pitt was one of those who had ceded his chop to Teichmann the day before.

Teichmann was sent aft to summon the cook. But Schmutzler didn't dare set foot in the mess and stood up by the hatch. "Come on down here, you swine, and we'll make hash of you," Pitt roared. 'I'll flatten him into noodles," said Löbbermann.

Schmutzler stayed where he was. He had made a mistake in the date, he said; he had thought it was Saturday.

Lauer said that was a damn lie; only this morning he had been making jokes about the hymns they had been singing over the radio. They sing them on weekdays now, said Schmutzler. That was a lie, Pitt shouted. Oh no, said Schmutzler, since the beginning of the war they had been singing hymns on weekdays, he was sure of it. Had he vomited into the food, or what kind of a sauce was this anyway? Meckel inquired. No, Schmutzler protested, he never vomited into the food, he wasn't that much of a pig, but today he'd been in a bit of hurry with the sauce. However, he'd be glad to look at the label on the can to see what it actually was.

"And what about the peas?" Löbbermann yelled. "You can count them on the fingers of one hand." He had lined up his peas beside his plate, flattening them with his thumb to keep them from rolling off the table. He was sure, he said, that there were more peas in the officers' mess, and he was going to show his peas to the CPO. The others began to follow suit, and shouted hurrah when they found a pea in their plate. Schmutzler, who was still standing up at the hatch, regarded this little game as a good sign and decided that the men were beginning to take a lighter view of the incident. By way of preparing a good exit, he called down, "You can have seconds." But before he could withdraw, a soup bowl hit him in the head. "That was good pitching, boy," said Osterbuhr, rattling his teeth with enthusiasm.

From the bridge Pauli saw Schmutzler keel over and then quickly pick himself up for fear that someone might come up to finish him off.

Pauli appeared in the crew's quarters.

"Who threw that soup bowl?"

Hinsch admitted his guilt.

"As soon as we're back in port, I'll lock you up. And meanwhile you can be sure you'll have nothing to laugh about."

By afternoon the sea was calm enough for the paravanes to be streamed. Hinsch was a specialist at setting the explosive cable-cutter. It was the most dangerous part of the work, and he had become remarkably skillful at it. But that day it seemed to Pauli that they were taking too long in getting the equipment ready and it was Hinsch's fault. "You're half asleep," Pauli bawled at him, "but I'll wake you up. All you know how to do is throw soup bowls around. You will make a complete circuit of the deck, and take that cable-cutter with you. Maybe on the way you'll remember how these little things are handled."

On the forecastle Hinsch stumbled over the port bollard. In falling, he held the mechanism over his head to prevent it from coming in contact with the deck.

"Once more around now, to teach you to open your sleepy eyes and keep your feet straight. But this time remove the safety pin."

The CPO ran to the officers' mess for the exec, who was off watch. But before Werner could say a word, the explosion came. Afterwards no one knew exactly what had happened. Hinsch had carried the activated cable cutter carefully in front of him. He had not run but had walked slowly. There was no apparent reason why the thing should have gone off. The seamen who had been aft working on the paravanes had only heard the explosion. Aside from the capstan, there was nothing on the forecastle that Hinsch could have stumbled over; the bollards were on the sides, and Hinsch was amidships when the explosion occurred.

Message to the flotilla leader: "K to C: Man fatally injured readying equipment."

Message from flotilla leader: "C to K: Send full report."

"I'll write that report," said the exec, who had mounted to the bridge. Then he went with Pauli to the captain's cabin.

There wasn't much left of Hinsch's legs. His face and the top of his body looked uninjured, but when he was examined more closely, there were innumerable little holes made by the

141

lead in the cable-cutter. When they laid him on the raft, the blood emerged from the holes like water from a squeezed sponge.

It was blowing up again, and that evening the paravanes had to be retrieved. Then Hinsch was buried.

For the next few days the flotilla swept mines off the islands of Terschelling and Ameland. Then the wind rose again to storm strength, the equipment was recovered, and that night there was a tremendous sea.

Teichmann and Heyne had the midnight watch on the after 20-millimeter station. Pitt had thought up the new watch schedule, and the men had quietly put it into effect.

At two o'clock Teichmann left his post. A few minutes later he came back as though nothing had happened. A little later someone in the stern said, "Ready?"

"All clear." That was Pitt's voice.

"Let her down slowly."

They heard a line paying off.

"We're making too much headway. He won't come into contact with the propeller."

"Haul her in."

They heard the chafing of the line against the railing as it was hauled in hand over hand.

"He ain't dead yet."

"Tie a weight to his legs."

"We've lost too many weights."

"Let her down again."

Almost simultaneously Teichmann and Heyne saw the chief going aft. They saw him too late. They had no time to warn the sailors in the stern.

"Haul it in."

That was the chief's voice.

Silence.

"Haul it in, I say."

"But, sir . . ."

"Haul it in, I said, and make it quick."

They heard a line being hauled in. It came very slowly.

"Sir . . ."

"How long are you going to take hauling in that line?"

142

They heard the chafing of the line again. And then it was still.

"There we are. And now lower him to starboard, straight down the side; that way he'll get into the propeller. The propeller turns to the right. You might have known that by now, you blubberheads."

They heard something splashing in the water and the line being paid out.

Silence.

"Take it in."

"Have a look around."

"All clear."

"Cut."

An ax struck.

"Hope he don't float."

"Nobody would recognize him."

In the lee of the stack Teichmann lit a cigarette.

"I've seldom seen a rottener character than that Pauli," said Heyne. "I've often wondered if he didn't, somewhere in that crumby carcass of his, have something resembling a heart. Never saw any sign of it."

After a while he went on, "But there's this consolation. If it's possible for one man to have so many bad qualities, maybe the opposite could happen sometime. I mean, maybe somebody could have as many good qualities as . . ."

"For God's sake, will you dry up!"

For a whole hour neither said a word.

"You don't happen to have a butt?"

"No."

"Then roll me one. There's the box."

Heyne hadn't learned yet to roll cigarettes, though he had finer fingers than Teichmann.

"There's nothing to be nervous about."

"My fingers are sticky, that's why it takes longer."

"Why are your fingers sticky? You sweating?"

"No."

"I wouldn't think so. You wouldn't call it a hot night."

"But the blood was warm and now it's sticky."

"It's going to taste mighty good, that little butt. That way

143

I get something out of the business. I would have liked to help. Would have been better than listening. This way the thing seems scarier than it really was."

"Maybe you're right."

At four o'clock they were relieved by Meckel and Halbernagel. Halbernagel said he had something to do on deck for another couple of minutes; would they mind waiting? Then he took some of the cleaning waste they used for wiping off shells before loading, wedged it under his arm like a waiter with his napkin, and went down on deck.

"Yeah," said Meckel, "we stuck that pig, all right."

"Where?" Heyne asked.

"In its pen," said Meckel.

"But we didn't hear him squeal," said Heyne.

"Ho, ho! No, we shoved his teeth down his windpipe. Unfortunately, he bled a bit."

Halbernagel came down for more waste.

At breakfast Pitt broke the news: Pauli had been washed overboard in the heavy seas that night; there seemed to be no other way of accounting for his absence.

The *Albatross* was flying the flotilla commander's pennant. She had become leader of the 52nd Minesweeper Flotilla. Lieutenant Commander Wegener occupied the captain's cabin. He had appointed Ensign Paschen captain, but Paschen had to continue on as exec until a new exec could be taken aboard. For the moment the flotilla commander was the actual captain of the *Albatross*.

Outwardly he had changed a bit since his days in Dänholm. He now wore a tattered blue jacket with leather patches sewed on the elbows. He wore his cap, which had once been white, tilted slightly to starboard; the gold embroidery on the visor was no longer present; he had had the staff officers' insignia stamped out in tin and painted yellow, but it was badly corroded and it took a good deal of imagination to tell what it was. Aside from his pipe, which he kept in his mouth even when it was not burning, his gold wrist watch was the only article remaining from the Dänholm days. The expensive-looking watch did not fit in with the rest of his rig, but he took very good care of it. The sailors said that that was why he always kept his left hand in his pocket.

The flotilla commander hadn't been aboard for twenty-four hours when Pauli came back. Teichmann, who had had the morning watch, remarked on it at breakfast. He spoke in a quiet conversational tone in order not to frighten anyone. "You're nuts," said Pitt. His eyes widened and began to flicker. "He's up on deck, you can go up and see for yourself," said Teichmann. Pitt jumped up, snorted violently, made wild incomprehensible movements with his hands, and mounted the ladder.

A squadron of T-boats had brought him. They had fished him out of the water, and having heard the radio message in which the flotilla commander had reported Pauli missing, one of the boats came alongside the *Albatross*—not quite alongside because of the heavy seas; there remained a gap of four yards—and tossed Pauli over onto the *Albatross* with a quick "Heave-ho." Then the T-boats sped away. Teichmann said it had been very impressive to see the T-boats, all of them brand new, come speeding in, sending up high spray, looking like Santa Clauses riding through the snow. "Looks as if your Santa Clauses have brought us a little present," said Heyne, and the others could think of no curses lewd enough to comment on Pauli's shameless and inconsiderate behavior.

Now he lay there on deck. He had been lashed to the starboard rail by a line around his left leg, to prevent him from being washed overboard.

"His face is gone," said Pitt on his return to the crew's quarters. The men went back to their breakfast. But just the same, there was something uncanny about this business. And this wasn't the end of it.

In the days that followed the wind rose to storm strength, turning the surface of the sea into a witches' caldron. When the night watches came on duty, Pauli was gone again.

All night he stayed away. The next morning before breakfast, the CPO called into the crew's quarters, "Three men."

Teichmann, Stollenberg, and Vögele reported and under the direction of the CPO hoisted Pauli back on board. He had been washed overboard and had spent the night in the water. Now they hoisted him on board by his line—a rough job on an empty stomach.

The announcement that Pauli was back again was greeted by a few moments of oppressive silence. Then Stüwe said, "The swine!" They hated Pauli dead even more than they had alive. They hated him for coming back and because they had a feeling that he was avenging himself on them and laughing up his sleeve at them. When they went on watch, they had to pass him as he lay there, a hunk of bloated flesh, tied like bait to a line, faceless. Only the back of his head was left, and his nosebone. The nosebone was very white and bashed in; it grinned out of the swollen flesh, as though mocking them. His pants were torn and half stripped off, revealing his underpants, which had taken on a greenish-yellow color. And one leg was bent back as if he were trying to scratch his behind with his heel. There he lay, as if there were still life in him, moving with the heaving of the ship, and the men resolved a second time to throw him overboard during the night—this time for good.

All day the ships pounded through the wild sea. Aboard the *Albatross* weird, unfamiliar sounds were heard. Although the engine was throttled down, the screw made an ungodly din when it emerged from the water at the crest of a wave and spun through the air like a top. Below decks there was a groaning and rattling, for everything that wasn't lashed tight had begun to lead a life of its own. In the crew's quarters the doors of the dish locker banged to and fro; dishes fell clattering and crashing to the deck, tables and benches slid about, and there was a constant thudding of sea boots. The contents of the storeroom shifted from side to side, and in the crew's quarters it sounded like a dozen old men in carpet slippers shuffling across the deck. But all the tones of this weird orchestra were dominated by the sea, as it broke raging and roaring over the *Albatross,* beating with the sound of rifle fire against the sheet-iron splinter shield of the forward battle station, thundering over the bridge, and descending with a crash on the after deck.

Even so, most of the men kept their legs and appetites.

The mess gang had to carry the food from the galley to the crew's quarters, and a cable had been stretched along the deck for them to hold on to, if they had a free hand, which they usually did not. That day, as they were getting supper, they waited in the shelter of the bridge for the moment when the deck would be free from water, and then ran for it. Vögele had managed to juggle his tray, piled with the men's rations of butter, eggs, and ham, without mishap from the galley as far as the bridge. Here he stood waiting until the sea would let him spring across the deck. The sea obliged him, but when he reached the crew's quarters his tray was empty.

"Pauli shnaffled it all avay," said Vögele, and sat down at the table, which was bare except for tea and dry bread. That was too much for the men. If Vögele hadn't been such a good fellow, they would have beaten him up even though he was innocent. He was innocent because, as he was trying to cross the deck, the sea had flung Pauli square in front of him; Vögele stumbled, fell down, and barely had time to save himself and his empty tray before the next breaker washed over the deck.

"Who's got the watch?"

"The chief."

"Let's go, then."

A minute later Pauli was gone for good.

In the next few days the flotilla swept thirty-seven mines. No. 5 ship hit a mine and was lost. The crew was saved, except for the captain, the exec, and the black gang. Then a shortage of coal compelled the flotilla to put into Den Helder.

Twenty nautical miles from the Dutch port the engines were running up to full speed and then to flank speed. Bülow, who had had the bridge watch, told the men at dinner that the engineering officer had notified the bridge that at that speed the coal bunkers would be empty in five hours. The commander had replied that a German reconnaissance plane had sighted a sub four miles off Den Helder, and he was going to get it if it meant burning all the bunks.

At 2000 Teichmann and Heyne went on watch. It was growing dark. The clouds hung low—thick, heavy rain clouds.

Only in the west there was a bright, salmon-colored strip, gilded by the setting sun, which still shone through occasional gaps in the clouds.

A little after 2200 it began to rain. It was very dark. The horizon could no longer be distinguished; sea and sky were equally black, and the sea rolled lazily like sirup. Three red rockets rose in the night sky. At the same time the alarm bells clanged and the Morse code sign for sub was repeated three times over the loud-speaker system. The chase began.

At brief intervals the ships stopped to let the men listen to the hydrophones, undisturbed by the sound of propellers. A spectral silence prevailed, as in a great deserted church, an unbearable silence that set the men's nerves on edge. They felt vaguely that warfare had become a purely technical business, and that there wasn't much men could do. Everything depended on the listening device. The men could only wait and be ready.

Shortly after 2300—the ships lay motionless, the silence broken only by the steady whish of the rain and little waves lapping against the sides—Teichmann and Heyne heard the engine-room telegraph on the bridge being swung back and forth three times. They knew that this could only mean "all ahead emergency speed." The sub must have been located.

"Ready depth charges," cried the flotilla commander from the bridge. The searchlights of the whole flotilla came to life. The *Albatross* turned hard starboard.

"Depth charges ready," cried the CPO.

Ensign Paschen came running aft, a stop watch hanging from his neck. He had two depth charges dropped in close succession, both set for a depth of 90 feet; and then a third set for 120 feet.

With a deafening roar the sea parted. Three times it roared with rage and sent three white fountains bounding into the night sky.

The sweepers stopped again. The sound men sat listening. The searchlights swept the sea, but found only dead fish.

"I don't like this kind of war, what about you?"

"No," said Heyne in a whisper. He was jittery. When Teich-

148

mann lit a cigarette, and the flame flickered from his cupped hands, Heyne said in an agitated, embittered tone, "Say, cut that out."

"Boy, oh boy!"

Every word that was spoken on the bridge could be heard at the after battle station; only the words came muffled as though by a curtain, and the voices sounded breathless, as if everyone on board were whispering. The bell of the engine-room telegraph sounded painfully loud in their ears.

"What are they being so quiet about? The sub can't . . ."

The engine-room telegraph sounded three times. The engine came to life. The *Albatross* seemed to leap forward. Then she heeled hard and turned fifty degrees to port. The flotilla commander turned up in the stern where the depth charge gang was busy and gave Paschen an order that Teichmann could not understand, because the next ship was dropping ash cans to encircle the sub. Then the commander returned to the bridge. Paschen ordered his men to set all charges for 120 feet. A blinker signal was given on the bridge and four ash cans were dropped.

After the detonations the ships stopped. The searchlights groped their way through the rain, searching the sea. The dead fish gleamed phosphorescent, and in among the dead fish an object was floating. From all sides the searchlights directed their beams on it, like the spokes of a wheel converging on the hub. The object turned into a man, and beside the man a piece of steel suddenly grew out of the water, remained motionless like a threatening finger for five, six, seven seconds, and sank. With it sank the man, as though a giant's finger had drawn him under. An oil slick appeared, iridescent in the beam of the searchlights.

For five minutes nothing happened. Only oil gushed to the surface. Then a man shot out of the water and lay still, shapeless in his pneumatic life jacket. Then three more came popping up like trout leaping from a stream.

The lifeboat put out and brought them aboard. Blood flowed from their mouths, their lungs had burst, and the oil had done the rest.

Until 0600 the ships remained at the scene of the sinking.

Then they put into Dan Helder and the British seamen were buried with military honors.

There was no liberty. Too much work on board. Provisions and ammunition were taken on, and that same night some of the ships loaded coal. The *Albatross* tied up at the coal pier the following morning, but the loading began only toward evening.

At 0300 the coaling was completed. The men, thoroughly blackened, were sitting on deck drinking their beer when Halbernagel rode up with a situation report on Helder and environs. Since Pauli's death he had become the flotilla commander's orderly; his official title was "commander's runner," but he liked to be called "commander's orderly." In this capacity he ostensibly had all sorts of things to attend to on shore. The flotilla staff had provided him with a bicycle and a permanent pass. He spent his time dashing from place to place, having a look around; this he called "shore duty." He now reported the discovery of a restaurant where for one gulden they served a first-class steak with pancakes and salad. The proprietress had two daughters who worked during the week in Haarlem and only came to Helder on week ends, but if the daughters had the same ideas as their mother, and the mother had dropped hints to that effect, there was business there. For urgent cases he had scared up a woman who was, well, a little older, but she was kind of expensive. Anyone interested in details should apply to him: whorehouse there was none.

"What rake-off does the pimp get?"

"Is that how you thank me? I'm just trying to keep you posted."

Grieved and offended, Halbernagel withdrew, pushing his bicycle. Meckel threw an empty beer bottle after him, whereupon Halbernagel hopped on the saddle and stepped on the pedals. The sailors laughed, but each of them would gladly have changed places with him.

Before they put out to sea again, the new exec came aboard, an ensign by the name of Rouff, who was dying with eagerness to meet the enemy. Rouff had already seen active service.

The *Albatross* remained flotilla leader and passed through the Channel at the head of the flotilla. Nowhere was there any sign of the enemies; the Tommies had drawn in their tails since Dunkirk. But over the white cliffs of Dover there were a few barrage balloons, the only reminders of war. The flotilla stopped at Le Havre and continued on to Saint-Malo. Between Cap de la Hague and the island of Alderney eight planes approached. They blinked recognition signals, but even so the alarm was sounded on the bridge, and the *Albatross* opened fire. The planes fired back and dropped bombs.

They were English planes. Two were shot down, and a third was damaged. None of the ships was hit by bombs. The flotilla lost nine men by machine-gun fire, and six were wounded. The dead on the *Albatross* were Becker, the boatswain's mate, Seaman First-class Lauer, and Signalman Striker Glatzel; Schindler, the other signalman striker, was wounded.

The English fliers had used a new trick. They had blinked recognition signals while far off, and the ships had taken them for German planes. The German recognition signal for the day was four green, two red. The planes fired three green, three red. They had picked the combination at random, to fool the ships. The watchers on the bridge of the *Albatross* had been deceived at first, but Stollenberg had reported almost at once that the recognition signal was wrong. The flotilla commander had given the order to open fire.

Stollenberg was rewarded with a week's leave. He went home by way of Berlin; the flotilla commander had asked him to take his wife a package. Halbernagel took him to the train.

That night the alarm signal rang through the ship. The men jumped from their bunks, slipped into their boots, and ran to their battle stations.

It was a false alarm. They stood by for fifteen minutes, but no planes appeared. After the command to secure from battle stations had been given, the harbor AA began to thunder. Fortunately, they didn't hit anything. Six Messerschmitt 110's came in from the sea and flew low over the harbor, hideous with the shark's head painted on their noses. They fired recognition signals only when they had the harbor behind them.

Out of sorts, the men went back below and shook the squashed cockroaches out of their boots. Most of the roaches had succumbed on the way to the battle stations. If you had narrow boots, it was easy to dispatch the roaches in the toes, though later on you'd have to reach in for the corpses. But if you had wide boots, you had to do toe gymnastics. The roaches that had taken refuge beneath the arches lived the longest, unless the wearer had flat feet; then all died at once. It was useless to smoke out their breeding places; they could not be exterminated. Where the *Albatross* went, they went too.

In the morning the ships received orders to put to sea. Some shot-down English fliers were floating around in the Bay of Saint-Malo; the flotilla was sent to fish them out. The weather was stormy and the men cursed.

Right outside the entrance the ship began to heave. Normally the sea around Saint-Malo was blue-green, but now it was grayish white. Great poison-green rollers spread a coating over the white-caps—it was like tarnish on silver. An impressive sight if you had solid ground under your feet. But the *Albatross* creaked and groaned in every joint, and anything that was not lashed down was washed overboard. Monstrous breakers crashed on the deck; the bow was pressed under water and painfully raised itself only to be submerged again. Like tenacious little mice, the ships worked their way through the watery waste. Around them the sea arched and writhed like great snakes in torment, springing furiously at the ships, entwining them, squeezing them, as though to crush them. But the ships cut through the bodies of the snakes with their iron bows.

It was in this weather that Schmutzler decided he had to take a walk on deck. A line had been stretched from the winch to the bulkhead of the crew's quarters. Clinging to the line, he made his way along the deck with a loaf of bread under his arm. A wave washed over the deck, and astride its foaming summit sat Schmutzler, clutching his loaf of bread and looking down at the bridge. He didn't cry out, he didn't even seem to be frightened; his face revealed only a boundless amazement. Then he was carried away. For a few seconds he was not to be seen; then he reappeared about a hundred yards off. A moment later he vanished for good.

In the afternoon the ships were back at the pier in Saint-Malo.

Halbernagel came whizzing up on his bicycle, which he carried aboard for fear of theft. "Have you got them?"

"Hell, no," said Meckel. "It was all for the birds. We lost a man and a loaf of bread and wasted a lot of coal."

As usual, Heyne disagreed. If nothing else, he declared, it showed our desire to rescue an enemy in danger at sea; in a higher sense, therefore, it had not been for the birds. "You try to explain that to Schmutzler," said Meckel. Then a good dinner was cooked up. The cook of the flotilla staff made his appearance, there was pig's knuckles with sauerkraut and mashed potatoes and compote—a beautiful meal; and now Schmutzler was really dead and forgotten.

After dinner Halbernagel delivered a lecture. He spoke like an official guide. He began with general considerations on the bathing facilities of Saint-Malo beach. Then he described the beauties of a stroll around the ramparts in the evening, and this led to the price of alcoholic beverages. Only when Pitt interrupted him with a curt "Get to the point, Halbernagel," did he reveal that an official Army brothel had just been opened in Saint-Malo. There were girls from Paris, whom he could highly recommend.

"Is that just what you say, or are you speaking from experience?"

"Don't worry about that. In return for the publicity I give them they let me try a few numbers free of charge."

"A few?"

"Sure, and quite a few come to think of it."

"Stop bragging," said Stüwe.

"Hell, you'd keel over after the first time," said Pitt.

Halbernagel was furious. "You won't get any more favors from me. Here I try to look after your well-being, but you don't deserve it. So do you know what I'm going to do? I'm going to visit all the other buckets and tell them about this unique opportunity, though the flotilla isn't supposed to be told until tomorrow. Today only the war profiteers on the flotilla staff are going. You can come tomorrow and wait in line."

"Hell, they probably won't be virgins even if we go today."

"No, they ain't virgins. They're already broken in and smooth as a gun carriage," said Halbernagel, beginning to go.

"You stay right here and keep your trap shut," said Pitt. "Later on you can take us to your first-class establishment."

They gave Halbernagel a bottle of schnapps. He sat down on the ladder leading up to the upper deck and drank while the men dressed for shore. Then they moved off under his guidance. Halbernagel felt like a sergeant taking out his recruits for the first time. Heyne, Bülow, and Vögele went along, "To case the situation," they told Teichmann.

Halbernagel had left his bottle of schnapps. Teichmann took a cup out of the dish locker and emptied the bottle. There were three and a half cups. After each cup he drank a bottle of beer. Afterwards he lay down in his bunk, and because he was dizzy he tried to concentrate his thoughts on something. He thought of his buddies, of Stollenberg and Heyne, and a little of himself. Nothing serious, nothing deep . . . and then he was asleep.

"What are you yelling about, Hans? Look, the guy lies in his bunk, drunk as a lord."

"It would have been better for you if you'd come along with us."

"You really missed something. You've never seen such military efficiency."

"Attention! Forward march! And in we go, still marching."

"It was a military orgy."

"Halbernagel, I hereby appoint you master of the whorehouse. No, you didn't exaggerate. As a sign of your new rank, we bestow—this rubber. On a ribbon."

"It can be worn in the buttonhole too.'"

"Here's to Halbernagel."

"Who drank up my schnapps?"

"Even Vögele got his."

154

"Did you have fun, Vögele?"

"I should say so. Ve had a vonderful time. We talked so good too. She gomes from Alsace."

"Did you tell her about the Black Forest?"

"Ha-ha-ha."

"Sure, and the Vosges. Vit illusdrations, see vot I mean? I showed her the moundains. . ."

"Ha-ha-ha."

"Den I showed her vere the Rhine vlows . . ."

"Ha-ha-ha."

"You didn't forget the tributaries, I hope."

"Naw, or Lake Gonstance."

"Ha-ha-ha."

"Quiet in the whorehouse."

"Ha-ha-ha."

For a week the flotilla did escort duty between Saint-Malo and Brest. When the *Albatross* tied up at Saint-Malo, Stollenberg came aboard.

"Regards from Berlin to the former members of the second company."

"She remembered us?"

"Sure. She sent you all her regards. She wanted to know who had shipped on the flotilla leader with her husband. Take a look at this." Stollenberg removed four little packages from his sea bag. Each package contained five chocolate bars and a card. On the card was written, "Edith Wegener wishes you all the very best of luck."

"That's nice," said Heyne, "very nice."

"We've got to thank her," said Bülow.

"Yes, write a few lines, and I'll take them ashore. I have to report to flotilla headquarters anyway," said Stollenberg. They all wrote something: "a pleasant surprise," Heyne wrote, and "Many thanks for your kind thought," and so on. "Most faithfully yours . . ."

Teichmann wrote, "Dear Emil, I'm sure you had a lot of trouble finagling those five chocolate bars for me and copying Frau Wegener's writing. You did a good job of it too, only you overlooked one thing—namely, that the name of a candy store in your home town can be made out on the wrapping paper. But I appreciate it. Hans."

That night Teichmann went to the whorehouse. Halbernagel had advised him against it. A new flak unit had just been transferred to Saint-Malo, and there was a terrible rush. But Teichmann went just the same. Stollenberg, Heyne, and Bülow joined him. Halbernagel advised them to ask for Madeleine; she was a little more expensive, but well worth it, especially if they said that he, Halbernagel, had sent them.

First they went walking on the ramparts of Saint-Malo and behaved as if they had never seen a sunset before. They went to a bistro and drank a few apéritifs, each more insipid than the last.

They had really picked a bad day. They had to wait; it was rush hour, and the flak boys were being waited on. "Nix Madeleine," said her colleagues. "Madeleine aujourd'hui malade, compris? Machine kaputt, compris?" "That much French we understand," said Heyne.

They took what there was. First they had to pass by a medic who checked their equipment and handed out "close-combat protection" on request.

"Allons, monsieur . . . oh la la . . . très bien, très bien . . . oh first-rate. chéri, wonderful . . . oh, oh, oh . . ." But it was all put on, included in the price. "Vingt-cinq francs, s'il vous plaît, mon chéri, merci beaucoup, au revoir, monsieur . . ." It was nothing, it wasn't even disgusting. It was like the annual medical examination at school. Outside the examining room stands the teacher, checking to see if they have all washed their necks. And afterwards you have a feeling of relief because it's behind you. The only difference was that the school examination was free of charge.

"Short-arm repairs," said the medics outside the door. One of the medics grew flustered at the sight of their identification tags, because of the designation Nav. Off. 1939 under the serial number, birth date, and blood group. It meant only that the possessor of the tag had entered the Navy in 1939 as an officer candidate. The medic interpreted the Nav. Off. as an accomplished fact and pointed out deferentially that the officers' brothel was situated in the Hôtel Napoléon.

"We're very much obliged to you for the information, my friend," said Bülow, "but for the present we're just the same as you, Ass-hole Third-Class, and whether we get to be officers depends on you. If we've caught something today, we probably won't. So please consider the solemnity of this hour and do your work well. You won't have to salute me later on, I'll remember you kindly."

The medic blew up. He would not be spoken to in such a tone, he wasn't any Ass-hole Third-Class but a corporal in the Army medical corps, he would soon be a sergeant, and they should immediately adjust their uniforms so their rank would be visible. He then proceeded to deal pretty roughly with them. Was rank important even in a whorehouse? Heyne asked. Yes, indeed, for the sake of order, said the future medical sergeant, and order was indispensable. He was not only a pedant but a sadist as well, and Bülow was the chief victim. "Take it easy, friend. Could I tell by your face that you'll be a sergeant in three years?"

"No, but you could see that I'm a corporal."

Bülow clicked his heels, gave the Hitler salute, and cried, "Seaman Second-Class Count von Bülow requests permission to leave the enlisted men's brothel upon completion of treatment." Then he did an about-face and marched out of the room in his under pants.

Back on board they drank. They had gone to a few bars, but they hadn't liked the sweet slop that was served them. They wanted to tank up fast. They now drank schnapps and beer—mostly schnapps. As far as they were concerned, there was nothing better or more beautiful. They drank it with veneration and fervor—not just to get it down. They took a big swallow that filled their mouths, held it a while until it penetrated every corner, burning and cauterizing, and to keep the fire burning as long as possible they breathed deeply and gave it oxygen. When the biting schnapps had burned the mouth clean, they let it slip slowly down into the stomach. Like an agile little snake, it moved, prickling and tickling, down through the esophagus into the stomach, where it diffused itself, creating warmth and well-being. This was glorious, but it was only the beginning. In a more advanced stage, they drank the schnapps more quickly, chasing it directly with a great gulp of cold beer, and perhaps in the long run this was even better than the slow stage.

But the best part of it all was that this clear, pure white liquid, which looked like water, transformed them into men. They thawed out and forgot that they had been trained to kill and that they would sooner or later drown in some part of the ocean. Everything was clear and simple when they had been drinking. The niggling trifles and absurdities, the inevitable boredom of daily life, receded into the background and vanished; the corners were smoothed off. Women could not take the place of alcohol. They were a totally different matter. Women were the little necessities of life that only became important when you had been deprived of them for a long time; they were petty annoyances like eating, washing, and having your hair cut; for most of the men they were an evil and nothing more. Intoxication came only from alcohol, and it lasted longer, much longer.

"The upper classes go to concerts or theaters, coolies take opium, and soldiers drink. And there's always a bit of despair in it—and do you know what else? No? Well, then, I'll tell you . . ."

"Gerd, man, are you boiled!" said Stollenberg, but his tongue was no longer quite able to do his bidding. "What have concerts got to do with despair? Can you tell me that?"

"Yes, I can . . ." Heyne had to belch but was still clear-headed enough to apologize. "Look here, my dear Emil— Oh, good God, Emil, you're so incredibly naïve; you really are, and it's the nicest thing about you, it's what makes you so lovable . . ."

"Are you trying to do a Schwalber?" asked Teichmann.

"That's what—don't interrupt me—what makes you so much nicer than big strong Teichmann, the burly bear, hee-hee-hee, boooh."

"You were talking about concerts," said Teichmann.

"Coming up. But first I want to talk about you," said Heyne, blinking his glassy eyes at him. Then he had to belch again. "Excuse me, please, my stomach . . ."

"Now he's competing with the chief," said Teichmann.

"Pipe down, Hans, and don't bother me. I'm talking about you, Hans, yes, that's right, about you. And I'm going to tell you what kind of a guy you are. Listen to me, Emil. The truth is that he has something the two of us lack, something we've lost or never had in the first place: he's fearless."

"Yes, that's right, you've hit the nail on the head, I noticed that even in school," said Stollenberg.

"I always said that I was a great psychologist. And that kind of thing is mighty rare nowadays. Fearlessness, I mean. Mostly it's something that exists only in the movies. And the remarkable part of it is that he knows a thing or two. He isn't ignorant—not by a long shot; he's got a few drops of poison in him, the subtle, slow, lethal poison that's known as reason. But only a few drops. They turned the faucet off in time, and that athlete's body of his is big enough to digest the bit of poison that's in it; it fights its way through . . ."

"You were talking about concerts," said Teichmann.

". . . and because he's fearless he can take a lot of punishment. And one more thing: he's very sensual; take a look at his lips. He radiates sensuality, he crackles with it, and the women feel it a mile off, and the result is that he'll always love life even if the going gets very rough."

"I'd be ashamed to drink so much," said Teichmann.

"D'you see, Emil? Now he's getting moral because I've taken a look inside him." Heyne reflected for a moment and then muttered as though to himself, "The fact is, I'm the brightest one of us. That's why I'm the weakest." He mumbled a few more words that nobody could understand, then pulled himself together and said to Stollenberg, "Oh yes, about concerts. Once there was a great man, and the great man was an artist. But after listening to one of Beethoven's symphonies—get me right, after the intoxication had worn off—he went home and hanged himself."

"Really?"

"It's a fact, Emil."

Maybe he felt too small, thought Teichmann while he was still capable of thinking; anyway, the fellow must have understood something about music . . .

159

The six ships of the flotilla lay at the coal pier in Brest when a report came in that a German plane had bombed a British sub off Brest; the sub had dived, but it left an oil track; the flotilla was ordered to go out and see.

Only two of the ships, the *Albatross* and No. 3, had taken on coal; the others were still busy loading. The flotilla commander ordered the *Albatross* and No. 3 to put out. His pennant was hoisted on the *Albatross*.

At 1100 the ships left Brest at full speed. An hour and a half later they reached the oil track. It led due north. The two vessels took the track between them and followed it. The depth charges in the stern were armed and set, ready to drop.

Shortly after 1300 the sub must have got wind of her pursuers, for she changed her course ninety degrees to starboard. The sweepers followed and ran some two miles on the new course. Here the oil track ended. The men stood aft and waited for the signal to drop the ash cans. They could not tell just where the track stopped for it lost itself in the eddies of the backwash. The signal to let go depth charges was given from the bridge. The first went overboard. After it detonated, the sweepers stopped and tried to catch the sound of the sub's propellers on the listening device; then they started up again, dropped charges and stopped, and the game began all over again.

After the fourth run the oil track broadened into a circular slick about five yards in diameter. The Albatross dropped two charges at once into the middle of the circle.

A minute after the detonation the sub showed her periscope. The *Albatross* headed for it. When she was barely a hundred yards off, the periscope was retracted. The *Albatros*s changed her course by ten degrees, taking the direction that the sub was presumed to have taken, and rammed it. All that could be heard on deck was a mild cracking sound.

"Why don't they stop playing hide-and-seek and just surface?" said Heyne. "All this horsing around isn't going to do them any good."

"We've smashed the periscope or the bridge at the most," said the CPO. "Otherwise there would have been more noise."

Someone called, "Submarine astern."

160

They had no time to look for it, for at the same moment the command came through the megaphone, "Ready lifeboats."

The lifeboats were lowered. The starboard boat collided with the side and capsized. Bülow had held the rudder to port instead of to starboard. The port boat was lowered without mishap. Its outboard motor started at once. Heyne held the tiller. Teichmann devoted himself to the motor. Behind the first thwart stood Stollenberg, boat hook in hand, and Pitt with a tommy gun at the ready. Forward stood the flotilla commander, the exec, and the CPO, each holding a hand grenade and waiting for the moment to board the sub.

The *Albatross* took the sub's bridge under fire. The starboard side of the bridge coaming had been bashed in when the sub was rammed.

The men in the lifeboat looked on. Their eyes saw the sub, but their brains were shut off. They were feverish with excitement, and their nerves were stretched to the breaking point. For a fraction of a second it seemed to them that the whole thing was a dream that would soon pass. Board a submarine on the high seas? It was too fantastic. And then suddenly what they were doing became immensely absorbing and they had no time to think of anything else.

The little boat darted through the water and a fine spray fell on the men, caressing their overheated faces. It felt wonderful.

"This is the stuff," the exec muttered to himself.

"If only the motor doesn't stall," said Heyne.

"If she stalls we're all fucked."

"Watch your language, Pitt," said the CPO. "There are officers on board."

"Yes, sir."

"Give her one notch more," said the exec to Teichmann.

Then they were there. Wegener raised his arm as a sign that the *Albatross* should cease firing. Heyne gave the boat a graceful turn that pulled them up alongside the stern of the sub. Pitt slipped and dropped his tommy gun in the water. Heyne secured the boat's painter to the after end of the sub's deflecting wire. When he and Stollenberg scrambled up on deck, the Tommies were standing there flashing their pistols. They had shot down Werner and Pitt and were tussling with Wegener, the exec, and Teichmann. In the melee they shot the exec through the head. Wegener succeeded in grabbing the pistol out of one of the Britisher's hands, but only after the other had fired at him. Teichmann had man-aged to give a great beanpole of a British officer a hook to the chin and was occupied at the moment in throwing another Britisher off the bridge. Heyne and Stollenberg jumped over the men lying on deck and flung themselves at the enemy. With the pistol he had captured, the flotilla commander shot two of them. But others emerged from the conning tower. Teichmann seized one who was still half inside the tower and smashed his skull against the hatch cover. The man lost consciousness and fell back on his shipmates who were try-ing to get out. Heyne closed the cover. Teichmann dispatched the one surviving Englishman on deck. Heyne took a hand grenade, pulled the pin, opened the hatch cover a crack, and dropped the grenade. Then he pressed the cover tight and stood on it. Teichmann and Stollenberg joined him.

The explosion blew the hatch cover open.

Below, nothing was stirring. The flotilla commander drop-ped down the hatch. Teichmann saw that his ear was bleeding.

Then the crew came up. They were barely able to stand. Their knees shook and their hands twitched violently. Some of them trembled all over. Their shoes were red as if they had gone wading in red lead. Thirty-two men came up, fol-lowed by the flotilla commander. "Get me a flashlight and a sea bag, quick. Don't know how long we can keep this coffin afloat; got to get the secret stuff off before she sinks."

"Is that the lot of them, sir?"

"The others have had it. They were in the control room when the hand grenade went off; the artillery shells they had ready exploded and they had closed the watertight doors. These fellows were fore and aft; the ones that were amidships are all dead."

The *Albatross* came alongside. The flotilla commander had his head bandaged; a bullet had grazed his scalp and another had passed through his ear. The exec, the CPO, and Pitt were dead.

Heyne produced flashlights and started down into the tower. Teichmann was going after him with a sea bag when Heyne cried, "Hold it!" He came back up again, held his head out of the hatch, and vomited.

Stollenberg had fastened the towline of the *Albatross* to the bow of the sub. He ran a second line through the hawse pipe, and since there was no proper pin available he dismounted the barrel of an English machine gun and stuck it through the eye in the line to keep it from slipping.

Wegener reboarded the sub and dropped down through the tower hatch. Teichmann followed him. It stank of powder, blood, urine, feces, iron, oil, and leather, and the farther down you went the worse it stank. At the bottom their feet sank into a spongy carpet that had once been twenty men who had been torn to pieces in the airtight compartment.

Slowly they made their way forward. The ground gave beneath their feet with a squeaking and a gurgling as if they were wading through a swamp. Great clods of muck seemed to be sticking to their boots. From the deck above them dripped a warm sticky liquid that stuck to their fingers. They had trouble keeping their balance. They followed the track that the British sailors had made passing from the forward section to the tower. Suddenly Teichmann felt himself held fast. When Wegener tried to pull him along, both of them fell down.

"Get up," said Wegener, rising to his feet.

"Somebody's grabbing my foot."

"Be sensible, man, dead men can't hold anybody."

"But they're holding me, sir."

"Can't you move your foot?"

"Yes, but it keeps getting pulled back again."

Teichmann braced himself against the carpet of flesh, blood, and bones, and when he was up he held in his hand a slippery, bubbly mass, which was warm and seemed to move. Wegener flashed his light on it; it was bright red.

"That's only a piece of lung. O.K., let's go now."

Then they passed through the open watertight door. They wiped their hands on the curtains of the bunks. In the radio shack they threw everything that bore the stamp "Secret" into the sea bag. Then they went back, and the going was better than they had expected.

"You're as pale as a chicken's ass."

"Shut your yap, Halbernagel."

"I've got to take a look at that."

"Take the light if you want to get your money's worth."

Halbernagel was soon back. He tried to say something, but then his mouth was full, and he barely had time to reach the rail.

"Haven't you even learned to talk and vomit at the same time?" Teichmann asked.

Before Halbernagel could answer, the sub began to go down. The stern sank slowly beneath the surface; the men got into the boat, and when it was full the rest jumped in the water and swam across to the *Albatross*. Meanwhile the bow of the submarine rose vertical and then slipped silently downward. The only sound was the cracking of the parting lines—there hadn't been time to cut them. A white wreath of foam was all that remained of the sub. Teichmann was glad that the coffin was gone.

The Britishers sat in the crew's quarters and drank schnapps. The wounded lay in the officers' cabins. The dead lay on deck in a neat row: Ensign Rouff, the CPO, Pitt, and the six Englishmen.

Heyne expressed the opinion that Wegener had sent the Englishmen below to prevent them from seeing the German ships in the harbor. Stollenberg maintained that he had done it out of tactfulness, to spare them the triumphal entry into port. After all, these fellows had started the war with the most powerful Navy in the world, and here they were setting out for prison camp on a herring trawler. Besides, the prisoners were not wild animals to be exhibited to the public, but human beings.

"Emil the Gentle has spoken," said Heyne. "I can only hope that you never get taken prisoner by the English. Because, believe me, if it had turned out the other way, the Britishers wouldn't have been so kindly. They like their little triumphs." From the masthead of the *Albatross* flew the

164

alphabet pennants, Tare, How, Peter, the signal that the flotilla commander always hoisted after a successful undertaking. There was a shade of irony in it; this was his way of commending the crews, without making a fuss.

7

On December 21, 1940, at 1132, the following incident occurred.

English bombers set out to attack Brest in three waves.

The flak was strong, and the first two waves suffered heavy losses. It was decided that the third wave would not attack Brest but drop their bombs on targets at sea.

Twenty-five miles northwest of Brest, the bombers sighted a minesweeper flotilla moving in column formation. They attacked from the quarter at a height of six thousand feet, out of range of the ships' flak. They dropped their bombs in a pattern, saw the ships blanketed in smoke, and continued on their way.

In this way the 52nd minesweeper flotilla was destroyed. Only the flotilla leader, which had been heading the column and thus had more time to maneuver, was still afloat. Tugs towed her into Brest.

Of the crews of the sunken ships, twenty-two men were fished out of the water. Ten of them died of their wounds.

8

They spent Christmas in Hamburg. Stollenberg had been home recently; Bülow and Vögele wouldn't have had time to reach home by Christmas, and Teichmann didn't know where to spend the holidays. They talked it over, and this was the solution.

On Christmas Eve the same people were gathered together as the year before, but they seemed almost unrecognizable. The general atmosphere was good, no comparison with the previous Christmas. Germany had been victorious and the feeling in the air was: Praise the Lord God, halleluia and hosanna!

Perhaps it was General Heyne who set the tone; he was looking fine. He had donned his uniform. He hadn't been recalled to active service; he just wore it in honor of the day, and for the same reason he had put on all his medals and insignia; after all, they were part of the uniform, part of the festivities. Again sister Luise was sitting behind him and a little to one side, with her rather long, bony hands folded in her lap.

Teichmann watched the general closely: self-assured and conscious of his dignity, the little man in the general's uniform stood by the Christmas tree and read the Christmas gospel. Did his hands, as they held the Bible, tremble a little, or did his voice shake a little in awe of the Word? Did he know what he was reading? Not a bit of it: the Bible lay firm and unflinching in his hands, and all one could tell from the tone of his voice was that it wished to be heard and was accustomed to commanding. The general seemed to be the right man in the right place. The general thought so too, of that there could be no doubt. What else, Teichmann reflected, would you expect him to think?

When the presents were given out, the sailors each received four boxes of cigarettes and a bottle of liqueur. Afterward the lights on the tree were turned off, the ceiling light was turned on, Christmas was over, Malaga was passed around, and a general conversation started up. Meanwhile, the children played war. Within half an hour they defeated the French Army; then they took on England. The Channel crossing gave them no trouble at all; they shouted "Hurrah" and Give it to them," and pretty soon they had conquered England.

This year two retired high-ranking officers had been invited; one of them had taken part in the War of 1870. They wore their old uniforms like armor, and took no part in the conversation. In addition to the Diebolds there were a pastor and his wife, who were addressed as Herr and Frau Ecclesiastical Councillor. The others were mostly businessmen. It was a distinguished gathering. All agreed that they were living in a great age, that by the grace of God still more glorious times were in store for them, that God held out his hand in blessing over the Führer, as the attempt on his life in Munich had shown, and that Germany under the inspired leadership of Adolf Hitler was on the eve of a colossal—"global," said one gentleman whom they addressed as Consul—victory. Heaven permit, said the ladies.

Then the ecclesiastical councillor spoke up and said that now God had granted victory over France, England would come down off her high horse; this was the last wartime Christmas that the younger generation would ever experience. The general added that every generation ought to fight one war; one war was good for it and built character. "The young people must face the storm before they can appreciate the security of the harbor," said the ecclesiastical councillor, and drank the sailors' health. "Am I right?" "Excellently put," said the general, and drank the health of the ecclesiastical councillor. The ecclesiastical councillor tried to drink in the military manner with pointed elbow, and sprinkled himself a bit in the process. The attack on the Protestant Church had been a mistake on the Führer's part, but he himself had seen that, and besides the quality of the SS was being improved. Such were the opinions of the ecclesiastical councillor.

"Of course," said the general. "They're young people, they have to sow their wild oats." "A dog's bark is never as bad as his bite," said a gentleman from the Chamber of Commerce. "Yes, yes, certain unfortunate things have happened," said a guest whom the others addressed as Senator, "but you can't make an omelet without breaking eggs." "And the omelet had to be made," said the general. "Our economy cannot be defeated; as far as we are concerned the war can go on for years."

"Exactly, Herr Commercial Councilor. I've heard that the Ruhr is going to increase its production by forty per cent next year, and . . ."

"Magnificent. . . ."

"I defy anyone to equal us."

"Yes, business is good . . . "

"There's even a chance to make money, ha-ha-ha . . . "

"We can't complain . . ."

All competent men, thought Teichmann, who've made something of their lives. They believe in God and money, or vice versa, and both are doing splendidly. A substantial lot.

The young people had retreated to the dining room. Dance music could be heard through the sliding door.

"Dancing on Christmas Eve! Who ever heard of such a thing!" said the general. "Luise, will you please tell them to desist."

Luise went into the dining room and came back with a young girl.

"But, Uncle, we thought just this once . . . the boys only have a few days' leave, then they'll be gone again . . . "

"My dear child," said the general, "one does not dance on Christmas."

Frau Diebold intervened, "Let the young people have their fun. They have so little chance to get together nowadays."

"After all," said the girl, "Christmas is a day of rejoicing."

"I wouldn't think of contradicting so pretty a young lady," said the general. "Very well, then. But restrained music, if you please. None of this insane modern stuff."

The pastor's wife drew Teichmann into a conversation.

"Why don't you dance?"

"I don't know how."

"That's not possible."

"I'm not musical enough."

"Oh, that doesn't matter. I know lots of people who are completely unmusical and they dance just the same. My husband, for instance, he has no ear for music at all and he dances quite well, clergyman and all, ha-ha."

"Yes, dancing really has more to do with sex than with music."

"Yes, perhaps, you're right. And that's why you don't dance?"

"I don't believe in detours."

"Oh, you wag. You wicked boy. But it's nice to be a little devious," she said with a confidential smile. "You wouldn't want to break the door down to get into the house."

"But suppose the house is wide open?"

The pastor's wife giggled. To make himself perfectly plain, he said, "To push perspiring women around the room is probably the silliest thing that a man can do."

"Did you say a man?"

This lascivious old cow thinks she has to teach me chapter and verse, thought Teichmann, annoyed at being so young. Then he lit a cigarette.

Champagne was drunk all around. They clinked and said "prost" and smiled. Then another guest arrived, a school friend of Gerd Heyne's named Alfred Nienhagen. He came on crutches; one foot was gone. As Heyne was introducing him, Teichmann heard the general whisper to his sister, "I told you we shouldn't have dancing."

"Thank you," said Nienhagen as Heyne moved up a chair for him. "I haven't had time to perfect my walking technique. I feel like a stork in a salad bowl."

"You have a sense of humor. I like that," said the general.

"Better wounded than dead, ha-ha-ha. The war is over as far as I'm concerned."

"Where did you fight?"

"At Amiens. That is, I didn't fight at all, all I did was lie

170

on my belly, and I didn't even do that right, not according to regulations, or I'd still have my foot."

"What do you mean?" asked the general.

"It's very simple. My platoon leader was lying on his belly too—those Frenchmen weren't bad shots. Well, my platoon leader calls out, Get those heels down. You know, when you're lying prone, you tend to stick your heels up a little, because it's more comfortable. . . ."

"Every recruit learns not to do that," said the general.

"That's true. But my leg was itching something awful; the little beasties, you know. France isn't as hygienic as we are; there's a lot of bugs. Anyway, I scratched and stuck my heel up. Then crack! and I felt something warm running down my leg. When I woke up—I can't stand the sight of blood, you know—I was lying in a wonderful white bed with fresh white sheets. There was a . . . an aroma of cleanliness, and there were pretty, yes, really pretty nurses that read your every desire in your eyes, so to speak. Only my left foot was gone, otherwise I was fine."

"Our military hospitals have always been exemplary," said the general.

"Yes, but the best is still to come. A few days later the head medic turns up beside my bed and tells me something about bravery in face of the enemy and lays an Iron Cross Second Class on my bedside table in the name of the division. Later I got the medal for the wounded too. As I found out, my company had suffered heavy losses, so a whole batch of I. C.'s were allotted to it, and that's how I got mine."

"And all that because a flea bit you at the right moment," said Heyne.

"That's just what happened. You could do a study on the principle of causality."

"Your health, Alfred."

"And yours, Gerd."

They drank the second glass to peace in the near future. The general did not empty his glass.

"Why don't you drink up? Don't you like champagne?"

"Why, yes," said the general, but it was plain that he hadn't liked Nienhagen's tone. "I drink slowly for the sake of propriety. Besides, one only drinks bottoms up when drinking the health of chiefs of state. As far as I can see, there are none in this room. Aside from that, of course I hope for peace in the near future."

"Heaven permit!" said one of the ladies in the background.

"But do you know," said the general, "there are no two ways about it. If the English don't give up of their own accord, we'll have to march on London. That's the only way to show them that we mean business. Then we'll have peace—and only then."

"I don't think it's so simple."

"Why, my good man, when *we* start marching . . ."

"First we've got to be over there, and that will cost a lot of blood. I would prefer a political to a military solution. But frankly I'm not entirely convinced of the ability of the gentlemen in the Foreign Office."

"Neither am I," said the general. "I don't trouble my head over politics, and I don't know much about it. We soldiers always have to swallow the broth that the politicians have cooked up."

"Right. And, begging your pardon, that is one of the reasons why I never wanted to be an officer."

"Oh no, young man, there you go too far," said the general. "In the end we have our little word to say too."

"I'm afraid by then it may be too late. I've got my own ideas on the subject."

"And so have we," said the general.

"The question is only whether they're the right ones."

"I *beg* your pardon."

"You will have to admit that in your profession faith and obedience stand higher than independent thinking. Well, I have faith in nothing. As far as I'm concerned, faith means ignorance. I don't often obey, and then only when the fellow that does the commanding seems to deserve it. But from time to time I like to think, though it doesn't exactly cheer you up. What I say is, obedience in itself doesn't mean a thing; any dog can obey if he's forced to, and I don't like to be forced to do something unless I'm convinced that it's right."

Before the general could recover from the last remark, Nienhagen took his leave.

But for the general the matter didn't end there. He had been attacked. He drained one glass and then another.

"What manners! I've never seen anything like it."

The general was hot under the collar; his face went purple, but that may have been from the champagne. He poured himself another glass and stood up.

"To tell me, an old general, that I can't think!"

"He didn't say that," Professor Heyne put in timidly.

"But it amounted to the same thing," said the general, running up and down the room. "We have the War College, after all. I've never heard the like of it!"

The general drained his glass. His hand trembled. "Why, he's still wet behind the ears. Utterly immature, and he has the gall to tell me . . ."

"Just the same," said Gerd Heyne, "he was almost mature enough to die a hero's death." His father cast a disapproving glance in his direction. The general poured himself more champagne.

"He's superficial, that's what he is. No real feeling. For him the war is over, he says. Never heard of duty and sacrifice."

"He did sacrifice his leg, though, if that's what you're after."

"And you defend him, Gerd . . ." The general began to scream. "A sacrifice must be voluntary, or it's no sacrifice. A fellow like him wouldn't even have volunteered to be a soldier. Their attitude is no good, these modern young fellows. And you're one of them too, Gerd. Know-it-alls, that's what you are. As a matter of fact, you're nihilists."

"Nihilists are honest, at least."

"Damn it all, you've got to be idealists."

"You can't command a man to be an idealist. Either he is or he isn't."

"And you aren't. But you should be idealists, I say."

"And if the ideals are false?"

"Ideals are never false. It's not a question of intelligence, but of character. Get that through your head."

The general drained his glass. "We soldiers are the only profession that stake their lives for their convictions. When

173

politicians make mistakes they resign and go on living. When a businessman stops making money, he liquidates or goes bankrupt and keeps on living. And your so-called intellectual workers, your philosophers, your men of letters and scribblers in general, they're full of ideas, but they never have to pay with their lives for the mistakes they make—except every now and then one of them hangs himself because he can't stand living with himself. They can make speeches and write books, but their books and speeches commit them to nothing. They can renege and amend and make compromises, oh yes, they can trade horses—it costs them nothing. But when it comes to character, they have none. And that's how you are too, Gerd, and your friends are exactly the same, they're simply—frivolous. Yes, that's the right word. Frivolous. Of course fellows of that sort don't die for their convictions; it's not possible, because they haven't got any, and besides, they want to go on living at any price . . ."

"What conviction have you got?" Heyne asked. Teichmann gave him a poke in the ribs as if to say, Oh, leave the old man alone.

"The convictions of my fathers," said the general. "The convictions in which we have grown great."

"Do right and fear no one," said Heyne.

"Yes, sir," said the general.

"Fearless and true."

"Yes, sir," cried the general.

"To be, not to seem."

"Yes, sir," cried the general. And then, "You know exactly what I mean."

"Yes, sir," said Heyne.

At this moment, resounding laughter was heard from the dining room, where the young people were still dancing behind closed doors.

"God in heaven!" cried the general. "Damn dancing. As if we weren't at war. Frivolous . . . frivolous . . ."

He pulled open the sliding door and stood in the doorway surveying the dancers. Teichmann couldn't see his face, but to judge by the reaction of the dancers, it must have been very martial.

"Desist at once," said the general. His voice quivered like a taut string.

After the last couple had left the dining room, the only sound was the phonograph finishing. "The Little Postillion." Lucky it's a march, thought Teichmann with an inner chuckle. Suppose it had been a tango.

When the record was done, the phonograph shut itself off. Without turning around, the general strode through the empty room—stiff, with measured tread, his toes at an angle, his narrow chest thrust out, his back arched, but teetering slightly. He tried to keep his knees stiff but couldn't quite manage it. He kept trying at every step. Possibly he thought that if the gait is good it doesn't matter in what direction you go; what counts in the end is the posture.

There he goes, thought Teichmann, looking like a nutcracker with too hard a nut in its mouth. Poor old general. This time there's no child to hold out his hand to you; this time you've got to walk alone. And you're a bad loser, you can't retreat properly.

After the general's withdrawal the others felt oppressed and spoke softly. Bülow came into the room and asked Teichmann what had happened: Bülow had been with the dancers.

"He was tight."

"Happens in the best of families," said Bülow, and suggested that the festivities might just as well continue. But Heyne collected his friends and took them up to his room.

There was wine in Heyne's room and there they sat, drinking Moselle and smoking black Havana cigars. Heyne smoked cigarettes. Teichmann went out on the balcony. It was snowing. On the garden path you could see the footprints of the departed guests. From above they looked strangely small and narrow, and Teichmann was surprised that men could take such short steps. The last guests were just leaving the house. Small and hunched over and uncertain, they moved homeward like a herd of frightened sheep who had lost their bellwether. Somewhere a church bell was tolling, on and on, as though no one had remembered to stop it. It was lovely to watch the snow fall. It floated down silently and made the night bright and friendly, and where there was dirt the snow covered it up. Teichmann felt the flakes settling on his hair, and it was a pleasant feeling, like a caress. There was something comforting and appeasing in the way the tiny silver crystals kept gliding downwards. He could have stood there for hours in the snow, listening to that solitary bell. And he wondered for whom it might be tolling.

In the room a lively debate was under way.

"We're reviewing the evening," said Heyne, who was in uncommonly high spirits. He didn't conceal his regret that the general's performance had been over so soon.

"What have you got against him?" asked Stollenberg.

Heyne explained that to him his uncle was like a red flag to a bull.

"Then why do you want to be an officer?"

"Cynicism," said Heyne. "I want to beat those bastards at their own game."

Heyne had all his arguments against the officer corps stored up inside; he opened the sluices and out they poured like a river long dammed up. All this didn't prevent Bülow from falling asleep. Teichmann found it quite amusing, and knowing that it was grist for Heyne's mill, he asked him how he felt about his relatives in general.

"Now why do you suppose I shipped on a herring trawler instead of going to the university? I would have gone to the North Pole to get away from them. The worst thing about them is their bigotry. Take a look at my father: outside, a fine figure of a man; inside, a wreck. They broke his backbone in his youth, the same way they wanted to break mine. They even got him to the point where he was proud of his broken backbone. Not by thine own strength alone: that's their motto. In the world ye are afraid; behold, I have conquered the world—but which one of them has conquered this world? Who even wants to conquer it? But all the while they hold that this world is God's creation and the best of all possible worlds. And their wholesome trust in God helps them to surmount any possible scruples here on earth. As long as their pocketbooks are full, they are happy. They ask no more. Why should they? It might give them a headache. But when death comes, then what? It's not of the world they're afraid, but of death—yes, death. To build a philosophy, a religion, on weakness, on fear—how absurd! How horribly absurd. Prost all around! And besides that, they behave as if there were no problems for them on this filthy planet. Every one of them has his telephone connection with heaven, his direct line to God. The least little bruise and they call into the phone, Hello! And God sends down adhesive tape. They try to sell everybody the same telephone number and can't understand why a good many of the people who call up get no answer, that for some the line is blocked as long as they live; and what they understand least of all is that there are some men who don't pick up the phone to ask for help every time they cut their finger. What would bravery be without loneliness, eh? But what's the use of talking to you jokers? You're asleep."

"Absolutely not," said Teichmann. "I just closed my eyes, I hear better that way."

"Oh. And what did you hear?"

"That you are a good Christian."

"*Wha-a-at?*"

"Yes, you're not an atheist at all. I always thought you were."

"And now you say I'm not?"

"No, my boy, you're not. You're the exact opposite of an atheist. What's more, you're an idealist. The general was wrong."

"And you, Hans, you're drunk."

"You know perfectly well that I am not drunk."

"Oho, you're stinko."

"You absolutely believe in that telephone connection, and now you're stamping your feet with rage because your connection is blocked for the moment."

Stollenberg had dozed off, but he'd caught the passage about bravery. "You won't get far with bravery," he said.

"Don't want to either," said Heyne. "I just want to get through with it, I just want to get out and leave this pigpen that they call creation behind me. That's all I want, do you understand?"

"No, I don't understand."

"I'd like to have your head, Emil."

"My head is fine, even if I have had a bit to drink. I know something about wine . . ."

"Why, Emil, that was a compliment," said Teichmann.

"Anyway, there's hatred in your talk," said Stollenberg.

"No, I'm only telling the truth."

"No, Gerd," said Teichmann. "Your voice gave you away."

"If you looked at things with the opposite of what we call hate, you'd understand them better," said Stollenberg, and stood up. "The people you are attacking may be dumb, but they're not bad. Say, where is the . . ."

"Out in the hall, second door left," said Heyne.

"But it seems to me that maybe you can be bad sometimes," said Teichmann.

"No, he's not bad," said Stollenberg on his way out.

"Vot's all dot bull flying around?" said Vögele, waking up. "Have a leedle drink."

They drank Johannisberger Cabinet, 1929. Stollenberg, who had come back, noted with satisfaction that it had cost thirty marks a bottle.

9

The new flotilla was commissioned. The *Albatross* was leader; the others were seven fishing vessels recently transferred from Germany.

It was late afternoon when the *Albatross* tied up at Brest. For six weeks she had been doing off-shore patrol and submarine escort duty in the Bay of Biscay with the 24th Patrol Flotilla.

Next morning a big cleanup was held: a number of ladies and gentlemen representing German cultural life were expected on board to celebrate the commissioning of the flotilla.

"They're here," Halbernagel announced at breakfast. "I've seen them. More ladies than gentlemen; celebrities, actresses, singers, ballet dancers, beauties, dressed fit to kill; some broads!"

The representatives of cultural life came on board. They wanted to see just everything. The ladies climbed down the ladder to the crew's quarters—no mean accomplishment in high-heeled shoes. "Goodness, how narrow!" "This is where you sleep?" "Unbelievable!"

"Yes, you've got to see it to realize what our boys are doing," said one of the gentlemen, removing his hat to keep it from being bashed in. The sailors couldn't think of anything to say and grinned with embarrassment. The star let herself down on one of the bunks and crossed her legs, displaying flesh-colored stockings. Then she began to chatter as she had learned to do on the stage and in the movies. She talked without interruption—and said nothing. It didn't matter; the sailors weren't listening but were more taken up with the visual aspect.

"Autographs? Why, of course. Overjoyed."

The sailors produced assorted scraps of paper for the star

179

to write her name on. Halbernagel stepped forward. "My diary, ma'am," he said, and held out a memorandum book from the previous year, in which he recorded his gambling debts. "That's verrry interesting," said the star, talking uninterruptedly and simultaneously turning out the autographs as she had learned to do in Berlin. It struck Teichmann that she was afraid someone might ask her a question she could not answer because the answer was not to be found in any play or movie.

After every sailor had at least one autograph—Halbernagel had got half a dozen; he would sell them later, he whispered to Teichmann—the group of celebrities went back up on deck. Here the ladies were taken in hand by some officers from the flotilla staff, who circled around them as a cat circles around a bowl of hot soup. Oh yes, they were hungry but they didn't want to get burned. These were important people, you had to be careful; they could mess up your career if you didn't watch your step. "Yes, madame, no, madame; yes, my dear madame," said the officers. The sailors put it in plainer language, but since the language was not fit for a lady's ears, they said it to themselves. It was the same thing in principle.

Halbernagel managed to persuade the ballet dancers to climb up to the battle stations. He explained the functioning of the guns and cranked them up high so the ladies could look through the sights. He bubbled over with efficiency and technical knowledge, though as "commandant's runner" he had his battle station on the bridge and never had anything to do with guns. He made little speeches, and his meaning was not always unambiguous as the sailors on deck could tell from the way the ladies giggled. There was the breech, and then there were bolts that you had to insert in various places; in the dark and especially with new guns, it wasn't easy to find the right opening. Loud laughs. Consequently, Halbernagel went on to say, he preferred a weapon that had been properly broken in. This the girls took as a compliment and there were more laughs.

The seamen on deck clustered around the ladders and watched the ladies climbing up and down. The star had no need to visit battle stations with Halbernagel; she was too big a name for that. Instead, she entertained the officers, and she could scarcely have found a more grateful public.

Then the ladies and gentlemen went to lunch. The gentlemen went first, and the ladies followed. The ladies were shepherded by a man in a heavy ulster and a homburg, who distributed greetings right and left and on every possible occasion took his hat off to the ladies, revealing his bald pate. He was addressed as "Professor" and, according to one of the officers, he was Goebbels' right-hand man.

"Wait just a minute, *Professorchen*," said the star. "I've just got to give out a few more autographs or the boys won't let me go."

"Very well, my dear," the man in the homburg called back, and waited as becomes a responsible leader.

The officers escorted the ladies to lunch. The first part of the "entertainment of the crew" was over.

"We're going to make a big stink," said Stüwe, "if they don't issue us some liquor. We can't hit the sack, we can't go ashore, and the officers take off with the girls."

But the petty officer in charge of the canteen refused to issue any liquor.

After lunch Boatswain's Mate Schwalber—he had been promoted to this high dignity on January 30—appeared in the crew's quarters. "My friends, I . . ."

"We ain't your friends," said Osterbuhr. "We pick our friends."

"Well, if you don't like being spoken to politely, I hereby order every God-damn one of you to get washed and put on your Sunday best. We fall in at four and march to the Service Club. They're putting on a Merry Evening."

"Why don't you turn your hose aft and go as a monkey?"

"I'll put you on report for that."

"You can . . ."

After this little colloquy the men were calm for a while.

But they were in no tender mood. Their next victim was the chief yeoman of the flotilla, who had been assigned to march the crews to the Service Club. The crew of the *Albatross* marched behind the yeomen of the flotilla staff.

"A song," cried the chief yeoman. "Let's go," cried the man in the last rank. "Three, four," cried the chief yeoman.

No one sang.

"You've got to tell us what kind of a song you want," said Löbbermann. The chief yeoman mentioned a few songs. "Don't know the words!" cried the sailors. "'The Blue Dragoons,'" cried the chief yeoman. "We're not dragoons," said Bülow. "We're blue all right, but singing won't help." "Shut your trap," bellowed the chief yeoman. "Do you know the words at least?"

"Naw," said Bülow.

"Don't know the words!" cried the sailors.

"Then we'll sing 'We're setting sail for England,'" said the chief yeoman.

"Never heard of it," said Bülow. The men laughed.

"Good God, men, what do you know?"

There was no singing. The men of the *Albatross* expressed their opinions about the flotilla staff, and the little yeomen looked very unhappy. When this topic was exhausted, topic No. 1 was resumed, and that was inexhaustible.

In the Service Club there were coffee and cake. Later there was schnapps. The flotilla commander made a speech.

Meanwhile Teichmann was busy behind the scenes. The commander had asked who knew something about music. "Teichmann," Heyne had said. "Good, then report backstage," the commander had said. It turned out exactly as Teichmann—and Heyne—had expected; he had to push the concert piano from the corridor out onto the stage and set up music racks. But then he obtained more interesting work, hanging a curtain to provide a dressing room for the ballet. Suddenly Halbernagle was on the spot. "Let me help you, you'll never manage it by yourself."

It was because of Halbernagel's help that they were not finished on time. But the girls didn't seem to mind; they were perfectly willing to undress without a curtain. When the curtain was finally in place, Halbernagel offered them his assistance; he was a specialist on zippers. The girls had no objection.

The accompanist appeared, his hair hanging down over

his shoulders, and said the piano was badly placed. He didn't so much as touch the piano, but merely indicated where he wanted it. Teichmann pushed this way and that way, and in the end the piano was back where it had been in the first place. He might have said thank you, Teichmann thought, that wouldn't have prevented him from being a great artist. But the virtuoso said nothing. He let himself down on the piano stool, ran his hand through his hair, and smoothed out his dinner jacket. The jacket was not quite new, and it was buttoned on the left side like a woman's dress; the sleeves were a bit short, revealing great expanses of cuff. But maybe that's the latest style, Teichmann said to himself. However, the jacket was visibly mended, and that couldn't very well be the style. The virtuoso struck a chord, inclining his head so that his left ear vanished beneath his luxuriant hair. Then he tossed his mane disapprovingly. A few thirds and fifths followed, but these too displeased him. Pretty soon, thought Teichmann, he's going to ask me to tune the piano, but the pianist merely dismissed him with a glance.

As Teichmann was passing by the curtain, he met the star. She had on a sort of dressing gown with red and yellow stripes. "Ah, young man," she said, "would you be kind enough to help me a little?"

"I should be delighted, ma'am."

"It's terribly nice of you."

They crossed the court to the annex where the artists were lodged. In her room she gave Teichmann an evening dress, a pair of shoes, a white kerchief and a red one. The white one was for her hair, she explained, to keep it from being mussed when she did a quick change. "Yes," said Teichmann.

When they were backstage again, she asked where she could change her clothes. "Here, if you please," said Goebbels' right-hand man, who now wore a dinner jacket.

"With the girls? You're out of your mind."

"For heaven's sake, I beg of you, don't make a scene now."

"The girls have to leave, or I won't go on."

"I beg of you . . ."

"I just won't appear."

183

The girls had to leave. They took their things under their arms and moved out into the corridor. The star moved in.

"Good God, what an odor . . ."

"I beg your pardon?"

"You really could teach those girls to wash once in a while. The smell in here takes my breath away. You know what a delicate sense of smell I have."

"I'm frightfully . . ."

"That's enough. Get out of here, I can't bear the sight of you, you, you *professor* . . ."

"Of all the stinking luck," said Halbernagel to Teichmann. "I was making a good start with the little blonde in the ballet. Well, never mind. I'll anchor alongside of her tonight just the same."

"Hope you strike bottom."

"Don't worry about that," said Halbernagel, and went back to his zipper work.

"Would you kindly stand outside the curtain and see that no one comes in?" said the star. Then she went on to say that she had never dreamt of having to change under such conditions. Oh well, it was wartime, she was willing to make an exception, but some people had their nerve all the same.

The star was now behind the curtain. Teichmann heard a rustling and swishing of material behind his back and caught a disturbing scent of perfume. A lieutenant who was a supply officer on the flotilla staff turned up and asked Teichmann what he was doing there. Teichmann told him. The officer ordered him to disappear; he himself would see to it that no unauthorized person entered.

"My good man," said the star, sticking her head out from behind the curtain, "you'll have to let me decide who is going to protect me."

"Certainly, ma'am; I beg your pardon, ma'am," said the supply officer, growing very red in the face.

"I've had bitter experience, you see; with officers, too, I'm sorry to say. And this young man strikes me as trustworthy."

"Very well, ma'am, of course, ma'am," said the lieutenant, lifting his hand to his cap as though speaking to an admiral; and swiftly withdrew.

"There's nothing wishy-washy about her," thought Teichmann, pleased at how she had told off the lieutenant. But he wasn't too happy about being referred to as a trustworthy young man. Damn it all, he said to himself. I'm no eunuch. Now Halbernagel, for instance—he wouldn't impress any woman as "trustworthy."

"While I am on stage, will you please see to it that none of these gentlemen enter my so-called dressing room? I don't like that kind of thing."

"I'll attend to it."

"Terribly nice of you. You can stay inside, you know, so you don't have to stand the whole time."

From his place Teichmann could not follow events on the stage; he could only hear what was said or sung, and see who went on and off.

The show was a success. The artists were warmly applauded, once even in the wrong place. The fiddler was playing Sarasate's *Gypsy Melodies;* when he lowered his bow after the slow movement, the audience thought the piece was over and began to clap. Then when he had got through the presto, not very accurately but quite effectively, they applauded again louder than before.

A buxom lady who sang Rusalka's "Song to the Moon" got the most applause of all. She had to repeat the number, and even then the enthusiasm did not wane. Teichmann had watched her before she went on and saw that she was half petrified with stage fright. She had no outward advantages; she was impossibly stout and had an ungainly, somewhat lopsided face that was surely no more attractive when she sang. It didn't look as if she succeeded in performing very often. She had nothing with which to captivate the public—nothing except her voice and the desire to do her best. And that she did.

She was happy as she left the stage. "These sailors *do* love music," she said, beaming from ear to ear.

Then came a male singer, accompanied by the piano virtuoso. "Oh Glorious Art" sang the vocalist, and the virtuoso played the piano for all he was worth. It was a large concert piano, and it was no joke for the singer. As a special attraction the virtuoso had conceived the idea of playing the whole left-hand part staccato. The result was a battle between singer and accompanist, each doing his best to drown out the other. The virtuoso won the first round; the singer hadn't yet found his voice. The number was greeted by polite applause. The next piece was "Softly my songs entreat thee." Again the virtuoso had his own little interpretation; this time he played legato, parking his right foot on the pedal while the singer screamed. Because it was Schubert, the audience applauded. The final number was Mozart's "Abendempfindung." This time the audience applauded because it was their last piece. The two performers bowed, the pianist's face disappearing behind a curtain of hair, and left the stage in utter exhaustion.

Intermission.

The second part of the program was devoted to the lighter Muse. A middle-aged gentleman came out and sang "Yours is my whole heart." He waited for the applause to come and go, and then sang a song with the refrain "Love is a heavenly power." Again he waited for the applause to come and go and said, "I'll be back." Then he went backstage and finished smoking the cigar he had lit during the intermission.

"How do I look?"

Before Teichmann had time to answer, the star was on the stage. She looked as if she had been poured into her dress—a black evening dress, low-cut and quite fetching, with a red rose in her sash; it was a paper rose, but no one could see that.

Thunderous applause. She spoke a few words. It seemed to Teichmann that she purposely spoke in a somewhat lower voice than usual and rolled her r's more than necessary.

More applause.

She began to sing. A recent hit. Teichmann couldn't believe his ears when he heard what his star had to offer. It was a mixture of singing and sighing and the singsong of small children, only an octave lower. Without the mike she would have been inaudible. Even so she ran out of wind with every few words and had to gasp for breath; there was something asthmatic about her breathing technique. And then came the worst: the last note of the song was off key, almost half a tone too low, and to complete the catastrophe she held it and held it.

What a flop! For a moment Teichmann felt sorry for the star, but only for a moment . . .

Down in the hall they were clapping, screaming with enthusiasm, howling like savages.

Another song.

Not one bit better. Tremendous applause.

Either I'm crazy or they are, thought Teichmann. Before he could think the matter out, the star came down from the stage. She must have misinterpreted his horrified look, for she said, "The boys deserve the best," and vanished behind the curtain.

On the stage the ballet was dancing. To judge by the enthusiasm the girls must have revealed some interesting sights.

The virtuoso with the hair approached Teichmann in a confidential tone. "Yes, that's how it's done. I watched you before, while she was singing. You mustn't listen; you've got to watch her when she sings. Then you'll know how it's done."

The star appeared again. She wore a red shawl around her shoulders and looked like Carmen. Teichmann left his place and observed her from the stage entrance.

Yes, there she stood, pining into the microphone, swaying her sinfully round hips a little, embracing the microphone, stroking it as though consoling an unhappy lover. On the middle finger of her right hand she wore an immense ring that made her plumpish fingers look a bit more slender. "Thank you," she said when the applause rang out.

Well, if the applause was for her singing, she had every reason to give thanks, Teichmann thought. He had seen enough and went back to his place. The virtuoso came out from behind the curtain. "Aha, so that's how it's done," said Teichmann, and felt like poking him one.

"Oh, please don't say anything, please . . ."

"Just put those things where they belong."

"Yes, but please don't say anything. I love her."

"You're not the only one."

"No, not that way. I don't want to possess her, only . . ."

"You wouldn't get very far."

"That's true. I know. But I love her."

"In your own way."

"Yes."

The virtuoso had grown small and ugly. Obediently he put everything back in its place and ran off.

The man with the cigar was due for a second appearance but was nowhere to be found. The ballet had to fill in—quickly. This time the girls had practically nothing on; it was even better than if they had come out stark naked.

Halbernagel turned up. "She's a baroness. A real one. Just my type."

"Who?"

"The blonde I was alongside of before. I told you."

"Oh, yes. And what about you?"

"Oh, I'm her type too. Love at first sighting."

" 'Sighting' is good."

"She's O.K.'d my plan of operations. Night maneuvers. I promised to let loose with a broadside. You know what she said?"

"No."

" 'Fire away,' she said. What do you think of that?"

"I think maybe she's an old hand as a target."

"The hell you say. She comes of a first-class family. Blue blood. But passionate."

"Well, then you're just a lucky bastard."

"Man, let me give you a piece of advice. In the beginning you've got to use your head. Later on you don't need it."

"It isn't everybody that's got a head like you, Halbernagel."

"O.K. I admit it. I've got something under my hair, top and bottom, ha-ha-ha. Maybe I could find you one if you could get away from here. They won't come looking for you, you know. With that dame, of course"—he pointed to the curtain—"you haven't got a chance. The most you'll get out of her is a tip."

"She'd better not try that."

The star had finished singing. The Merry Evening was ended, and the artists were mingling with the audience.

"It would be terribly nice of you if you'd take my things

188

back to my room. Well, the room is locked, but you wouldn't mind waiting just a little while, in the hall, of course?"

"Not at all, ma'am."

"It's terribly nice of you."

Teichmann watched the performers and decided that they were a good-natured lot. They had distributed themselves among the various tables. The ballet girls let food be piled on their plates. The men helped themselves to mountains of cake and rivers of coffee and schnapps. The girls affected no indifference to food, but after the fifth piece of cake most of them said no thank you, on account of their figures. Schnapps? Oh yes, please, that could do no harm.

The star sat at the flotilla comander's table. Here, in contrast to the other tables, a considerable decorum prevailed, even two hours later. The star favored the proprieties and maintained her reserve. She spoke rather condescendingly with the gentlemen at her table, mostly about the problems of art. The officers listened attentively and nodded their heads.

By midnight the difference in rank between petty officers and men was pretty well effaced. But before the situation could get out of hand, the ballet girls left the room, escorted by officers who did not return. The flotilla commander announced that the party was over; anyone who so desired could stay on; liberty was extended until four in the morning, but no more schnapps would be given out.

The star took her leave of the gentlemen at her table.

"Oh, that's too bad; won't you stay a while?"

"I'm so sorry; I'm terribly tired."

The officers bowed and maneuvered in an attempt to kiss her hand.

"Thank you, it has been a delightful evening, but the trip . . . You *do* understand?"

"Why, of course, of course. Sleep well. A pleasant night."

Teichmann went backstage.

"Ah, there you are. I'd forgotten all about you. It took a little longer than I expected. Is that very bad?"

"I've been enjoying myself."

"Have you really? I'm so glad."

The supply officer was back again.

"Madame . . ."

"What do you wish?"

"Oh, madame, I have so many wishes."

"I hope you'll have the decency not to express them."

"I wish you a pleasant night, madame."

"Oh, don't worry."

Teichmann wouldn't have expected that from her; he liked her more and more. She went ahead, and he, carrying her things, followed her downstairs, across the court and then again upstairs. If I wanted to play the well-bred young man, he reflected on the way up, I should really take the lead; but after all, she has on a long dress, it won't bother her if I stay behind. She opened the door to her room and said, "Come . . . ," and pretended to be drunk.

In the crew's quarters things were looking pretty wild. The men had been given liquor, not enough to make them drunk, but too much to leave them sober. They had been given a glimpse of flesh, and then it had been spirited away from under their noses. By the time the party was over, the whorehouses were closed. The sailors went aboard, filled up on beer, lay down in their bunks, and tossed empty beer bottles at each other, from starboard to port and port to starboard. There were few serious injuries; the curtains broke the impact. When all the bottles were smashed, they took down the fire extinguishers and squirted the contents from bunk to bunk.

The artists stayed in Brest for another two days, entertaining the infantry and the AA gunners. Halbernagel spent the nights with his fiancée. He had become officially engaged to the blonde ballet dancer and applied to the commander for permission to marry. As the flotilla prepared to put to sea on the third day after commissioning, he strolled back and forth on the pier with his fiancée to give his comrades a look at her. She was very pretty; it was no disgrace to be seen with her. Yes, a few years older than Halbernagel, but that wasn't too evident. You could see, though, that she wasn't exactly an impregnable fortress. As he strolled beside her,

Halbernagel seemed rather tired. Just before the lines were cast off, he jumped aboard.

Heyne remarked that he looked pooped. It was worth it, said Halbernagel; he had fixed things so she'd have to be faithful to him; he'd done all he could to give her a baby, so she'd have to take him. Heyne asked if he wished to be addressed as Herr Baron. Not yet, said Halbernagel.

Before dusk, the ships streamed the paravanes. Orders were to sweep the Brest-Saint-Malo-Le Havre sea lane. After midnight the equipment had to be taken in for a short time on account of shoals. The body of a man was hanging from the cable-cutter of the starboard paravane. His flesh was bloated and flabby and looked green under the flashlight. The sleeves of the Navy uniform had burst at the seams, the face was unrecognizable, a shapeless oval resembling a half-deflated football that had been lying in the mud. Stollenberg discovered a little cleft in the ring finger of the right hand and tried, without success, to get at the ring with a pair of pliers. Teichmann took his knife and scraped the flesh off the bone. It cut easily and fell off like wet newspaper. Then they were able to pull the ring off. It was a wedding ring; inside it were engraved the letters H.K. and the date 28 Aug. 39. They threw the corpse overboard.

Shortly afterward the order came to restream the gear. This was the first time that they used the new otter paravanes at night, and there was a good deal of confusion. Jellyfish Löbbermann directed the work with blood-curdling obscenities.

The *Albatross* was the first ship of the flotilla to report its sweeping gear ready, and that was Löbbermann's doing. As Löbberman's left foot was caught in the tail fin of the depressor. The tow line of the port cutter ran between Teichmann and Löbbermann. Teichmann yelled, "Jellyfish, get your foot out of there!" But apparently Löbbermann didn't understand him .All he said was "Shut up." Bülow, too, saw what was happening and tried to pull Löbberman away. Löbberman fell down, and before he could extract his foot from the fin, the cutter jerked the depressor overboard. Löbberman pulled himself up as though trying to take a sitting position, and his head knocked against the stern rail. It sounded like a bowling ball smashing against a stone wall. And then the depressor was overboard and Löbberman with it.

It would have been useless to attempt a man-overboard maneuver; the depressor held Löbbermann under water, and it was night. Stüwe became master-at-arms.

The next morning the flotilla anchored off Saint-Malo.

"I've got to get ashore," said Halbernagel.

"That's all you need. You can hardly crawl aboard and twenty-four hours later you want to go ashore again," said Heyne. Halbernagel gave a forced laugh. He didn't go ashore; no one did. The flotilla put to sea again early in the afternoon, heading for Le Havre.

In the washroom after supper, Halbernagel let down his pants flap. "What do you think of it?"

"Go see what the petty officers say."

"Oh, no. I won't give them the pleasure. Anyway, it's not sure. What do you think?"

"I haven't had any experience—not yet."

"Maybe it's just a cold?"

"In this weather?"

"Well, maybe not. Anyway, what can I do?"

"Wait and drink tea."

"But you keep your trap shut, see?"

"Don't worry about me. The crew will find out soon enough. They'll split a gut."

"A lot of good that does me. I'm done for."

As they were docking at Le Havre the stern line got tangled in the screw. The *Albatross* had to drydock. The first night the chief, on his way back from shore, fell into the drydock. They found him in the morning; his neck was broken and he stank of liquor. They put "heart failure" in the log as the cause of death. "Heart failure" is always acceptable. No one knew a thing about the chief except that he drank and had a weak bladder. He was said to have no relatives. The picture of a very beautiful woman was found in his billfold. But it was faded and seemed old, or else it must have been handled a good deal. In any case, the chief's funeral was rough going;

the pastor didn't quite know what to say, and everyone was glad when it was over.

The flotilla remained in Le Havre for two weeks. The sailors had a good deal of free time and plenty of money; the girls took the money where they found it—when possible, without using their hands. One of the girls let out a frightful yell; Heyne had held the coin over a burning match. It took a bit of hush-money to quiet her screams. "It's too bad Halbernagel couldn't have seen that," said Osterbuhr. They decided to send him a picture postcard and inquire when the wedding would be. Everybody signed it, the girls too. Heyne wrote the address: to Commander's Runner, Baron von Halbernagel, Military Hospital, Rennes, V. D. Section.

On the return trip they lost the buoy ship. It happened in a matter of seconds, and no one was saved.

It was a moonless night. No. 3 was buoy ship, steaming along a thousand yards astern of the rest of the flotilla. And all of a sudden there they were. They came from aft, emerging from a low-lying haze. No. 3 sighted them first and fired recognition signals. When there was no answer, she opened fire, but the MTB boats—there were six or seven of them—came roaring in at more than forty knots, firing their torpedoes from a considerable distance. The buoy ship heeled over ninety degrees to port; her tracer ammunition sent up sheaves of light, as though trying to shoot down the stars, and then there was nothing more to be seen of her. The MTBs were gone too; the nightmare was past.

The sweepers took in their gear and turned back. At the scene of the sinking, they found nothing but a few planks.

Then there were a few quiet weeks, quick patrol runs between Saint-Nazaire and Lorient; submarine escort duty, and off-shore patrol in the Bay of Biscay. There was no sign of the enemy; these were pure pleasure cruises.

The vacation from war ended abruptly, when the flotilla was assigned back to the Channel. The fireworks started off the Pointe du Raz, on the west coast of France. Early in the morning, as the ships were running through the Bay of Douarnenez, they were attacked by a dozen English pursuit planes.

They came out of the sun that had just risen, split into three groups, and descended on the ships from three sides like a swarm of hornets. Their bodies glittered gold in the sunlight, and when they were close enough they sprayed the ships with fiery red poison; the tracer fire looked like long stings darting into the ships. Then they flew away—great glass insects reflecting the sun.

The flotilla shot down two of them; six sailors were killed and four wounded. No. 7 ship could only do five knots, as her boiler had been damaged. The commander ordered the whole flotilla to run in formation at five knots, but even so No. 7 was lost the very same day.

When they entered the Bay of Berthaume, the flotilla's anchorage off Brest, the *Scharnhorst* lay gleaming white in the midst of the smooth blue carpet of water, bordered by pale green hills. And when she veered, turning her whole length toward the sun, she glittered like finely chiseled silver. At her mast waved the white pennant with the black Luisa Cross. The fleet commander was on board.

She seemed to be lying still. The sailors on the mine-sweepers stared at her, and now they knew for whom they were sweeping mines. Most of the men had never seen a battleship before.

Tugs were towing the flagship of the German fleet toward the southern side of the bay, and now the sailors saw the *Scharnhorst*'s great gun turrets, first the two forward ones, then the others, swing to starboard and point their guns skyward. The yellow-and-blue-striped air-raid flag went up the mast, and on the bridge a blinker gave the message "To all: Come alongside at once and give torpedo protection."

The picture changed in a flash. At top speed, throwing up an immense wave, torpedo boats came racing from inside the bay, with sirens howling. The 12th minesweeper flotilla, which lay on the north side of the Bay of Berthaume, weighed anchor, sent up thick black clouds of smoke, and moved toward the *Scharnhorst*. The 52nd minesweeper flotilla, with the *Albatross* in the lead, headed at top speed for the battleship; a blockade runner came in from the sea and sped past the minesweepers, creating the wake of a giant liner.

Even before the other ships could see a thing the *Scharnhorst*'s 280-millimeter guns began to roar. Far out at sea there was a bursting of great black clouds and out of the clouds planes came rolling down like parts of an exploded rocket. Here and there three or four fell at once. Still the planes kept on coming. The staccato bark of the 40-millimeter Bofors and the 37's mingled with the howling roar of the heavy shells. But before the 20-millimeter automatic guns of the torpedo boats and minesweepers could get into action, the planes turned aside. They had no chance in this hail of fire and steel. But other planes appeared from behind the green hills: flat, elongated machines that looked like dragonflies and dropped great cigars that landed with a splash and vanished beneath the surface of the water. Tracing a streak of bubbles, they ran toward the flagship; three of them struck the barrier of ships around the flagship and exploded, sending up great columns of water. One of the ships, belonging to the 12th Minesweeper Flotilla, broke in two parts that sank at once. The other, hit by two torpedoes, went up in the air; that was No. 7. Being the slowest, she was the last ship to have reached the *Scharnhorst;* she had made it just in time.

The English lost twenty-three bombers and eight torpedo planes. The flagship was not hit.

In the next three months the 52nd minesweeper flotilla did not lose a ship. In the months of August and September it lost five. The battle odds had become too uneven.

The men on the herring trawlers, minesweepers, patrol craft, torpedo boats, and T boats here along the French coast had long been wondering why the British fleet did not appear or at least send out a few of its cruisers that would shoot the Lilliputian German fleet to kingdom come; but apparently the ratio of forces still struck the British as too risky. The cruisers did not appear. But there were plenty of planes.

They made things easy for themselves. They came in swarms, attacking the little ships from all sides. Since the ships had only two or at most three 20-millimeter guns on board, and could not fire in all four directions and upward at the same time, the assailants waited until the gun crews had been shot down by machine-gun fire. Then they dropped their bombs on the defenseless ships. The German Air Force was in Russia.

This was what the war had become. The English called it the "nonstop offensive." For the German minesweepers it was a forlorn struggle that began when the lines were cast off and continued unremittingly until the ships made fast again—or failed to return. There were no breaks, no breathing spells, no withdrawals, because the sea is flat and smooth; it offers no hiding places. On this battlefield everything could be computed; the computation was clear, simple, deadly, and the only factors that really counted were speed and fire power. The side that was superior in both was the winner. The only remaining imponderable was courage. But it had ceased to be a decisive factor. It had become a matter of dignity. A sailor was expected to sell his life as dearly as possible. At sea there was no such thing as a white flag.

The little ships kept putting out to sea; they went on sweeping mines, they kept afloat as long as they could, and after that—they went down.

In the last days of September the two ships that were left of the flotilla—the *Albatross* and No. 5—embarked on a patrol run from Saint-Malo to the Channel Islands. Afterward they were scheduled to join the 34th minesweeper flotilla in Helder for merchant escort duty.

In the Bay of Saint-Malo they were attacked by a plane. The visibility was poor, and the plane came in quickly. The *Albatross* opened fire, and after the first burst the plane was aflame. Its left wing broke off, and the plane fell into the water and sank. The *Albatross* steamed to the site. There was nothing more to be seen of the plane. But then, about eight hundred yards away, they made out the wing of the plane, floating and sparkling in the sunlight. Through the binoculars they distinguished the German insignia.

"It's his own fault," said Stüwe. "Why does the damn fool fly straight at us without even firing a recognition signal? We couldn't get out of the way, could we?"

"There's a sensitive soul for you," said Stollenberg.

196

"Sensitive hell! Orders are orders. When a plane comes straight at you, you fire, and that's that."

"With such sentiments you'll end up as an SS leader," said Heyne, who had been at odds with Stüwe ever since Stüwe had been master-at-arms. Stüwe came in for more harsh words. Later on, when they were readying the paravanes on the after deck and Stüwe began holding forth though the others knew a good deal more on the subject than he did, Meckel—accidentally, he claimed—gave him a kick in the behind. Stüwe sprawled forward and his head hit the paravane. "I never knew a mushhead could make so much noise," said Heyne. With that kick the sailors' mental equilibrium was more or less restored.

When the noon watch was relieved, Teichmann lay down in his bunk and fell asleep. When he awoke, the wall clock said 1855. He noted that his wrist watch had stopped. Before he could set and wind it, the air-raid alarm rang. He leapt from his bunk, and when he couldn't find his shoes he ran up on deck barefoot. As he staggered up the ladder, stubbing his toes, he could hear the clear, purring tone of Rolls-Royce engines, and when he reached the hatch he saw the stack leaning over to port. Then he was flung to the deck.

He stood up. The pressure was gone from his ears. Beyond the bridge everything was shrouded in whitish-gray mist. The *Albatross* veered hard to starboard. The wind was now abeam; when the mist cleared, Teichmann could see that everything was gone. Stack, flak stations, galley, captain's cabin: all had vanished. The starboard rail was gone too. And on the starboard side the coal bunker was torn open at the level of the waterline.

Teichmann climbed the ladder to the forward battle station. Osterbuhr, who was No. 1 gunner, lay in a pool of blood. Meckel, who was No. 2, was leaning over him, trying to stop the blood with a blue Navy handkerchief. "Watch out," Meckel said, "they're attacking with machine guns." "I can see that, you idiot," said Teichmann. "Get back to your gun and put in a new magazine."

He watched the British planes coming on. They flew close together in a cluster of eight to ten; he couldn't count them exactly. Meckel wasn't able to get the magazine in. It was the heavy sixty-shot magazine of the Oerlikon; Meckel was excited and couldn't find the grooves. Teichmann saw the planes swerving about for the attack and making straight for the *Albatross*. What No. 5 ship was doing he couldn't see. He did his utmost to keep calm. "Don't you know how to handle that thing?" he asked Meckel.

"Sure, but it don't go in."

Teichmann snatched the magazine out of his hands and shoved it in.

The Britishers fired. Meckel took aim and pressed the trigger. Teichmann had the feeling that Meckel was shooting accurately. As the British tracers whistled past their heads, it flashed through his mind that Meckel had better be shooting accurately if they were going to get out of this mess alive. Then he saw the whites of Meckel's eyes and he saw that Meckel wasn't shooting right. Both eyes were wide open. The damn fool, he can't aim like that, Teichmann thought. He stared at the planes, and there was terror in his face. Meckel closed his left eye. Ah, at last, the stupid bastard—then he opened it again; there was a clot of blood under the eyelid, and Meckel toppled over. Teichmann felt a pang under his right knee, but the pain only lasted a moment. It was the way it was in school, when the little friend behind you hit you in the calf with a wad of paper shot from a rubber band, and you can't let on that anything is wrong. Then the planes were gone. The pain was back again and now it really hurt.

The Britishers had been using phosphorus bombs; the phosphorus was burning on the floor of the battle station. Teichmann danced around, not knowing where to set his bare feet. He jumped up on Meckel, who still lay prostrate. He hoped that Meckel couldn't feel the phosphorus. In the end he jumped up on Osterbuhr. He certainly can't feel anything, he thought.

When the phosphorus was burned out, he felt his way down the ladder with his hands. Bülow carried him to the crew's quarters and laid him on a bunk. He disappeared and came back a moment later with butter, which he smeared on Teichmann's feet. Then he bandaged the right leg in a jersey shirt and wrapped a neckerchief around it. Then he was off again. Teichmann wondered where Bülow had found the butter now that the galley was gone. He decided to ask him about it.

Heyne and Halbernagel came down the ladder, carrying Osterbuhr. They laid him down on a bunk. The petty officer who had taken the quick medical course came down and tinkered with Osterbuhr. "Take his teeth out first or he'll swallow them," Teichmann heard Halbernagel saying. "Doc on deck," someone called down the hatch. "I've only got two hands," the petty officer called back. Teichmann heard him working with scissors and cursing and finally saying, "He's dead as a doornail. What do you want me to do with him, you dopes?"

Several more wounded men were brought down. Teichmann couldn't see who they were. God knows when somebody'll have to look after me, he thought. But then Vögele appeared, sat down on Teichmann's bunk, and began to tell him what had happened. While he talked he tore off Teichmann's bandage and poured iodine on his wounds.

This time, he explained, they had opened fire too late, for fear of shooting down another German plane. The whole swarm of Britishers had concentrated on the *Albatross;* nothing had happened to No. 5; the stern of the *Albatross :* . .

"Go easy on that iodine."

"No, dot's important." The stern of the *Albatross* was half under water, the boiler had been hit, and the firemen . . .

"Man, you're killing me."

"Don't worry. I pring you back to life." The firemen who had been on watch had been killed, and so had part of the flak crews. The *Albatross* could no longer maneuver . . .

"Ouch, damn it."

"If it shtings, dot's a good sign." So she'd have to be towed ashore. The torpedo boats would do it; for them it was child's play. So the *Albatross* would have to be towed in, she'd taken a hit in boiler and . . .

"You've told me that twice already."

"Might be. I'm almosht finished. Dere. And now you better shleep."

199

When he had replaced the dressing on the leg and bandaged the feet, he let Teichmann be.

"Shleep now," said Vögele, and went off to the other wounded with his iodine bottle.

Teichmann did not sleep. When he closed his eyes, he saw Meckel's left eye before and after being hit, and when he forced himself to look, Meckel's eye grew larger. Once, when Teichmann had persisted in looking, the eye grew to the size of a globe; a gelatinous mass represented the mountains. Then after the shot the mountains collapsed, covered over by a red deluge. Terror-stricken, Teichmann opened his eyes and occupied himself with his pain.

Then he fell asleep.

Shortly after midnight he awakened. He felt pretty well, only he would have liked something to drink. He touched his right leg. There was no feeling in it; he could poke it anywhere he pleased, it gave no sign of life. Oh, all right, he thought, maybe it's still asleep. He leaned back and tried to stretch out again, but then he was struck from below; his body was tossed upward and fell back onto the bunk. He lay there as before. His bones hurt, he ached all over, and his head was befuddled. That had been a hard blow; a sledge hammer couldn't have hit any harder; he wasn't quite clear in the head yet. Suddenly something sticky squirted into his face. Then it stopped, started again, stopped and started again. He resigned himself to the idea that this would go on forever.

Somebody was moving around with a flashlight. The fire extinguishers had been thrown out of their holders and were filling the whole place with foam. The extinguishers lay on the floor, rolling with the motion of the ship, squirting first to starboard, then straight up, then to port, and then back again, and that went on until they were empty.

An emergency light was rigged. The crew's quarters looked like a snowstorm. Some men came in. Teichmann recognized Stollenberg. A bomb had fallen into the water close to the side, Stollenberg told him, the *Albatross* had taken a bit of a jump, the stern was torn off, but there was no cause for alarm, as the bulkheads were holding.

Then the flotilla commander was standing there. "We're

trying to save her. You'll be informed in plenty of time if we have to abandon ship. The wounded will leave first."

They carried Bülow in and laid him on a table. His face was as white as the foam from the fire extinguishers. That was all Teichmann could see of him. Later they took him back up on deck. Then the other wounded men were taken up, and Teichmann too. They were laid between the door of the petty officers' quarters and the winch.

Ship No. 5 came alongside and the *Albatross* was made fast by her bow and sternlines. Bülow was taken off and then Stüwe. All the wounded were supposed to be transferred to No. 5 but Teichmann didn't make it. The *Albatross* was sinking fast and was weighing down No. 5, which was listing dangerously. The flotilla commander gave orders to cast off the lines. That was no longer possible, and they had to be cut.

"Make for port with all the speed you've got," cried Wegener to the captain of No. 5.

"I request permission to stay near you, sir, in case you have to abandon ship," cried Lieutenant Hoff, captain of No. 5.

"All right, I guess the fireworks are over. But keep far enough away so you have a field of fire."

"Yes, sir."

The *Albatross* had settled still more. The men were trying to pump the water out of the coal bunker. The commander ordered Halbernagel to ready the rafts. Halbernagel scrambled up the starboard shrouds and loosened a raft, so it could just be slipped down if needed. On his way to the port shrouds he stumbled over Teichmann's legs. He fell down, saying "Hoppla," picked himself up, apologized very politely to Teichmann, and said that if the coal dust didn't clog the pump they could keep the old tub afloat. Then he clambered up the port shrouds like a weasel and readied the second raft. At this point he lost his balance and fell. His toe caught in the rigging, and he crashed headfirst against the bulkhead. There he lay. Teichmann wanted to call out, but he heard the pump: it was working evenly, and that took up all his attention.

For him it was an awful feeling to be helpless, unable to move, dependent on others. But then to prove to himself that he wasn't entirely done for, he slid over to Halbernagel, dragging himself along the deck with his hands. It was slow going, and in between he listened to the sound of the pump. He felt Halbernagel's head and found the hole at once; it was like sticking his fingers into a pudding.

The pump was working perfectly. The water flowed outboard in an even stream. When the men relieved each other, the stream grew thinner for a few seconds, but then resumed its normal force. Teichmann slid back to his old place. He felt relatively safe. The *Albatross* was afloat: if nothing went wrong, she'd stay afloat for a long time, and No. 5 was only a few hundred yards off.

Stollenberg lit a cigarette. After two drags he gave it to Teichmann and went back to the pump. Teichmann slid closer to the winch so he could lean his back against it, and cupping his hand around it, he finished smoking Stollenberg's cigarette. There was a slight hissing when he crushed it out on deck; the blood, he decided, came from Meckel, whom they had laid down behind the winch, firmly wedged in between the winch and the bridge structure.

The pump worked smoothly, sending out an even stream of water. It was a pleasant, soothing sound. But along with it Teichmann heard, first swelling, then diminishing, then increasing again, the sound of engines. They came on quickly. A glaring white light burst, as though for a flash exposure; he was blinded, and a monstrous crash struck his ears. A wall of hot air pressed him against the winch; the bow of the *Albatross* was lifted up, fell back on the water; waves crashed over the deck; on the bow only the *"night watchman"* was still peering out of the water.

"Abandon ship!" he heard Wegener shouting. The water squished and gurgled under Teichmann, and he could feel the ship sinking. The rafts were slipped. Stollenberg and Vögele lifted him over the rail and let him down on the port raft. A couple of firemen who had been off watch jumped in after him. Vögele and a fireman let down the port lifeboat, threw the men in the raft a line, and took the raft in tow. Then the flotilla commander and the captain jumped overboard, swam to the raft, and hung on to it. The sodium lights were lit on the ends of the raft as a sign that its passengers had been shipwrecked.

Teichmann saw the men on the starboard raft paddling along, making good headway, because the current was driving them toward No. 5. Hoff came toward them and took them on board.

"The *Albatross* has sunk, sir," said Ensign Paschen in a calm but toneless voice. "The time is twenty-three eleven."

"Very well," said the flotilla commander.

The planes attacked again. Hoff's men shot down two of them. The Britishers dropped a bomb on the stern of his ship and then attacked the raft. They came in low, firing their guns. Twice in quick succession Teichmann felt the same pain as in the battle station when he had first been hit. He knew he had been hit twice. They must have got the other leg somewhere, he thought.

And again they came on, again flying low. Teichmann rolled into the water, gripping the raft with his hands. He saw Paschen waving his arm at the attacking planes; then, shot in the face, Paschen let go the raft and drowned.

The sodium could not be extinguished. In their terror the firemen tried to hold the sodium containers under water, but it was useless. They couldn't hold both of them under water at once. It was like a seesaw; when one end was down the other was up, and when the chemical came into contact with oxygen, it burned. They tried to turn the raft over. This too was impossible, for no one was willing to release his grip on the raft.

The planes came on again. Before they attacked, a fireman threw himself on one of the sodium containers, let out a roar, and fell into the water.

The machine-gun bullets splashed in the water, sending up little white fountains. Then they got the range of the raft. Teichmann closed his eyes. He felt a blow in the belly; unconsciously his brain registered the word "foul," and he waited to be dead.. He heard his comrades cursing and screaming and in the end just screaming. He couldn't see how they died.

When he opened his eyes, he saw the flotilla commander.

There was no one else. Wegener had rested his chin on the edge of the raft, and in the glow of the burning sodium Teichmann saw that his hands were red and the sleeves of his jacket torn in several places.

"You've been hit?"

"In the arms."

Teichmann made his way to him, hand over hand, thrust his right arm under Wegener's shoulder, and gripped the raft again with his hand, holding Wegener between himself and the raft.

The current drove the raft and the lifeboat, on which nothing was stirring, some five hundred yards past the stern of Hoff's ship. Hoff was again under attack. Teichmann saw the last ship in the flotilla firing all its guns. One plane fell in flames.

"Can you hold out?"

"Sure, for hours."

But suddenly Teichmann felt a tearing pain in his stomach. He remembered that they had shot him in the belly, and the realization came as such a shock, it was as if he had just been hit.

The current was strong. They were driven away from No. 5. Hoff was still fighting it out with the planes. Teichmann's legs burned like fire; the salt water was taking effect. But he had the feeling that he could hang on to the raft like this for ages; I'm not the least bit tired, he thought. And that's the truth.

Suddenly the tearing pain was back again. It ate into his bowels like a hungry rat. Gall rose to his mouth, and the bitter liquid reminded him of his worst hours of seasickness. His legs burned as if they had been thrust into boiling oil. He moaned.

"Can you hold out?"

"Sure."

The rat was still there. It bored into his body. He felt as if he were buried in the ground up to his neck; he was unable to move, defenseless, at the mercy of the rat. The rat was in a metal tube; one end of the tube was above the ground but red hot; the rat couldn't get out by that end and the other end was aimed at his belly button. The rat could get out if it chewed its way through, and that was what it was doing. Teichmann roared with pain.

"You can let go now."

He felt the rat burrowing through his bowels as through a pile of straw. And then it was gnawing again. He felt its sharp, pointed teeth cutting everything that was in their way. He groaned with pain and exertion; his arms and hands began to tremble.

"Come, let go."

He grew dizzy. His mind was a fog.

In the dreamy distance he heard Wegener's voice: "Let go." Stick it out, stick it out. He repeated the order to himself through clenched lips.

"Lie down on the raft. I can hold on with my teeth."

Teichmann let Wegener go. His fingers dug into the wood of the raft, he closed his eyes, pulled himself up, let himself down on the raft, and lay still. His brain was giving him some order; he vaguely sensed it, but he no longer obeyed. He merely stretched out his right arm instinctively in the direction where he assumed Wegener to be; and then he sank into unconsciousness.

A frightful pain wrenched him upward. He doubled up and when he tried to lay his hands on his belly where the pain was, he could move only one hand. Slowly and very cautiously he ran his hand over his belly and he felt as though he were investigating a foreign body. He felt a warm wetness and knew that it was blood. I'm bleeding to death. It's perfectly plain, I'm bleeding to death. All right. Then I'll bleed to death. He knew that he was giving himself up for dead, but that didn't strike him as anything very unusual. It was so simple. Everything was simple once you'd given up wanting anything. . . .

When he woke up again, he lay still at first. He was surprised. Something was moving in his belly: a dull, even pounding, like someone knocking on a door with his knuckles. It's my heart, he thought. He was cold. Cold shivers shook his whole body. He felt the cold with every fiber of his being, and for a little while his brain functioned with precision, telling him that he was finished. He felt alone and miserable. His limbs were cold and brittle as if made of thin glass, and he couldn't stop shivering. Suddenly a wild despair came over him. He was filled with a furious rage against the pain, although at the moment he felt hardly anything. He tried to raise himself, to prop himself up on his hands, but he had only one hand free. He couldn't tell where the other hand was.

The sodium containers had burned themselves out and where the east must have been it was growing faintly light. With a groan Teichmann turned over on the other side and looked into Wegener's face. He had sunk his teeth into Teichmann's hand and that was how he was holding himself above the water. Teichmann looked at him for a while. He saw his own hand and the white teeth, which were something to see under the cracked upper lip. He did not notice that the hand was his own. For him the hand was a part of the raft. Wegener had closed his eyes. He looked as though he were biting into something sour and bitter. A dill pickle perhaps? Teichmann giggled and then took fright because he was giggling. What's the matter with me? Wegener opened his eyes. Teichmann saw the blue pupils and the red eyelids inflamed with the salt water. He sat up and seized Wegener's hair in his left hand. He slid close to the edge of the raft, took Wegener's hair between his teeth, reached his arms under Wegener's shoulders, and pulled him up on the raft. During the effort he was almost unaware of the pain. It was only after he lay down again that he felt as if someone had cut a great slit in his belly.

He lay exhausted, incapable of thinking. Everything ached. His body was burning with fever. It seemed to him that he was lying in a field of nettles, but he made no attempt to move.

"Take off your shirt and cover your wound with it."

It took all his strength to obey this order. He raised himself a little and stripped off his shirt. It was red and sticky in front. Trembling, his fingers groped for the hole in his belly. He had pulled his pants down a little and then he could feel the bullet hole. He was seized with disgust, and his mouth twisted into a grimace of horror. He laid the bunched-up shirt on the wound.

"Lie still now."

When the sun was up, he felt better. He listened inwardly, waiting for the pain. He knew it would come again, but for the moment it was bearable. He propped himself up on his elbows and looked down at himself, and at the sight of his legs he vomited. The smell was revolting, it filled him with loathing for himself, and again he gagged. He raised himself almost to a sitting position, but then he sank back again, and the gagging continued. What was it I ate last? Anyway I didn't drink enough or it would be easier. He vaguely noticed that he was beginning to bleed again; his shirt felt like a wet mop. He cursed aloud.

"We've got to have the boat."

Teichmann was furious. That voice—he has no right to give me orders. God Almighty, doesn't he see that I'm dying? Damn him. But he knew that the voice was right and that he would obey, and that increased his rage. The pain in his body mounted. he felt as if a balloon covered with thorns were being blown up inside him. He took the bloody shirt away from his wound and held his hand by his belly to catch the blood that was oozing out. When he put the shirt back, it was like a heavy flat stone. He wanted to sleep and closed his eyes. He tried to pull up his knees; it wouldn't work and it hurt. He turned over on his side. Then he saw Wegener lying prone, trying to pull in the line of the boat by his teeth. Is he stronger than I am? He pulled himself up. Chills shook his legs and after catching a glimpse of them he looked away, gagging again. They were alien legs; they no longer belonged to him. He crawled over to Wegener and took the line, and infinitely slowly, as in a slow-motion film, he pulled it in hand over hand, and the boat came closer. A few times he wanted to stop; it was too hard, and he was too weak and too tired. He looked at Wegener and he went on working. Damn it, he has no right to look at me like that.

When the boat was alongside the raft, he was exhausted. His body was empty, bathed in sweat; he was finished. The blood kept oozing out of him, and a sharp, piercing pain sawed at his abdomen like a jagged knife. He tasted the blood in his mouth; it tasted like iron, and he began to sob softly.

"Come into the boat."

He heard but he didn't care what happened. The voice was so far away, it couldn't have anything to do with him. I'm going to die now, he said to himself, and he was pleased with his decision. Just to die.

"Come on."

Good God, can't he leave me alone? They don't even let you die, oh . . . He let out a deep, hopeless moan, and then he heard the motor. It was as if in a dream. They're coming to get us . . .

They're coming . . .

He was a new man. If they operate right away, everything will be all right. I still have a chance, I'll live through it, I'll . . .

"Come on."

He raised himself and saw Wegener in the boat. He had pulled the starter cord with his teeth. The motor was no longer running. But it had been running. It could run again, thought Teichmann, and summoned up the strength to get into the boat.

In the boat lay Vögele and a fireman. Under the gunwale, a hand's breadth above water level, there was a leak. The boat hadn't taken in much water but she rode low.

"We'll have to throw one of them overboard."

"Yes, sir."

Vögele lay on top of the fireman. Teichmann pulled him out of the boat. He wanted to pull him onto the raft, but the body fell in the water and sank. The leak was now twice as far above the waterline as before. Teichmann tried to start the motor again. After the third try it ran a few minutes and then stalled again. He pulled the cord again and it ran.

"Course one seven zero," said Wegener, and then he collapsed.

On the floor of the boat lay the dead striker and in the bow lay Wegener, crumpled up, unconscious. His arms hung limp, as though dead, and seemed like a superfluous appendage that no longer concerned him in any way. His right hand lay palm upward between his thighs, his index finger out-stretched—an obscene posture despite the three gold stripes on his arm.

Teichmann steered the boat, keeping the sun to port. He wanted to get a bearing himself by his watch and fix a course toward the French coast, but his watch had stopped running. He pondered a long time whether to do it, because the motor would probably stall again, but then he did it after all. He crawled forward over the fireman, and when he saw that the second hand was moving he took Wegener's wrist watch. With the help of the watch and the sun he figured out the direction to the coast. He could tell by the wake when he was off course. The motor had not stalled.

Later he grew too tired to look back. He looked toward the sun and sometimes he thought he saw the coast. And then the coast was gone; it had been clouds. The sun blazed down on him and a dry, hot fever seared his body. I'm being baked inside and out, he mumbled to himself. The heat of the sun made his limbs heavy and tired. They no longer hurt so badly; he had a feeling that his legs were no longer there. A warm drowsiness enfolded him, as the monotonous sound of the motor lulled his senses like a drug. I'm drunk, he thought pleasantly. His eyes closed . . .

"I've got to hold out," he heard himself whisper. He blinked into the sun and then he saw the endless surface of the water, glittering silver. There was a swimming before his eyes, and he turned them on Wegener. It was a cheerless sight. He lay doubled up on the floor, motionless. His hands were brown with dried blood.

The rat was back again. It gnawed about wildly in his body, dispelling his weariness, because he had to scream. He felt that the blood was trickling out of the wound in his belly. He saw it collecting in his open pants flap, and he was amazed at how much blood he possessed.

Then the thirst came. He knew that he mustn't drink the sea water. But his thirst was overpowering. He no longer had any will to oppose it; he was too weak. He was half mad with struggle between the desire to drink and the will to hold out. He felt that two millstones were rubbing together, crushing him between them. He had used his last reserves of strength in fighting the pain. Now he was worn out, defenseless, apathetic. He felt his body shaken by a convulsion. Beads of sweat stood out on his forehead and collected into big drops; when enough of them had gathered they ran down into his eyebrows. Stopped in their course, they gathered again, and when they had swelled sufficiently they flowed into his eyes. The salt sweat stung fiercely. It took him an eternity to decide whether or not to wipe it away.

His hands began to tremble on the tiller. He had to clench his teeth to keep his head from drooping forward, to keep from falling asleep. And then again he felt the consuming fire of thirst. Everything was burning inside him. He saw revolving circles before his eyes and closed them. Someone inside him said, You've got to stick it out. His eyes opened. But then the pain had him in its clutches again. He wanted to scream, but phlegm clogged his throat. He rubbed his tongue against his parched, leathery palate. His mouth was completely dry and his lips were as rough as a coarse file. He ached all over. Now and then he let out a furious, desperate scream because the pain was unbearable, and the rest of the time he just moaned. But he didn't let go of the tiller.

The screaming exhausted him. He wept silently. Now and then he had to cough, and bloody phlegm collected in his mouth. He gagged, and looked on as the blood ran down over his chin to his chest. A few drops remained in the corners of his mouth, and when he coughed they became red bubbles. He spat, the spittle stuck to his chin, and he felt it slowly drying and growing hard. He mumbled something unintelligible. A deep, oppressive weariness overcame him. His eyes closed.

Stick it out.

He made a feeble attempt to change his position without letting go of the tiller, and then the motor stalled.

For a minute he did nothing, just waited. But the motor wouldn't start by itself. That was what he had been secretly hoping. He looked at Wegener as though for advice. Bah, he's just as dead as the fireman. We're all dead. I'm just putting on airs.

He wound up the starter cord and pulled it. He was surprised at being able to, and when the motor ran he looked at it in amazement.

Frequently he spoke to himself—an incoherent, unintelligible garble. Now and then he giggled for no reason at all. But then a time came when he was too tired to talk to himself. He just looked obstinately straight ahead of him. When his head drooped over, his fists gripped the tiller like two steel vises and he pulled himself up again.

By noon the sun was so crushingly hot that he could no longer sit up. The sea swam before his eyes in the glare. He dropped his head like a boxer who has decided to let himself be counted out. His face was covered with sweat; he saw the half-dried, sticky, bloody mucous in his pants flap and closed his eyes. Just for a little while, he thought, then it will all be over . . .

The motor coughed a little and that woke him up. It coughed again and then stopped entirely.

The air was torrid, and there was no breeze. The unaccustomed stillness kept him awake. But his will was broken. I've got through the fourth round—that's when the tiredness begins. I've got through the seventh, that's when you really begin to feel pooped. I've got through the ninth, but what I don't know is whether this fight is going to be ten, twelve, or fifteen rounds, or more . . . anyway, I've taken all I can, I'm going to give up. Somehow he felt better after framing this thought. He felt that this time his decision was irrevocable. He knew that by his own strength there was nothing more he could do. It's all over. Rotten luck. But it's over. Everything's over. Over . . .

Shortly before losing consciousness he began to wonder who would miss him, and he found no one. Once again he looked over toward Wegener. He suddenly remembered who would miss Wegener, and the thought came to him like an immense fear. He had lost the connections between things. But what he had tried to forget, what had almost been the end of him at the time, lived before his closed eyes. A wondrous, voluptuous image. Every minute detail was there. Her face was so close to him that he could see every pore in her skin. And her fragrance was there too. He saw her standing by the dog-rose hedge while the duty sergeant was lecturing him. He saw her as she gave him the buns; her dress was light blue and she had on a narrow golden belt and white shoes, and the rectangular neckline of her dress was bordered with a white stripe, and under it lay her bosom, and her golden hair glittered in the sun . . .

In his memory she was good and beautiful. He had forgotten everything else.

He propped himself up. His hands were trembling so hard that the cord dropped from his fingers. Clumsily and with great difficulty he wound it round one finger and, while a fierce pain raced through him, pulled the cord. The motor ran. He held the tiller. His stomach muscles were scraped raw by the constant struggle with the pain. He leaned forward with his back hunched over. He had discovered that this position was the least painful. He held his head upright and with chin thrust forward looked up at the sun or squinted now and then at Wegener's watch, which he had strapped to his wrist. It was still running.

But the monotonous droning of the motor lulled him. An irresistible, stifling weariness settled over him. A leaden blanket descended on his body, extinguishing all life. He resisted the blanket, but knew that in the end the resistance would be useless. And then, as though falling back into a bottomless deep dream, he saw *her* before him. The contrast between his memory and what he was enduring now was so enormous that he let out a groan. He was sorry for himself.

But still he held out. The pain mounted. It was no longer a dull throbbing but a furious hammering, and his body was the anvil. He hurled himself at the hammer, he summoned up the last little remnant of his will to defy it. Hammer away, you swine, he thought, screaming beneath the merciless blows. And when the hammering let up, even a little, the thirst was on him. Instinctively he forbade himself to look at the water. His mouth felt like parchment. He gagged and fought for breath, but there was nothing left to vomit up; everything in him had dried up. His breath rattled as if it were not air but wood. From time to time the spray fell on his face; for a moment it was very pleasant, but then the thirst was redoubled. It had grown worse than the pain.

Suddenly he felt a distinct knocking in his head. First single strokes, then many, and then they came rattling down on him. It was like a rolling of drums on his skull. He closed his eyes. Red dots appeared in his lids. They danced. They grew darker, and in the end they were black. The black dots multiplied at a feverish pace until everything was black—black and indifferent. Teichmann let his eyes do as they pleased, and the boat too. . . .

A scream awakened him from his faint. Wegener was screaming. Teichmann came to slowly, his mind still clouded. But then he understood why Wegener had screamed, and he sat paralyzed with horror. He wanted to howl, but no sound came out of his throat. He thought he wasn't seeing right. Good God, it *can't* be . . .

A berserk rage brought him to his feet, and half mad with fury he stumbled over the dead fireman to Wegener. The gulls flew off. He took Wegener's head in his arms and a toneless, desperate sobbing shook his body. He thought he would go out of his mind when he realized that he had slept while the gulls were eating Wegener's eyes. Wegener had been unable to move his arms to chase them away; they had picked out first one, then the other one. Two red streams flowed from the empty sockets.

He laid Wegener over the fireman. Then he dragged himself back into the stern. Wegener's head was now barely an inch from Teichmann's legs. The gulls did not come back.

His body was ablaze. He felt it with his hands. He felt the oozing blood and it seemed frightfully hot. A cramp convulsed him and when he tried to cry out thick blood rushed into his mouth. Filled with nausea, he let it flow down over his chest. He tried to swallow, but in spite of the blood the inside of his mouth felt like sandpaper.

He could no longer think anything at all. Automatically he took the starter cord between his fingers and tugged at it.

The motor ran, but he had no consciousness of it. The words "hold out" were burned into his brain, but he no longer knew it. He cowered there clutching the tiller, waiting for death.

10

He heard the snipping of scissors, and from time to time he
felt as though electric currents were racing through him. He
raised his head but could see nothing. His throat was clogged
and he was afraid he would suffocate.

When he came to, he saw a little Teddy bear above him,
hanging from a string that was attached to the handle of a
sea chest; the sea chest was on a locker. The bear was
swinging back and forth. If he keeps on like that, Teichmann
thought, he'll rub his ass sore on the locker door. He followed
the Teddy bear with his eyes and then with his head. But
soon he gave up; it made him dizzy. He felt very tired, but
he persuaded himself that it was very important for him to
keep his eye on the bear. To keep awake, he wondered very
hard what the bear's name was. He knew that these bears
have a little button with their name on it in one ear. What
could the name be?

He dozed off for a while and when he opened his eyes the
bear hung motionless. That frightened him; he decided to ask
the bear why he had stopped swinging. But then Teichmann
was lifted up. Something spun in his head and then he was
in the open.

The air did him good. It was pleasantly warm and yet
fresh. His head became quite clear; he could lift it without
feeling sick, and he noticed that he was on a stretcher,
wrapped in a gray blanket that reached up to his chest.
Over his legs the blanket had a broad white stripe with
LUFTWAFFE written on it in big letters. When he turned
his head a little, he saw the top of a sharp-looking boat,
and while he was wondering how many knots it could make,
he felt himself being lifted up. It grew dark around him; a
door slammed: not the door to a room, it sounded more like

the door of a van truck. He heard the driver stepping on the starter and the motor springing into action. The car gave a jolt and Teichmann felt a terrible pain. Then the motor was still again. That jerk of a driver left her in gear and has killed the motor, he thought. The driver started again and this time set the car cautiously in motion.

He drove like the devil himself, or so it seemed to Teichmann. On the curves he ran on the front wheels and let the hind wheels come sliding after. At such moments Teichmann had the feeling that the hind wheels had lost contact with the road. When the car took a right curve, he was thrown against the left wall of the car; on left curves he was afraid of being flung off the stretcher and landing on the floor. He wished there would be only right curves, but this was not the case and he was terrified the whole time. Sometimes the driver braked abruptly; then the blood shot into his legs; it felt as though giant ants were biting his legs and that was worse than all the curves together. He lay there defenseless while thousands of great, fat, but very hungry ants bit into him at once, eating him alive. Every time the driver braked, they bit, and when he braked hard, the giant ants bit great chunks out of his legs.

It can't go on like this, he thought, I've got to tell Mr. Speed King. He yelled something and pounded on the partition with his fists. The man up front drove on as though he had heard nothing. Teichmann screamed with rage.

The car stopped. Now I'm going to tell that gorilla what I think of him. It grew light and someone said, "Well, what's the matter with you?"

It wasn't the driver but an Air Force master sergeant. He spoke as if asking what time it was. Teichmann kept quiet for a moment—I'm too exhausted to answer properly; I've got to collect my strength, he said to himself—and then he screamed, "Turn me around the other way, you ass-hole."

"Take it easy," said the sergeant, "you're not in the Navy now."

"I know, but I expected better treatment from that baboon of a driver."

"In the first place I'm not driving; in the second place

216

I'm not a baboon," said the master sergeant and called forward, "Paul, come quick, we've got to turn him around the other way."

Teichmann heard the driver getting out and coming around in back.

"Don't raise a stink, son. We're almost there."

"You can kiss my ass."

"Easy does it."

They pulled the stretcher out and shoved Teichmann back in the car headfirst.

"We'll be there in two minutes, son."

The journey continued. Now when the driver stepped on the brake, innumerable little worms wriggled in Teichmann's legs. He would have liked to scratch . . .

"Well, how are you?" somebody said.

It was a woman's voice. Teichmann opened his eyes and saw a veiled face over him. He could see no features behind the veil. The woman said something he could not understand and then indistinctly he could hear her say that the chief staff doctor would soon be there; he was an authority in his field, he'd soon set Teichmann straight, his abdomen had already been operated on. "It didn't hurt, did it?" He closed his eyes.

A little later he opened them again because he heard several voices. They came closer. He saw the woman's face again—now he could get a better look at her—and then he located two or three men who also had veils over their faces. The figures kept moving together and then bounding apart. Below their heads everything was white. The biggest head, which was round as a pumpkin, was addressed as Herr Chief Staff Doctor. One of the heads said something in Latin in a high voice; it ended in -us; the big round head nodded and said "Amputate."

The veil before the faces became thinner. The high voice said something, and then the mouth of the big head gave forth the words "Probably both."

The veils were gone. Teichmann saw the faces of the

heads. The chief staff doctor had a dueling scar that extended from the corner of his mouth to the lobe of one ear.

"I think he's awake," said the woman dressed like a nurse.

"Impossible," said the head with the high voice, and turned away with the other heads.

"Oh, yes I am," said Teichmann.

The heads spun around and goggled at him. The whole thing seemed to him like a dream that has suddenly turned to reality. Three men in doctor's gowns and two nurses were standing around him. He wasn't greatly impressed. The nurse who stood to the left of him, and had not yet said a word, looked as dry and bony as a scarecrow; she had the pinched mouth of an aging old maid, surmounted by a mustache. Beside her stood a young, slender, black-haired doctor who looked like nothing at all. Then came the chief staff doctor and then the doctor with the high voice. He wore glasses with thin metal frames. His overhanging nose and thick lips didn't go with the thin metal frames. To the right of him stood the nurse who had spoken to Teichmann. Her breasts looked like huge sugar loaves. That was the first thing Teichmann noticed about her—he had captured her most notable feature.

"Yes, we may have to amputate. Only one leg, though; perhaps . . ."

"I heard everything you said."

"Oh, well, then you're all set, ha-ha. Your abdomen's O.K.; in fact . . ."

"When?"

"What's that?"

"I mean, does it have to be right away?"

"No, not necessarily. We can wait for tonight. If the pus drains all right, it may not be necessary."

"Otherwise tomorrow?"

"Yes. But we'll see you before that. Now sleep well. Good night."

The man was glad when he could leave. Teichmann felt certain that he wouldn't see him again before the operation.

A nurse laid her hand on his forehead. It was a cool,

smooth, pleasant hand. Then she took a cloth and ran it over his mouth.

"I'd like something to drink, please."

"No, not yet."

"Oh, please, just a little sip."

"Should I notify Edith?"

"Who?"

"Your wife."

"What are you talking about? I haven't any wife."

"I thought Edith was your wife." The nurse gave a clucking laugh like a hen. "I thought the watch was from your wife."

"What watch?"

"There on the bedside table. We took it off when we were washing you, before the operation. You had a watch on each wrist. Looked kind of funny. One of them isn't running; water must have got into it, but the other is still going. Here, see for yourself."

Teichmann examined it closely. It was gold and rather heavy. It was still running. On the back of the case he read the words "Edith for Erich 2/5/39," written in tiny jewels.

"You can put it on again. Your arms won't be amputated, and probably not your legs either; I don't think so. Anyway, things will look better tomorrow. You'd better sleep now."

He asked the nurse to put the watch back on the bedside table.

"Yes," she said. "And my name is Bertha. I'm on duty tonight. If you need anything just call for Nurse Bertha."

She came in several times in the course of the night although he had not called her. She seemed very much concerned about him. And once a doctor came in and stuck him in the arm with a thin needle.

He had asked for the watch again, wound it, and put it on. Somebody might make off with it, he said to himself; after all, it's valuable.

At dawn he fell asleep, against his will; he wanted to be awake when they took him to the operating room. He wanted to speak again to the chief staff doctor. . . .

In the afternoon he woke up. Through the window he saw

the blue sky. The sun shone into the ward and fell on the row of beds across from Teichmann. He lay in the shadow; more restful for his eyes, it occurred to him. Behind him a window was open; he heard birds twittering.

In the bed to the left of him someone was snoring gently. The bed on the right was empty. Farther off they were playing a game on a board; it sounded like *Mühle;* must be good players, they take their time about moving. Across the ward someone was playing "Red Poppy" on a harmonica. Teichmann felt good. It's better to have an amputation than to die, he thought. He was aware of a stiff bandage on his belly. He couldn't feel the belly itself.

A short, powerfully built man came in. He walked slowly; every step seemed to hurt. Under his right arm he carried several thick books. He sat down cautiously on the empty bed next to Teichmann and leafed through the books. Then he piled them up on the bedside table, took the topmost volume, removed his slippers without using his hands, lay down on his side, and began to read. Teichmann had to squint hard to see the man. It was tiring; he rested his eyes from time to time by looking into the blue sky. But it was interesting to look at the man. He was holding an oversized red pencil and making marks in the book with it. Teichmann could tell when he made an exclamation mark, a wavy line, or a big question mark, and when he underscored. He did everything at least double. Once he marked a paragraph with five thick lines and threw in two exclamation marks after it. The man was beaming.

His neighbor on the left had awakened. He stuck his legs out of the bed, put on his slippers, apparently with great care, and went out of the ward. When he came back he said to Teichmann's right-hand neighbor, "Hey, Ernst; it's free."

"Then I'll go lay a big fat egg," said the man with the books. He rolled out of bed, stepped into his slippers, and went out, moving carefully around Teichmann's bed.

Teichmann noticed that all the patients wore the same slippers. Theoretically there ought to be a pair under my bed. He leaned over to the right. No slippers. That's nothing, he said to himself, ninety per cent of the time slippers are on the left side of the bed; but for a time he lay still. If he has to, a man can do all sorts of things without legs.

The man named Ernst came back. Coffee cups were rolled in on a little cart. Behind it came a man with a big pot and poured coffee into the cups. Teichmann smelled it. The man with the cart and the man with the pitcher went to every bed. When they were still two beds away from Teichmann, he bent over to the left. There was *one* slipper. He lay back again, trying to figure out to which foot the slipper belonged. Oh, hell, you can do all sorts of things with one leg, he said to himself. You can stand on it, for instance. Then suddenly a number of men were standing around him, examining him like a rare animal.

"Well, how's it going?" they asked.

"Do you want anything? Do you need something?"

"Coffee," said Teichmann.

"Say, you're in luck. They've just brought it in."

"First-class coffee."

"You wouldn't get better at Kranzler's."

"Peacetime quality," said the man with the pot. One held his hand behind Teichmann's head; another held the cup. The coffee was hot and steaming.

"Take that stuff away, you idiots. He's not allowed to drink."

"Oh, I'm . . ."

"Later, friend. You'll have to wait a little while."

"Do you need anything else?"

"Can we do something for you?"

"No, I don't need a thing. I just want to sleep a little."

More men came to his bedside and looked on as he tried to sleep. When they had taken the coffee away he wanted to cry; he thought of his missing leg again. Just to be saying something, he asked if there were any more Navy men in the ward.

No, they said, he was the only one. All the rest were sick men from the Army and Air Force.

"No wounded?"

No, there hadn't been any in quite some time. There was nothing doing here in the West.

Teichmann closed his eyes and soon fell asleep. From time to time he woke up because he was thirsty. He asked for water but he didn't get any. He was so chagrined that most of the time he fell right back to sleep. Now and then a nurse appeared and gave him an injection. He would have liked to know which leg they had amputated but he was afraid to ask.

One day they put something damp between his lips. It was unbelievably wonderful. In that moment, when his parched lips felt the moisture—only the tiniest little bit—it seemed to him as though he had just come into the world. He was reborn. And there was something voluptuous, unique, incomparable about this rebirth. He felt that his tear glands were functioning again and he didn't know which way to look. They stood around him, and a nurse smiled at him as though to give him courage; everyone smiled at him and one man said, "Looks like he's pulled through."

"Can't we give him something to drink now?"

"No, I'll attend to the drinking."

"What's your name, nurse?"

"What's that? Be quiet, you fellows."

"I'd like to know your name."

"Margot."

"Thank you," said Teichmann.

"Gangway!" cried a thundering voice, so loud that the whole room trembled. "Can't you make room, you landlubbers?"

At the foot of Teichmann's bed appeared a giant of a man in Navy dungarees, with a flat sailor cap on his head. The hat band was pulled so tight that the N of NAVY was under the eagle.

"Hail, shipmate and fellow sufferer," the giant roared. He smelled strongly of liquor. Teichmann took a closer look at him. His features were coarse but pleasant. He shook Teichmann's hand without hurting him.

"Karl Bockhammer. They call me Karlchen. I'm from your flotilla." He looked at the name plate at the head of the bed. "Say, Hans, why, we're good friends."

"I thought I was the only one here from our outfit," said Teichmann.

"I looked in on you right away. That's clear as mud. But fella, all you did was sleep. I've been here about twelve times. Had your sleep out?"

"Sure."

"Say, that's good." And still in the same roar, "Got to welcome an old shipmate. We've seen action together, you and me, ain't we?"

"Sure have," said Teichmann, though he couldn't remember ever having laid eyes on the fellow. It would have been better if he had said nothing, for now Bockhammer began—"Say, do you remember . . ."—to spin hair-raising yarns about battles with the Tommies, overjoyed to have the whole ward listening. Teichmann would have liked to tell him not to strain his vocal cords, but he couldn't get a word in edgewise. Bockhammer invented the wildest episodes. He and his buddies had shot down the four-engined bombers of the Royal Air Force—he pronounced it *Rohschelle Eiervotze*—like sparrows. He and his buddies had sunk everything that came within range of their guns: "Mine sweepers, subs, PT boats, destroyers . . ."

"With your fish bucket?" asked an Air Force man.

"Yes, it so happens. We rammed her, you greenhorn. We caught her on the beam and down she went. You were there, Hans, you remember?"

"I must have been on leave," said Teichmann.

But later he said yes and amen to everything, in the hope that Bockhammer would soon run out of yarns.

A nurse appeared and announced that in ten minutes the Chief Staff Doctor would be there for his evening rounds. This didn't disturb Bockhammer in the least; on the contrary, it seemed to stimulate him. When he ran out of exploits he began to talk about conditions in the hospital. He complained about the bilge they were given to eat, and as if it weren't bad enough already, they had to mix dangle-powder with every meal. Life in the hospital was no joke; no liquor, no liberty, they didn't even let you slip out to the whorehouse, and the nurses wouldn't let anybody near them. How could a man be expected to get well when he wasn't allowed to lead a normal life?

"Here it's different," said one of the men in the ward.

"Yes, in your section. But in ours there's nothing doing. We're up the creek."

"Any more Navy guys in with you?" said Teichmann.

"Sure, a whole stableful. But say, I've got to go now. Where did you catch it?"

"In the legs and belly. And you?"

"Burned my pecker."

"And the others?"

"Ditto."

"Then you can hardly expect the nurses to cozy up to you."

"Just the same, they could be friendlier. They could be a little more . . . sympathetic, see. We're two decks up. We'll come down and see you. You'll see, it's a swell bunch."

"Maybe it's better if I come up and see you when I can walk."

"O.K. We've got plans for you, see. Something we need you for. We'll talk about it later on. Be good, son, but not for too long, or it gets to be a habit. So long."

The head physician cast a glance into the ward and said, "Everything all right?" Then he disappeared without waiting for an answer.

Then came supper.

Teichmann got to talking with his neighbors. Ernst's last name was Esch; he was a man in his early forties. He was a Pfc. in Air Intelligence, a mechanic in civilian life, and he was here for hemorrhoids. Teichmann's other neighbor was Adolf Köhler, a corporal, about the same age as Esch, and a baker by trade. He'd been in the hospital for twelve weeks, he told Teichmann, originally on account of appendicitis; then he had caught cold and got pleurisy, with fluid—"up to here"—it had almost reached the heart. By the time that was over, he had malignant bedsores in various places; now he had them on his heels. He weighed only 128 as compared to his normal weight of 180. He had completely lost his appetite; sometimes he thought he was fated never to leave the hospital alive. As he related his troubles, the tears came to his eyes; but otherwise he was a good fellow.

When the wagon with the evening soup was wheeled into the ward, Köhler stood up, limped over to it, and came back with a full dish. You had to hurry, he explained, because the ones who could get up always made a rush for it and filled their bellies first and there was never anything left for the bed patients. He knew, he had been in bed long enough. Then, sitting on his bed, he hurriedly emptied his plate, smacking his lips in such a way that Teichmann felt justified in asking how it tasted. "Not so bad," said Köhler.

After supper Esch briefed Teichmann on the hospital routine. He promised to tell him about the doctors and nurses next day; it was too much for one session.

They straightened Teichmann's bed, shook the pillow, and smoothed out the sheet. If he needed something, he should tell them; he mustn't get up under any circumstances. And as long as he wasn't allowed to get up, said Köhler, he would continue to use his left slipper: it had a softer back than his own; he had to turn the back of his left slipper down to keep it from rubbing against his sore heel. He'd already been bawled out twice by the head doctor, for damaging government property.

"Oh, our head doctor," said Esch. "He's a brass hat if ever there was one."

"You can say that again," said Köhler.

"Look who's talking. If you didn't kiss your superiors' asses, you wouldn't be a corporal."

"And they lay off you because of your gold Party medal."

"They'd better if they know what's good for them."

In the course of the night Nurse Margot came in three times to look after Teichmann. She was very nice. . . .

Teichmann woke up; a very ordinary perfume tickled his nose. He heard a few unmentionable words, and saw two women on either side of the bed. They were made up like whores, their age was indeterminate, and they giggled like teen-agers. Then a third joined them and in her turn uttered a term not usually heard outside of whorehouses; then all three withdrew to one corner of the ward, lifted their skirts, thrust their broom handles between their legs, and began in this way to sweep the ward.

Esch explained to Teichmann that these were the native cleaning women who came every morning. They were not to be blamed for their terms of greeting; the soldiers had taught them that these words meant good morning in German. There was still a fourth, Esch related, who was very serviceable; she lay on the table in the washroom.

Teichmann observed how one man at a time went into the washroom and how when he came back the next man went in. There were seven in all.

"On payday there are twice as many," said Esch. "She's expensive."

"She must be strong, though. Is she pretty?"

"I can't say. I don't go with such women. I'm a National Socialist."

"Do the doctors know it?"

"Of course. There aren't very many Old Fighters left."

"I mean about the woman in the washroom."

"Yes, most of them. Not the chief staff doctor. But Weckerlin knows, all right. He's the biggest pig of the lot."

"The one with the glasses?"

"Yes. He encourages it as part of his therapy. He says it quiets the men down and makes them happier and that helps them to get well. He's fixed himself up with a nurse—had her assigned to his station. The little fat one with the balloons out in front . . ."

"Bertha?"

"Yes, she's his steady. He's not the only one. All the doctors have their Mercurochrome Minnies. Nurse Olga, the head nurse, is a rotten pervert. She's at least sixty and very proud of her virginity. Oh, the surgical department's a well-organized pigsty, and the biggest pigs are the ones that run around in white."

Esch related all this in the tone of a man of high moral principles, who is unhappily married. Teichmann couldn't make head or tail of him; he couldn't tell whether Esch really deplored the conditions he described or only pretended to.

After this situation report Esch told Teichmann a little about himself. He called the Führer and Chancellor only Adolf. Oh well, thought Teichmann, that's not so bad; he's an Old Party Fighter. But then Esch said, "When in the year 1923 I marched to the Feldherrnhalle with Adolf, Erich, and Rudi—ah, those were the days, those . . ."

"Who was Erich?"

"You don't know General Ludendorff?"

"By name."

"Ah, yes. Unfortunately, good old Erich left us for Valhalla much too soon."

"And who was Rudi?"

"Man, you're not exactly an expert on German statesmen. Didn't you ever hear of Rudolf Hess?"

"Sure, the guy that flew to England."

"Yes, yes, that's right; he *is* in England now. But in those days, in my time, he was normal."

But you don't seem to be, Teichmann thought. He had the impression that the heroic age of the National Socialist Party was Pfc. Esch's only capital, and that he was still living on it.

Esch got up and did his gymnastics in spite of his hemorrhoids and the laughter of his wardmates. When he had finished his exercises he said to Teichmann, "I want to tell you one thing. He who rests rusts. And the mocking of those fools doesn't bother me in the slightest. They're too dumb to understand. In the early days of National Socialism the same people laughed at us. One of these days they're going to laugh on the other side of their face."

He put on his gray Army jacket over his hospital dress, though it was quite warm in the ward. On the left side of his jacket he wore the gold medal of honor of the National Socialist Party. Slowly, doing his best to keep his buttocks from wobbling, he left the ward in the direction of the latrine.

Meanwhile the Frenchwomen had finished their work and took their leave with the same obscenities as had marked their arrival. Köhler brought Teichmann a basin of water, and Teichmann tried to wash. Someone called "Attention!"

Silence in the ward. According to regulations, bed patients as well as up patients had to come to attention; they lay on their backs, arms at their sides, hands outstretched, their head turned toward the officer.

Dr. Weckerlin entered the ward, accompanied by the sexless head nurse and by Nurses Bertha and Lisbeth. Nurse Margot came in last. The men had eyes only for her; a nod of good morning from her sufficed to make a man happy. She was a feast for the eyes. Her figure was slender, yet well rounded; she had a shapely, sensual mouth and copper-brown hair. And there was something tantalizing about her bearing. She was unapproachable and polite. It was plain that she looked on the men purely as patients. And to top it all, she was from Berlin.

"At ease," cried Dr. Weckerlin, and passed from bed to bed with his covey of nurses. Teichmann was washing when he approached his bed. Nurse Margot had wanted to take the basin away, but he had held on to it. Weckerlin expected each patient to salute by coming to attention as he approached.

"Haven't you learned to salute when an officer approaches you?"

"Yes, sir."

"Well, good God, man, why don't you salute, then?"

"Because I'm washing."

A brief pause ensued. Esch could be heard flushing the head. Weckerlin, it struck Teichmann, looked like a little spitz that wanted to bark and couldn't. Then suddenly the doctor's face was metamorphosed. Deep furrows creased his high forehead and he compressed his thick lips. A battle seemed to have broken out between the upper and lower parts of his face. His lips had taken on the look of a cracked windowpane.

"Well, well, my young friend, perhaps we have you in the wrong place. Perhaps you belong in the psychiatric ward?"

"My trouble is in the legs and belly, sir. Not in the brain."

"In that case, what prevents you from saluting an officer?" Weckerlin roared.

"I have learned that salutes are not given at battle stations,

228

in the washroom, and in the head. Since I cannot leave my bed, I am in the washroom, so to speak. Consequently I am not obliged to salute."

Another brief pause.

Dr. Weckerlin took off his glasses—rather theatrically, as though unsheathing a sword. Then he ran his hand over his forehead, his mouth opened a little, the corners of his mouth turned upward. He was grinning.

"You seem to have a head on your shoulders. I like that." He held out his hand. "My name is Weckerlin. And you, I see, are Herr Teichmann. Very pleased to meet you." He asked with real solicitude how Teichmann was feeling. Then he had the bandages removed from his legs—the nurses were very careful, but Teichmann would have been glad to scream. The pus had drained well, Weckerlin said; if no complications set in, he could keep his legs.

"That would be very nice, sir."

Weckerlin laughed and everyone else laughed, even the usually sullen Nurse Olga.

When Teichmann awoke from his afternoon nap, Stollenberg and Heyne were standing at his bedside.

"Still alive," said Heyne. "Looks as if they can't kill you."

"Not me. You rejoiced too soon."

That was the tone: "You can't lose a bad penny." "Weeds live forever." "It's only the good men that die." When the formalities of greeting were over, they told Teichmann that the flotilla commander was in the hospital in Paris and would soon be transferred to Berlin. Bülow was here in Rennes, but in a private room; he wasn't in very good shape. Hoff's ship had been attacked several times by low-flying planes, and Bülow had been hit again, in the gut, but they thought he would pull through. Vögele was missing. . . .

"He's dead," said Teichmann.

"There's only one ship left in the flotilla. But the flotilla staff is full strength."

"Then the war can go on. Here's the old man's wrist watch. You can take it with you."

"It's no use to him. He won't be able to see it."

"Never mind," said Teichmann, "he'll wear it."

"All right. We'll take it and send it to his wife. We've got to shove off now. Our train leaves at five. We've got to go back to Saint-Malo; then we have leave until further notice."

"Here's something for you," said Stollenberg, and shoved a bottle of Hennessy under his blanket. "Maybe you don't need it now, but it will do you good later."

"Don't show it to the nurses," said Heyne, "or they'll take it away."

"Don't worry about that."

"Well, be good."

"You too."

"Your buddies are O.K." said Esch when they had gone.

"You'll get some, too. I won't drink it by myself."

"That's not what I meant. You mustn't think that. But you'll have to hide it from the doctors and nurses."

"I can't keep it in bed the whole time. I might shove it out while I'm asleep. And that would be the end of it."

Now that Stollenberg and Heyne were gone, it seemed to him that he had only dreamt their visit; to make sure that they had really been there he clutched the bottle. After a while he caught himself fondling it.

He kept it in bed until the light was put out at ten o'clock. Then he handed it over to Esch. Esch tied a string around the neck and slipped the string over the bar at the head of his bed, on which his uniform hung. Then he let the bottle down until it disappeared inside his jacket.

"Should we try and see if it works?" asked Esch.

"Sure."

Esch pulled the string and turned the bar a little to release the bottle; then he let go of the string, and the bottle landed on his pillow.

"Like a block and fall. Why, that's a wonderful invention," said Teichmann. The only drawback, he reflected at the same time, is that I can only get at the bottle by way of Esch.

"The string is a bit thin," said Esch.

"You mean the bottle is too heavy."

"Well, maybe . . ."

"Should we make it a little lighter?"

"That would be the safest way. The string really is . . ."

"Open it."

The bottle was tossed from Esch to Teichmann to Köhler and back again. Teichmann was glad that he was in the middle. It went back and forth four or five times until Köhler, who had dozed off, got hit in the head and let out a yell. After that it shuttled back and forth between Teichmann and Esch. When he took it from Esch, it always felt considerably lighter. Teichmann suspected Esch of rewarding himself with an extra snort for his ingenious mechanism. Before he could bring the matter up, the bottle was empty. He pretended there was still something in it and threw it to Esch. Esch did the same. For some time they tossed the empty bottle back and forth and pretended to drink. Neither wanted to admit having emptied it. When it fell to the floor and smashed, Esch cried, "Damn it, man, can't you be careful. Why, it was half full."

"You threw it."

"Me?"

"Who else? A good National Socialist doesn't do such things. It's an outrage."

"I am a good National Socialist. I didn't throw it. Maybe it slipped out of my hand."

"An Old Fighter's hand never slips," said Teichmann sternly.

"You're perfectly right. It won't happen again. I promise."

"We'd better sleep now."

"O.K.—if you're tired."

"Don't forget your prayers, Esch."

"I never pray."

"Then I'll do it for you."

"That I will not permit."

"As you please. But then recite a verse from the song book at least."

"I haven't got any song book."

" 'Great God, we praise thee.' You must know that by heart."

"All right. But I'm going to say, 'Great cod, we braise

231

thee,' if you don't mind. And afterwards you have to recite one of my songs."

They said the first verse of the hymn together, and since they didn't know the second they repeated the first.

"Quiet, you bastards," cried a voice in the ward.

"Now one of my songs," said Esch.

"Which one?"

" 'When the golden evening sun' . . ."

"Don't know it."

"What do you know?"

" 'Raise the banner.' "

"Will you shut your traps, you drunken bums."

"Then we'll say that."

After reciting the first verse three times, each time louder than the last, they began to sing. In the end Esch was singing alone. But when his solo showed no sign of ceasing, Teichmann joined in and sang, "Fox, you've stolen the goose. Give it back again." Esch stopped singing and said what Teichmann was doing was a desecration of German culture. Teichmann said no, it was a canon. Then it was all right, said Esch, for Hermann had said cannons were better than butter and butter was good. Then the night nurse came in; it was Nurse Margot. She stumbled over the broken bottle and was very angry because Esch and Teichmann were drunk. She laced into Esch and called him an old jackass and the whole ward agreed with her, even if Esch did have the gold Party medal.

Esch said he'd report her to Adolf as unfit to be a nurse. Nurse Margot said, "If you don't pipe down immediately, I'll report you to the Chief Doctor." And Esch piped down immediately.

Right after lunch six men came in, the giant in the lead, roaring, "Well, how's she going, old-timer?" and "Wake up, sailor, time to take a leak." They sat down on Teichmann's bed, and Bockhammer introduced his crew by name and nickname. The obscenity of the nicknames exceeded Teichmann's experience and made him feel ashamed of his fellow sailors, especially as Bockhammer spoke so loud that the whole ward could hear him. "We've brought you a bottle of slivovitz; wasn't easy to come by. Let's pass her around; after all, we've all got the same thing. . . ."

"Navy disease, see."

"You can begin. It's smooth as an admiral's ass."

"How many times have you bent your watering can, Hans?"

"With seven of us it's hardly worth the trouble," said Teichmann, hoping to get out of the drinking—and God damn it, he thought, we haven't got the same ailment. But there was nothing he could do. One of them said, "We'll go easy so there'll be plenty for you."

Teichmann told himself that alcohol was a disinfectant and set the bottle to his lips. After the first swallow he noticed that he hadn't quite digested the Hennessy, and hoped Nurse Margot would come and take the bottle away. But when she passed through the ward—he had by this time had three turns—Bockhammer adroitly spirited the bottle away. Teichmann could only join his companions in rejoicing that Nurse Margot had seen nothing. His pleasure was not entirely insincere. For Nurse Margot had said nothing about the night before, and he would not have liked to offend her now.

Then they told him their sorrows. Oh, the cold, hard world in which they were forced to live! And after considerable beating around the bush they came out with their plan. What a stroke of luck to have found a buddy like Teichmann here on the second floor! All he had to do was lend them his sheet; they'd wet it and the rest would be child's play. Nobody would notice if they let themselves down by it; the second story wasn't very high. They would come down tonight and rehearse the maneuver.

It took Teichmann some time to make it clear to them that they couldn't take his sheet until his legs were in shape. They finally saw the light. Shortly before the evening rounds they withdrew.

"Thanks for the fine schnapps."

"Don't mention it."

When Nurse Margot took Teichmann's temperature that evening, she was again very angry—which was extremely becoming, as he noted. He explained that certain social obligations were hard to avoid. This made her even angrier. He promised to reform and swore by everything that was holy that he'd never take a drop again. He had the impression that she didn't believe him, and that hurt his feelings.

"You don't even know what you're saying. Why, you're drunk again."

Now he was really offended. "When seven men share a bottle of schnapps together, nobody's going to be drunk."

"An eighteen-year-old boy isn't a man."

"Bet you can't carry me in your arms."

"No, you're not that little. And now I hope that you'll get a good night's sleep. At your age you need lots of sleep."

There's another witch for you, thought Teichmann, and lay awake for quite some time.

The next days and weeks passed very slowly. His belly was in order, but his legs took time. The lying in bed got on his nerves. Esch and Köhler and the nurses too were very nice to him. Köhler explained to him in great detail how bread is baked and told him about all the different kinds of rolls he had made every day before the war. Teichmann learned that a baker can be a great artist. Esch said nothing about his peacetime activity. Esch read books. Sometimes Teichmann read a bit too. Esch provided him with reading matter. There were certain books, Esch pointed out, that Teichmann would have to read if he wanted to hold up his end of the conversation. It never entered Esch's head that Teichmann didn't give a damn about holding up his end. Despite his illness, Esch went to the hospital library every other day. It was situated on the fourth floor and at the opposite end of the building. He read few books through; for the most part he picked out pointers for discussion. Teichmann had been singled out as the victim. But Esch didn't get his money's worth. Teichmann had no desire to discuss Rosenberg's *Myth*, Chamberlain's *Foundations*, and Nietzsche's *Zarathustra*. His indifference in this field was incomprehensible to Esch and infuriated him—and what infuriated him most was Teichmann's way of avoiding discussion, namely, agreeing with everything.

But Esch was obstinate. He had taken it into his head once and for all that Teichmann must participate in his intellectual battles. Every morning when he had finished reading the Army newspaper, he handed it on to Teichmann and waited for him to leaf through it. Then he said, "What do you think of the situation?"

Usually Teichmann said, "Nothing."

"How so?"

"Because there's nothing I can do about it."

"Yes—but our troops are marching on Moscow."

"Sure, and even if they march back again, there's nothing I can do about it."

"They will never march back."

"Well, then everything is O.K."

One day he came over to Teichmann's bed with an outline of the history of Western philosophy and held his finger under two words. Could Teichmann tell him what they meant? Teichmann told him they were Greek, that those words had been inscribed on the temple in Delphi, that they meant "Know Thyself" and were pronounced *"Gnothi seauton."*

This bit of information impressed Esch immensely. He looked at Teichmann respectfully and a bit enviously and said, "Yes, that's something I lack."

"Very few people know themselves. You're not the only one."

"No, I mean that I lack Greek. It must be terrible for somebody who knows Latin and Greek to live in this atmosphere. Don't you mind?"

"Sometimes the people that teach you Latin and Greek are pretty terrible too. To be able to read Homer in the original is wonderful. But of my twenty classmates, there were maybe three who realized that. For the others—and I was one of them—it was plain torture, like lots of things at school."

"But, man, education is always valuable. A man can't have enough of it."

"Education, the knowledge you learn, is rot. Book reading is a waste of time. Do something yourself, that's worth more,

235

for you at least, than reading what others dish up. Reading won't make you any smarter."

"What can I do that has value? To know that, I've got to be educated. That's why I read books."

"Nonsense. If you'd pick a pretty bunch of flowers outside in the garden and put it on the table, we'd all get something out of it. That would have more value than reading all those headache books."

"The others might get something out of the flowers, but not me."

"That's too bad."

"You don't like to read any books at all?"

"For pleasure, yes. There are some books that you can read for pleasure."

"And what else do you like besides flowers?"

"A mug of beer and Wagner's music, for instance."

"Man, that's a funny combination."

"I know, they're both pretty low-class, but I like them."

"Because when you're drinking beer you don't have to think."

"Maybe. Thinking isn't always very pleasant."

"It's wonderful to think; you're too young to understand that. And what's wrong with Wagner? He's marvelous, he's terrific; I can listen to his music for hours. *Meistersinger* is my favorite opera. . . ."

"It's Adolf's too."

"Ah, yes, Wagner. Wagner's all right. Anything by Wagner has class. But beer?"

"Beer has class too. It just depends what kind of thirst you've got."

"By the way, I wouldn't want any misunderstanding about Wagner; when I say I like him that doesn't include *Parsifal*. *Parsifal* makes me sick to my stomach. I must admit that I've only read the libretto, but it's trash. I'll never forgive him for that. But otherwise he's all right."

Teichmann said to himself, be nice to him, he can't help it. But he found it hard not to insult him. There are people, he reflected, who, when they were young, had too little money or too little gray matter for a higher education. It can take two forms. Some take it as a deficiency and try to compensate, hurriedly and unsystematically, for what they supposedly missed in their youth. Others make a cult of their ignorance.

In Esch it took the first form. Teichmann tried in vain to convince him that pure book learning merely skims the surface: real education is precisely the process of getting rid of the notions they funnel into you at school. Living, said Teichmann, is more important than learning; knowledge unfits you for life; the men who have really made something of their lives have never been wise; wisdom is too discouraging. A man who has found out that all is vanity will never do anything.

Esch replied that Teichmann was a cynic. Once he said that Teichmann was profane, and when Teichmann asked him if he didn't mean frivolous, he said yes, that was the right word. Teichmann said perhaps he came of a frivolous generation. But it troubled him somehow that a mechanic and a general should have expressed the same opinion.

One Sunday morning Esch confided in Teichmann that he was writing a book. He would call it a philosophical novel, that was something new, wasn't it, or had Teichmann ever heard of a philosophical novel?

"No, I never did."

"Then listen carefully. This is what happens: There was once a young doctor . . ."

"As in the fairy tale?"

"Don't interrupt me. That's just the beginning. Very well: the young doctor is very pious, very Christian, a good Evangelist, who . . ."

"You mean a Protestant?"

"Yes, but I say Evangelist; I prefer the word. Anyway, he was a fanatical Evangelist, who always asked God's advice before he did anything, and . . ."

"Was he married?"

"No. I've told you he was very pious. And now listen carefully. This doctor is working in a field hospital near the front. After an enemy attack three badly wounded men are brought into the hospital at the same time—don't miss that, or the whole meaning of the story will escape you. Very well, they are brought in at the same time: a Protestant—do you see the subtle distinction I make between Evangelist and Protestant—very well, a Protestant, a Catholic, and an atheist. All three of them are equally seriously wounded. . . ."

"Do I have to remember that too?"

"That they're equally seriously wounded? Yes, of course. That's the most important thing of all. You've got to remember it, because now the story gets a bit complicated."

"All right. Fire away. I'm remembering what you told me: brought in at the same time and equally seriously wounded."

"So far everything is clear to you?"

"Perfectly. I'll tell you the moment something isn't clear to me."

"Good. So all three are equally seriously wounded, one foot in heaven so to speak and the other . . ."

"You can't use expressions of that sort in a philosophical novel."

"I don't mean to. I write a cultivated German, something like Rosenberg. Well, all three of them need to be operated on at once if they are to live. And now our pious doctor has conscientious scruples: he doesn't know which of the three to operate on first. It's certain that the one he gets to last will bleed to death, and he can only operate on one at a time. So there's the question: Which one is he to take first? I suppose you think he takes the Protestant? Oh no. He thinks so too at first, but then he remembers that the Bible says to love your enemies. But then he doesn't know who is the greater enemy for a fanatical Evangelist like him: is it the Catholic or is it the atheist? To make a long story short, he can't solve the problem by himself; he decides to ask God in person. He kneels down—the wounded men on all sides of him; what a scene, eh?—and prays. Maybe God is in no hurry to answer; maybe something else goes wrong—I leave the question open, the reader can decide for himself—in any case, all three have bled to death by the time the doctor is finished praying. But the whole incident is observed by a stretcher bearer, an enlisted man. This stretcher bearer happens to be an old Party member, and he supplies a de-

of conversation. Maybe, Teichmann hoped, he'll feel better when he's home with his people.

Teichmann was no longer the chief curiosity of his ward. Two fliers had been brought in who had cracked up in an emergency landing. One died twenty hours later; the other screamed for a night and a day and another night—there was no morphine, said the head nurse, and besides it was bad for the health—and then began to recover.

One day when Bülow didn't want to go out, Teichmann explored the city and made purchases for his friends. Many things were unavailable in Rennes; women were abundant and cheap, but these he couldn't very well buy for his wardmates. The cleaning women, whom Dr. Weckerlin made available in line with his therapeutic principles, took shameless advantage of their monopoly; their prices were exorbitant. The result was the exact opposite of what Weckerlin intended: the soldiers saw flesh but couldn't get near it. As the prices mounted they became more restless than ever.

Then came Christmas.

The Christmas packages had arrived and been distributed some days earlier. Teichmann received three packages: one each from Stollenberg and Heyne; the third was from Berlin. It was a very pretty package, with evergreen sprays, Christmas paper, gold ribbons, and a letter that was again phrased as if Wegener had written it. He repeated his invitation; his wife and he wished Teichmann a Merry Christmas and all the best for the New Year.

Bülow was scheduled to be sent back to Germany, leaving on the morning of the twenty-third. At five o'clock Nurse Bertha found him on the floor beside his bed. He had cut his throat with a razor blade. Dr. Weckerlin sewed him up and gave him a blood transfusion.

On Bülow's bedside table lay a letter addressed to Teichmann. Teichmann wondered for some time what to do with the letter; there was nothing about not opening it until after Bülow's death. When Bülow hadn't regained consciousness that evening and Dr. Weckerlin said there was nothing more he could do for him, Teichmann opened the letter. Bülow wrote that suicide was the only way out; it wasn't just his legs that had been cut off, and he could no longer expect anybody to regard him as a man. Enclosed there was a little letter addressed to Fräulein So-and-So. Teichmann decided to keep it for the present.

A medical corps general had announced his visit for the morning of the twenty-fourth. Everyone was awakened at six o'clock. The Frenchwomen had to polish the whole ward till it sparkled. The sheets were changed, and some of the bedside tables were adorned with cactuses. The head physician sent word that the patients were to wash and shave and comb their hair with special care.

The bed patients had been shaved the night before. The doctors discussed the possibility that the general would not arrive at ten o'clock, but later, perhaps not until the afternoon. In this event, they decided, the bed patients would have to be shaved again.

A little before eight o'clock the Chief Staff Doctor came in and objected to the artistic manes on some of the patients. The barber was summoned, and the hair had to go. The doctors, too, had made themselves pretty; they looked like barber's apprentices in their freshly washed white coats. They went from bed to bed, memorizing the patients' ailments both in German and in Latin. The nurses wore fresh aprons; in honor of the day Nurse Bertha had put on a brassière.

Teichmann lay in bed until nine o'clock. Just as he was rising the assistant physician came running through the ward and said, "Maybe Your Lordship ought to begin to get moving."

"Yes, sir," said Teichmann. The doctor had it in for him because he was from the Navy. There were people like that.

Teichmann reached the washroom just in time to see somebody busy on the table with the cleaning woman. The man was exceedingly vexed; apparently Teichmann had come in at the crucial moment. He was just on the point of saying, "Man, you've got nerves," but because it was Esch he only said, "Don't mind me. Make a fresh start when I've finished washing." Esch said it wasn't very important; he'd just wanted to give it a try, and after all it was Christmas. Then he

242

argued with the woman about the price; he wanted to pay next to nothing because the venture had been unsuccessful, but she said that was a risk he should have weighed before he started. Esch said that no one else would want her this morning anyway. Thereupon he put on his Army jacket and disappeared.

After washing, Teichmann went back to bed. Esch had lain down too. He explained to Teichmann that you must experience everything if you want to form an opinion. He had done it by way of research. Well, now he knew: French-women *were* great swine. And the queer part of it was that her German had been very good. He couldn't make out how she had learned German so well; why, the German language must be very hard for a Latin. But then, the educated Gauls had always been drawn to the Germans, because they themselves were superficial; no, they were not stupid, just degenerate and lacking in depth. And then he began to talk about Romain Rolland.

The general did not come at ten o'clock or at twelve o'clock or in the afternoon; he did not come at all; but he sent word that he would come next day.

For the Christmas celebration a tree was set up. "O Tannenbaum" was sung; a Catholic priest and a Protestant pastor gave brief talks, and meanwhile Esch read Rosenberg's *Myth of the Twentieth Century*. He held the book so that everybody could see it. Afterward "Silent Night" was sung, and the celebration was over.

Bülow came to for a few minutes on Christmas Day. In the evening he was conscious for half an hour. The doctors said he was over the hump.

Then the general came. On the dot of ten, the day after Christmas, there he was. Having awaited him in vain the day before, the doctors were unprepared.

The general was very magnanimous. He was in the middle of the ward before anyone called "Attention!" But he chose to overlook this. The whole medical staff ran along in his wake. The general took little notice of them, said thank you after every report, and passed the beds at high speed. He stopped only once; a man was sitting bolt upright in bed. He asked what was the matter with the man, and when he was told he turned red in the face. To cap the misfortune, the man cried out a moment later in a shamelessly loud voice that he was finished. Nurse Lisbeth had to smuggle the bedpan out of the ward behind the general's back.

When the general had completed his round, he cleared his throat and said in a hoarse voice, "I wish you a Merry Christmas."

That was nice of him; the soldiers would have liked to say thank you and wish him the same, but this the regulations did not permit. The regulations forbade enlisted men to thank their superiors in words, and prescribed that on such occasions they must stand at attention. The men lay at attention.

Two days later Teichmann was able to talk a little with Bülow. Then he went down to the garden and burned Bülow's letters. Later he went back to Bülow and told him the little house they had been arguing about was used for burning dirty bandages. Bülow believed him.

11

They had heard glowing reports about the Naval Academy in Flensburg-Mürwik. The best officers in the Navy were said to serve there as instructors; you were treated like a thinking being and given a chance to show what you had under your hat.

These are the circumstances of Teichmann's first time on report:

On their arrival they were received at the head of the stairs by a midshipman who assigned them their rooms. Stollenberg was sent to the east wing of the building where the Second Company was lodged; Teichmann and Heyne were sent to the west wing; they had been assigned to the third platoon of the First Company. Teichmann shared his room with five other cadets. They had a living room and a bedroom and shared a washroom with the next room, to which Heyne had been assigned. While Teichmann was putting his things into his locker, the door was opened and someone bellowed, "I want one man." Teichmann went out. The light was on in the room, but it was dark in the corridor; he could not immediately see who had called. The result was that the voice continued to bellow. As far as Teichmann could make out, he was being ordered to report with packed sea bag: "I'll teach you how to salute your superiors: I am Lieutenant Wissmann. Remember that."

Teichmann made a mental note, as he would have done even without any special recommendation. But before he went to pack his sea bag, Wissmann ordered him to black out his, Wissmann's, quarters—that was why he had called for a man. Teichmann went to Wissmann's room, at the end of the corridor, and fixed the cardboard panels in the windows. Then he reported to Wissmann with packed sea bag. Again Wissmann bellowed, "Got all your stuff in that bag?"

"Yes, sir."

"Can't trust you fellows. I'd better check."

Teichmann had to carry the bag back to his room; Wissmann went with him. He asked to see Teichmann's locker. It was empty.

"That's lucky for you, or I would have put you on report your very first day. Now take that bag and run around the compound. I expect you back in three minutes flat."

Teichmann hoisted the bag on his back and ran off. It never entered his head to regulate his pace by Herr Wissmann's watch; he took it slow and easy. When he reappeared in the corridor, he was received with more bellowing: "Come in here on the double or I'll show you the reason why."

Wissmann's face was crimson with rage. Between thumb and forefinger he lifted a razor and held it under Teichmann's nose. "What's this? Can you tell me what this is?"

In the washroom each cadet had a little wooden shelf for his toilet articles. Teichmann hadn't thought of that, as he now attempted to inform Herr Wissmann, but Wissmann wouldn't let him get a word in.

"So you're a liar to boot. Well, fella, I'll teach you which way is up. Once more around."

It got to be three times around, because Teichmann didn't run fast enough. Then he was permitted to unpack. This he did too slowly to suit Wissmann. "Pack it up again," he bellowed, "and once more around."

"Oh no," said Teichmann. "I'm finished." The whole altercation took place in the doorway; the cadets in the other rooms could hear every word.

Such a reply was new to Wissmann. He was caught up short for a moment; then he said in a trembling voice, but softly, "Do you know what you've just done?"

"Yes, sir. I have refused to obey an order. But I've just come out of the hospital and I don't feel like taking treatment that's going to send me back."

"What you feel like and don't feel like is of no interest to anybody. And why were you in the hospital?"

246

"I was wounded."

"Oh, you were wounded. Well, just let me ask you one question: why don't you wear your wound insignia?"

"It's on my pea coat and my pea coat's in my bag."

"Oh, so that's the story. Don't you know that you are expected to wear undress uniform when you report to an officer?"

"No, I didn't know that."

"Well, I'm telling you now. What's more, undress uniform includes all decorations and insignia. You can't expect me to smell that you were wounded. Anyway, I'm putting you on report."

The dinner bell rang.

In the mess hall they remained standing for fifteen minutes. Then an officer appeared, passed along the tables, inspected the fingernails of a few of the cadets, sent two of them out of the room, went to his place, banged a wooden hammer on the table, and said, "Be seated." The cadets sat down to a meal of beet salad, bread, and hard cheese.

Next morning Teichmann reported to the company commander and received a reprimand.

These are the circumstances of Teichmann's second time on report:

The company commander made a speech of welcome. He was a corpulent gentleman with fat puffy cheeks; from afar his beaming baby face looked like one of Raphael's angels, except that the top of the head was bald. He began his address, "Gentlemen, some of you have come from France; but it is not true that you must have had gonorrhea at least seven times in order to be a good sailor. I am getting married soon. . . . It's no laughing matter, damn it. There is no connection between that and what I was saying before. Of course not. . . . Well, in any case, you'll soon be laughing on the other side of your face. I am not referring to marriage . . . I forbid you to read double meanings into my remarks . . . I simply wanted to point out that you must at all times prepare yourselves for your future marriage; you, too, will have to marry someday. Yes, yes, 'have to' is too strong . . .

You will marry only if you wish to, if you've attained sufficient maturity. . . . Yes, men, the naval officer corps believes in cleanliness, inside and out. For a naval officer marriage is the unique, the only, possibility of having children. . . . Will you please stop that silly laughing. I will not stand for it. You are simply childish. You are not mature enough for a serious talk. I'll make a note of that. . . . I mean, of course—for the officers' wives it's the only possibility of having children. . . . There are many fine women here in Flensburg. . . ." And the talk ended with three cheers for the Führer.

Teichmann hadn't laughed the loudest, but the speaker had noticed his bass voice, particularly because he was standing at the end and the company commander already knew him. He was put on report.

In the course of the day a midshipman by the name of Ramer, of the previous class, appeared in his room and traded his NPP including directions for use for two boxes of cigarettes. NPP stood for Navy Prize Packages and referred to the girls who attended the dances at the Naval Academy. These girls possessed a certain rarity value because there were not enough of them to go around. They were handed down from class to class, and that didn't make them any younger. But Ramer had every reason to be pleased with his trade, for his looks were against him. He was of dwarfish stature with a great bloated face and a bulbous uptilted nose, a mouth like a tadpole, and stubble for hair. When he walked you had the impression that he had to counterbalance his head in some way to keep it from falling off.

The midshipman also had the texts of the commander's speeches. The speeches were the same for every class, he said, and it was very interesting to follow with the text in hand, and see how many mistakes he made in delivering his three obligatory addresses marking arrival of the new class, promotion to the rank of midshipman, and impending departure after the final examination. But the midshipman found no takers for his texts.

There wasn't much fun to be had with Ramer: after pocketing his NPP and directions, he took an immense tome out of his locker and began to study Swahili—out loud. He was absolutely convinced that he was cut out to be governor of German East Africa, and he never for a moment doubted that the German colonies would come "home to the Reich" after the war. And he had other little foibles that made him hard to live with. He not only regarded himself as Africa's coming man, but also as a great drinker. Actually, half a bottle of schnapps gave him the heebie-jeebies. When he came home from his schnapps safaris, his roommates had to undress him, give him a cold shower, and put him to bed, and in the course of the process he regularly vomited up the schnapps. His third foible was a weapons collection allegedly comprising forty rifles and seventy-three pistols. Fortunately, he had been obliged to leave it home. But every day his comrades were subjected to his profound regrets on the subject.

"We have met before," said the company commander when Teichmann reported to him next day. This time Teichmann received a "severe" reprimand.

These are the circumstances of Teichmann's third time on report:

He offended against tradition, and without tradition there wouldn't have been much left of the Naval Academy.

The tradition began with the different categories of ship. It all depended what kind of ship the tactics instructor had served on. If it was a battleship, these vessels were traditionally the backbone of the German Navy; but if he had served on a torpedo boat, then torpedo boats were traditionally the backbone of the German Navy; and the same was true of destroyers. None of the tactics instructors had served on a submarine. In classroom exercises a reconnaissance patrol would be made up of several battleships, aircraft carriers, a number of cruisers, and a dozen destroyers. It didn't disturb the instructors in the least that at that time the German Navy possessed not one aircraft carrier, two small battleships at the most, and three or four cruisers.

Teichmann's platoon leader was thoroughly at home in this atmosphere. His hobby was military etiquette, behavior toward superiors, and so on. Much thought was given to such problems as how you introduce two couples when you don't know which of the ladies is the older. Sometimes the instructor brought his wife to class, and the cadets had to practice kissing her hand.

Another of his preoccupations was the uniform. The cadets must dress in accordance with tradition. Their pants must be sharply creased, and when they became midshipmen they must wear stiff white collars. In this rig they were compelled to do rifle drill twice a week with Dutch rifles. The tradition also forbade wearing low-cut shoes on duty; you had to wear naval officers' laced boots. It was also traditional to wear a narrow white scarf when you went out in a coat. When you had to wear pea jacket or coat was determined by the post commander; his order was binding, regardless of rain or shine.

On a fine Saturday afternoon Teichmann went out without a pea coat. But the post commander was feeling cold that day and had prescribed pea coats. Teichmann came up on report and was punished with one day of arrest.

They stood outside Wegener's house. Heyne pressed the bell.

On April 20th they had been promoted to the rank of midshipmen. Then they had gone to Berlin in a special train to hear a speech by the Commander-in-Chief. They had spent the first night in Berlin at a night club. Next morning they were marched to the Sportpalast, to hear the Führer's speech, and had shouted "Heil" on command. In the afternoon they had seen *Julius Caesar,* and that in itself made the trip seem worth while. Then, armed with three bouquets, they had ridden out to Dahlem. They were invited to dinner.

Teichmann was afraid. Damn it all, he said to himself. He was at the end of his strength. He hadn't answered Wegener's letters or thanked him for the Christmas package, and that was the least of it. If he could only report sick.

It was more than fear; it was despair. I'm an idiot, he said to himself, but that was no help. I've got to pull myself together, he told himself, but his knees were shaky, his breathing came hard, and his face was damp, though the evening was cool and windy. It was the same as in his early school-days when he had started for school in fear and trembling because he was a poor student and the teachers took the stick to you; he remembered that he had prayed on his way to school to dispel his fear and keep from thinking. But this method had lost its effectiveness.

He tried to follow the conversation of his friends, who were talking about the play, and suddenly a sentence flashed into his mind: "Of all the wonders that I yet have heard, It seems to me most strange that men should fear." He was glad those lines had come to him, and he thought back to see if he could still say them in English. Yes, he remembered them in English too and he began to recite them alternately in German and in English. He kept on reciting until they reached Wegener's home. And then it was no use, Shakespeare couldn't help him; he felt miserable and very ridiculous. He was furious with Heyne, who had called up without consulting him. But now he had to swallow his anger. He set his hopes in Stollenberg, whom he believed to be more tactful than Heyne.

The buzzer unlatched the garden gate. Heyne pushed it open. Crossing the garden, they passed a lilac bush; Teichmann saw that his bunch of lilacs was the same color as the bush, and that gave him an idea of something to say if he had trouble getting through the greetings.

A woman was waiting for them at the door. When they came closer she turned out to be a young girl, apparently doing her year of labor service. They left their caps, gloves, daggers, and dagger belts in the cloakroom and removed the paper from the flowers. Then Frau Wegener stood before them. Teichmann did not look at her, but he knew that she was there. He crumpled up the paper and clenched it for a moment in his fist, as if unwilling to part with it.

She was wearing a white silk blouse buttoned up high, a black skirt, and a broad, wine-red belt. She greeted Heyne and Stollenberg first and then turned to Teichmann. He bowed somewhat lower than the others and took his time; this way he didn't have to look into her eyes. Her hand seemed small and unusually warm; her fingernails were shorter than before. He didn't utter a word. Stollenberg, on whose sense of tact he had been counting, blushed as usual and said, "Perhaps I ought to say that he didn't pick his lilacs in your garden." Frau Wegener laughed and said that would have been difficult, it was still broad daylight and the lilacs were a little high for him. Yes, but Teichmann can climb, said Heyne. It couldn't have turned out sillier, thought Teichmann; he would have liked to smash everything into little pieces, and he swore that he would never go through anything like this again as long as he lived.

They were shown into a room with a piano in it and landscapes on the walls. In a corner hung a portrait of Brahms. Frau Wegener opened the sliding door and Teichmann heard her saying, "Your young friends are here." He couldn't make out what was said between them.

"My husband will be right in," she said when she came back, and asked them to sit down. Heyne did most of the talking. They smoked cigarettes—Teichmann was afraid to light one—and they drank cognac out of little glasses that made it look like liquid gold. Frau Wegener did not smoke, but she said she liked the smell of tobacco. She treated her guests with equal friendliness and made things easy for Teichmann, acting as if they had met for the first time. He was in doubt as to whether she was a gifted actress or whether she no longer had any reason to overplay. In any case, she played her part well, so well that she struck him as a stranger. It seemed to him that she was making things too easy for him, and once when she laughed aloud he was seized with anger. But when he looked at her, he was no longer angry.

Wegener wore a dark blue civilian suit that looked scarcely different from his Navy uniform, and he had his pipe in his mouth. Even so, he seemed very changed; the dark glasses made him look like a different man.

"Well, Teichmann, how are you?"

Teichmann went toward him and as he held out his hand, he saw that the sleeves were empty. He had to swallow hard. He felt that his knees would crumple under him if he didn't hold himself hard. He didn't know what to do and blushed in his helplessness. This greeting was worse than everything he had feared.

Before he had time for another false step, Frau Wegener stepped between them and said to her husband, "That valet of yours is going to have to learn how to tie a tie." She took the pipe out of his mouth, gave it to Teichmann to hold, and retied the tie. She seemed to Teichmann like an unexpected ally.

"Yes, gentlemen," said Wegener, "I've taken on a valet. It's a wonderful thing; I hardly have to do anything by myself." And to Teichmann, "As long as you're holding my pipe, would you please pack it? Otherwise the tobacco falls on the floor and my wife doesn't like that."

"There's a gadget you can use on the little table," said Frau Wegener.

Teichmann pressed the tobacco down with his thumb and put the pipe back between Wegener's teeth.

"Now tell me," said Wegener, "what the Kaiser's favorite arm of the service has been doing to you in the meantime." The tone was that of a man determined to be gay.

Teichmann told about his stay in the hospital and thanked them for the Christmas package; it had given him great pleasure, he said without looking at Frau Wegener. In the course of the conversation it occurred to him to say something about Dr. Weckerlin's original therapy, but he knew it was childish and out of place, and besides he couldn't find the right words. When Frau Wegener went into the kitchen, he lost all inclination to talk about this aspect of hospital life.

The dinner was of peacetime quality. Frau Wegener owned a farm near Eberswalde; they could eat with a clear conscience, she said. She took the pipe out of her husband's mouth and fed him from her own plate. The midshipmen ate slowly. When they drank to the health of their hosts, Frau Wegener held two glasses.

After dinner a lively conversation sprang up, almost entirely between Wegener and Heyne. Despite Frau Wegener's presence—which at first preoccupied Teichmann and distracted him from the conversation, although she did nothing but just sit there—he had to admit that the conversation fascinated him, and he was amazed that Heyne knew so much about the Navy; he seemed to know things that he had never so much as mentioned even to his most intimate friends. As might have been expected, he attacked—he attacked just about everything that was held sacred in the Navy. His attacks were witty and sharp, and when he occasionally overshot the mark, Wegener, who listened calmly the rest of the time, corrected him. Teichmann was startled and almost shocked to discover that Wegener's views were not so far removed from Heyne's, for when Heyne spoke with an irony bordering on cynicism about the spirit of the Naval Academy, Wegener said. "You must be fair, Heyne. All this fuss about tradition in the Navy has its psychological grounds; it comes from an inferiority complex. See here: in a country where for centuries the Army has set the tone in all military matters, where the Army can boast a real tradition, it hasn't been easy for a newcomer like the Navy to make a place for itself. In the Kaiser's day, the Navy was blown up too fast for its health. Everything was done to make it popular. Criticism of the Navy was almost *lèse-majesté*. Intellectually Tirpitz was head and shoulders above the Army men of his time. I don't mean to say that his ideas on foreign policy were sound, but I do think he was the only outstanding mind that the Navy has produced to this day. Just read his memoirs . . ."

"I have, sir," said Stollenberg a little too eagerly, and then blushed, although Wegener could not see him.

"Well, then you know. And after the Kaiser had abdicated, there wasn't much left of the Navy. The mutiny and its aftermath made people forget its achievements in the war. And rightly so: an officer whose men don't obey him has ceased to be an officer, regardless of the reasons for the mutiny. The mere fact that they mutiny is enough . . ."

"But, sir," Heyne put in, "do you know that these things aren't even mentioned at the Academy? At least they haven't been so far. . . ."

"They never will be, my boy; they weren't mentioned in

254

my day either. But that mutiny had passed judgment on the officer corps of the Imperial Navy. And the Kaiser was gone. The officers were left to themselves. Their colleagues in the Army thought up a lie—I'm sorry, but there's no other word for it. I'm referring to the myth that the Army was 'undefeated in the field.' Incidentally, the formula was Ebert's but the generals were only too glad to take it up. And the admirals echoed, 'Undefeated on the high seas.' While the Army boasted of Tannenberg, Verdun, and the Isonzo, the Navy spoke of Coronel, Skagerak, and Weddigen. That was the beginning of the Navy tradition that the Academy is still chewing on. After the lost war, the Navy officers without ships immersed themselves in history and discovered Prince Adalbert and the Great Elector. Where they couldn't discover enough, they invented; every German who'd ever set foot on a ship became a great naval genius. Well, this kind of history is what the Academy lives on. They hang the portraits of our great naval heroes on every wall and exhibit the 'world's finest ships' in glass cases. All that comes from an inferiority complex. And it is a complex, because actually the German sailors were anything but inferior. We were the only sailors besides the British who counted at all; we were the eternal underdog, but what it was possible to do with our insufficient forces we did."

"Most Navy officers," said Heyne, "would call what you've just been saying 'fouling our own nest.' "

"That's just where the inferiority complex comes in: men who can't stand any criticism have no right to command. Well, maybe you are surprised to hear me saying such things—but I am no longer in active service, and you fellows can stand more than criticism."

Wegener laughed and the others followed suit, but the laughter was rather forced. Frau Wegener filled their glasses. They were drinking a sparkling, slightly tart Moselle, and perhaps it was the wine that gave Stollenberg the courage to ask Wegener whether the present leaders of the Navy had learned nothing from the past. "To that question," said Wegener, "I can only give you a very heretical answer. I'm afraid not."

"It seems to me," said Heyne, "that the German Navy hasn't always been very intelligently led."

"But there again, Heyne, you've got to be fair. You've got to bear in mind that we've always been numerically inferior to the British. That means that every German commanding a ship of any size, not to mention a group of ships, knows that he can't take any risks. To lose a single big ship is to decimate our fleet. With the British it was very different. . . ."

"What about the *Bismarck,* sir?"

"Just a moment. I'm coming to that. It's my opinion—and I don't think anyone would seriously contest the principle—that small fleet should not be exposed to a far stronger enemy at the beginning of a war. I think the Admiralty was perfectly right in the First World War to keep the fleet in reserve until it was really needed. After the war they were sharply criticized for this very decision, which was even blamed for the November revolution. The result? In this war, to avoid being accused of the same supposed mistake, they send a battleship like the *Bismarck* to sea, escorted by only one cruiser, knowing all the while that the enemy has at least five times our naval strength. It's true, the *Bismarck* had bad luck, taking a torpedo hit in the rudder, but I tell you frankly, it was a great mistake to send her out in the first place, before the *Tirpitz* was ready. Because now we're finished as far as surface warfare is concerned. All we have left is our submarines, and in the long run that isn't much—you can't win a war at sea with one category of ship. I know that I'm destroying your illusions"—"Not mine," said Heyne, but Wegener didn't hear him—"but it's better that I should do it than others, than those others who are just waiting for us to lose the war, those who hate us. . . ."

"Wegener is bright," said Heyne on the way home. "But not so very bright at that."

"What do you mean?"

"I would have been interested to know all that he thinks about our fighting this war," said Heyne.

"Anyway, he's a regular fellow," said Teichmann, fully conscious of what he meant by those words. And secretly, perhaps because of the wine he had drunk, he was amused that *this* visit should have ended with a discussion about naval warfare. Now what really was I afraid of?

"He's a very good man," said Stollenberg. In the darkness no one saw whether he blushed, but he spoke with enthusiasm. All the way home he continued in this tone.

"I like his wife even better," said Heyne, and began to whistle.

These are the circumstances of Heyne's first time on report:

The history of naval warfare was taught by an Imperial Navy officer, a little man with a goatee and a starched wing collar. He had taken part in the battles of Coronel and the Falkland Islands, and on this stored-up ration he was living out the rest of his life. In the course of the six-month term he described these battles and his own part in them four times.

The climax of his narrative was always the sinking of the ship on which he was First Officer. As the sailors were swimming for their lives, they had supposedly begun to sing "Deutschland, Deutschland über alles" . . . Thereupon he, also swimming, had cried out over the waters of the Atlantic, "Suspend singing. Save strength." To him it had been vastly edifying to hear the men calling to each other, "Orders of First Officer: Suspend singing."

Three times the midshipmen listened to this tale and kept their peace in deference to the old man. But as he was starting a fourth time, Heyne, sitting in the last row, called out, "Rest in peace."

For a moment the lecturer complied with Heyne's recommendation. Heyne's neighbor broke the silence with a kindly "Oh, all right, sing it again."

The naval historian didn't catch this last remark but the ensuing laughter was not to be ignored. He attributed it to Heyne's words and called him to account. What had he meant by his remark? Heyne said he had meant that the story was already sufficiently known.

"We cannot speak often enough of German's naval heroes."

"I am not of that opinion, sir," said Heyne. And then he

257

started in: The word "hero" had been overdone; misused bravery was worthless.

Before the naval historian could recover from his shock, Heyne was in the middle of a lecture on "the economy of bravery," as he called it. He began with the War of 1870 and the so-called death ride of Mars-La-Tour. A German cavalry brigade had been ordered to storm a French artillery position; reportedly there had only been two survivors in the whole brigade. The history books called this a German victory. In Heyne's opinion the German general who gave the order to attack should have been court-martialed. But the most glaring example of this kind of thing was Langemarck. He assumed that the facts were known to all, though he himself did not know what had been done to the general who had commanded ill-trained volunteers to attack a well-camouflaged enemy in a terrain entirely unsuited to such an attack. Here again a military fiasco had been represented as a victory—chiefly because the attackers had supposedly sung "Deutschland, Deutschland über alles." Actually, nothing could be more stupid than to sing while storming an enemy position, and the same in his opinion could be said of sailors singing in the water. Altogether, he had no use for the traditional techniques of dying, all this clutching of banners and so on. What was more, he did not believe that the volunteers of Langemarck had died with "Deutschland, Deutschland über alles" on their lips. Men who were dying did not sing. He'd seen men dying, and if they said anything it was mostly indecent.

The historian of naval warfare blanched.

"Yes, sir, most of them just cursed. A young fellow, just eighteen, called out twice for his mother before he drowned. That happens too. Now and then God is mentioned. Some call for help while they're floating around in the water, though they know it's useless. It's perfectly possible that I'll call for help when I'm on the point of drowning, and I don't know what you, sir, will do when you get a load of salt water in your throat and you know that the comedy is over. I doubt if you sing 'Deutschland, Deutschland über alles.' Though once in a while a man sings to keep up his courage."

With this Heyne sat down.

"Nevertheless, I shall put you on report."

"I thank you for the 'nevertheless,' sir. I know that tradition requires you to put me on report."

"No, that is not the reason," said the naval historian, and tried to explain why he was putting Heyne on report. But no one understood him.

The next day Heyne received a reprimand from the company commander.

These are the circumstances of Heyne's second time on report:

On the morning of the examination, the company commander had the men awakened at four o'clock, in order to give them one last chance to prepare for the momentous hours in store for them. But instead of busying themselves with books, a good many of them, in their rage at being hauled out of bed at such an hour, devoted themselves to alcohol. One of these was Heyne. He and his roommates began to drink the provisions they had been storing up in their lockers against the farewell festivities. They had three good hours for this occupation, and Heyne made such good use of them that by seven o'clock he was thoroughly boiled. He had made a bet with one of his roommates that he could stand on a chair and drink a pint of rum without removing it from his lips. He won his bet. But he was not accustomed to drinking on an empty stomach and ten minutes before the examination he was still incapable of walking straight. A written test devoted to celestial navigation was scheduled for the first hour. Heyne was the best mathematician in the platoon, but in his present condition an examination was out of the question. His roommates went to Teichmann for counsel, but Teichmann could think of no solution. He couldn't report sick, any corps man in the infirmary would have known what was wrong. Then Ramer had an idea, which was a rare occurrence in itself, but what made it all the more remarkable was that he was on the outs with Heyne.

One of his many foibles was his sister, who, as he never

wearied of telling his friends, was more beautiful than Greta Garbo, and *so* intelligent. Unfortunately, he had no picture of her available. This sister had been assigned to the German civil administration in Poland, and he felt that he must give her a weapon from his collection with which to defend her life and honor in those remote parts. This presented a difficult problem. It had to be a small pistol that would fit in a lady's handbag, and it had to be one that would function if necessary. For a whole week he consulted his roommates and the men in the adjoining room on this knotty problem. When Ramer asked him for the hundredth time, Heyne was fed up. "Why don't you trade faces with her?" he suggested. "Then not even a Pole would touch her."

Since then Ramer had not spoken one word to Heyne. Yet it was his suggestion that helped Heyne out of his difficulties. Ramer had learned from Stollenberg, who often came to Teichmann's room, that for the Second Company the written celestial navigation did not come until ten o'clock. From eight to ten the Second Company would be examined orally in secondary subjects, but this was a pure matter of form, and Stollenberg, who was midshipman of the watch that day, did not have to attend. The examinations were supervised by outside instructors, who did not know the men by name but merely counted them. Ramer's idea was that Stollenberg should take the written examination for Heyne.

On the stroke of eight the Commanding Admiral of the Navy arrived. Stollenberg called out the watch, made his report, and dismissed the watch. Then, as the admiral listened to the oral examination of the Second Company, Stollenberg sat on the bench behind Teichmann in the First Company examination, and calmly wrote the examination paper of Midshipman Gerd Heyne, who lay in his bunk sleeping off his rum. He was one of the first to finish. With a grin on his face he handed in his paper and retired to the guardroom.

When Teichmann had finished he ran to the canteen and bought as many tablets of dextro-energine as he could get. This was the only edible substance obtainable without coupons. He gave them to Heyne, who ate them but had trouble keeping them down. Then he drank a bottle of soda water at one gulp; the carbonic acid was supposed to help. Thus fortified, he repaired to the oral.

The admiral appeared in the examination room and listened to what the midshipmen knew. What they did not know was not asked. Heyne was not called upon; he had taken full cover behind the big celestial globe. But while leaving the hall, he teetered suspiciously—the effect of the carbonic acid had worn off. The platoon leader saw that he had been drinking and put him on report.

Heyne explained to the company commander that he had taken a few drinks in his fear of the examination—he had always suffered terribly from stage fright. And the company commander believed him.

Among the four in Teichmann's squad who flunked and had to repeat the class was Colonial Warrior Ramer. It was a bitter blow to him. They tried to comfort him by pointing out that he would get to the colonies in plenty of time and that as long as the war was going on the Naval Academy was certainly the best place in which to perfect his Swahili. Ramer said he could not make up his mind which weapon to shoot himself with.

All who were fit for submarine duty were automatically volunteered for that branch. Teichmann and Stollenberg were assigned to the Third Submarine Flotilla, Heyne to the Sixth. They parted in Paris; Heyne changed trains for Lorient, while Teichmann and Stollenberg remained in the special Com Sub train and went on to La Rochelle.

Teichmann and a midshipman named Rosencranz were assigned to a submarine commanded by Lieutenant Lüttke, while Stollenberg was to ship with a Lieutenant Wehner. But after a bit of drinking with the flotilla adjutant, Teichmann and Stollenberg were assigned to Lüttke and Rosencranz to Wehner.

12

The submarine steered a westerly course.

When Teichmann went on watch, the Cape Finisterre light was flashing on the port quarter. Fifteen minutes later it had vanished. The lights of a few fishing boats were still to be seen; then they too were gone, and only the gulls remained. They slept on the light swell and seemed incredibly white in the moonlight; from a distance they looked like snowballs.

The men on the bridge were tired and cold, but their eyes were vigilant, trying to penetrate the night that lay before them. Behind them in the east a pale-green strip appeared above the horizon, and when the strip took on a yellow tinge, the exec called down the tower hatch, "To captain: It's beginning to get light."

The captain came up. The exec reported as officer of the watch and indicated course and speed. The captain said nothing. He had the sextant handed up to him, took a star sight, and went below again.

Without removing his binoculars from his eyes, Teichmann said to the exec, "Is the old man always such a clam?"

"Not when he's bawling you out."

It was quiet for a moment. Then they heard, behind them, a stream of water splashing on the deck. The exec turned around and said, "Morning, Doctor."

"Morning, gentlemen. Funny thing I like to do it when the sun isn't looking on. The sun makes me bashful, ha-ha."

"But next time you come up on the bridge you will please say, One man to bridge."

"Yes, of course. But why?"

"I've got to know how many men are on the bridge besides the watch. In case we have to submerge in a hurry."

"Oh, I'll remember that. And now, one man leaving bridge."

"You learn quickly, Doctor."

"Always did."

"You could have said good morning to Herr Timmler," said the exec. "Whether we like it or not, he's our war correspondent."

"I don't like him," said Teichmann.

"That's how the skipper feels about us."

"But we're not war correspondents."

"I can't make out what you have against war correspondents. Timmler's a Ph.D. and in private life he's a writer."

"I've got nothing against war correspondents. On the contrary, I've always heard good things about them. But tell me the truth. Do you like him?"

"I can't bear the sight of him."

Then the sun appeared and suddenly everything was changed. Thin as silk threads, the first tender rays felt their way hesitantly across the horizon. Gradually they took the form of glittering arrows that pierced the night-black clouds and turned them to flame. Then the great fiery ball thrust its upper edge over the horizon. While the heavens blazed and the gulls flew up screaming, the great light rose from out of the sea. The veils of mist that lay on the waters were torn, the ocean appeared to be steaming. The gulls circled the vessel, holding their wings motionless like great eagles. With long plaintive screams they greeted the morning; and there was one that came flying toward the ship, holding its wings rigid longer than the others. . . .

"All ahead full. Left full rudder. Fire when ready," cried the exec.

But it was too late. The bomb had been released. It fell in the water ten yards to starboard. The bridge watch got a good splashing. The plane vanished.

The captain appeared on the bridge. The exec reported what had happened. "Bastards!" said the skipper. No one could tell whether he meant the Britishers or his bridge watch.

Then he ordered them to submerge.

The captain and behind him the two after lookouts dropped down the hatch; after them Teichmann, and last the exec.

Teichmann went to the control room and sat down at the place of the bow hydroplane operator. To the right of him sat the stern planeman. Behind them stood Winkler, the engineering officer.

The men at the vents of the diving tanks reported:

"One ready."

"Two ready."

"Three both sides ready."

"Four ready."

"All five ready."

"All vents ready," the engineering officer called up to the tower.

"Flood," the exec called down to the control room.

"Flood," said the engineer to the men at the vents.

Teichmann set his hydroplane at "full dive"; the stern hydroplane was set at "level." The vents were opened, water poured into the forward, then into the after ballast tank. The sub tipped forward in a dive. At fifty feet the engineer called out, "Negative tanks." With a deafening roar the water was blown out of the quick-diving tanks with compressed air. At fifteen fathoms Winkler leveled off. Then he reported to the captain, "All vents cycled and shut."

"Depth forty meters," the captain ordered. "All ahead dead slow. Trim the ship."

The engineer repeated the captain's command and with the help of the trim tanks brought the boat on an even keel. At the same time he called out orders to the planeman. When the submarine had steadied at twenty fathoms the hydroplane operators worked independently by the water level in the Papenberg differential pressure gauge, the engineering officer merely giving a correction now and then.

"That fella'd better take his wrist watch off," said the captain to Winkler, with a gesture toward the bow planeman. Teichmann wondered whether the skipper had forgotten his name again or just didn't want to make use of it. That would be like him. Anyway, I won't take Wegener's watch off. On the other hand—I don't need it on board, and when there's a sea on the bridge it gets wet, and that doesn't do it any good even if it is guaranteed waterproof. So I guess

I'll have to take it off now and then. But not now, not just because that stuck-up bastard with the lieutenant's stripes thinks he can call me "that fella"—that dandy with his pointed fingernails and his lavender lotion. . . .

Teichmann underestimated him. Lüttke was unpopular but he *was* a U-boat skipper. He had sunk more than a hundred thousand tons of enemy shipping and was an expert in his field. His men knew that, and although it was their fifth trip with him, they feared him as on the first day and yet were secretly proud of him. They wouldn't let anybody say a word against their skipper and defended him even if they hated his guts. They forgave him most of his faults— but that didn't bring them one inch closer to him. They even forgave him for making them remove the Knight's Cross which, like all crews whose captains received it, they had painted on the conning tower of their ship. After the crew had congratulated him on his decoration, he had said, "What business is it of yours? Get that bird off my ship. I hadn't heard anything about the crew being decorated." That was Lüttke. But ashore, and when leaving or putting into port, he wore his medal. He even wore it in the officers' brothel.

After breakfast there was a deep-dive drill. The sub dived to eighty fathoms and then surfaced. At 0800 Teichmann was relieved.

He and Stollenberg had their bunks in the petty officers' quarters, and there they slept. But they had to spend the rest of their off-watch time and take their meals in the chiefs' quarters. The captain wanted it that way. This was not to the liking of the petty officers or the chiefs, and it didn't suit Teichmann and Stollenberg either. They would have liked to remain in the petty officers' mess for their meals, because the galley was right next door; the food for the officers, chiefs, and crew had to pass through the petty officers' mess, which was a sort of customs station. Yet even when it reached the chiefs' mess, the food was very good. The midshipmen had not eaten so well since they had come into the service. But that was the only pleasant thing about life on a submarine.

In the beginning they kept bumping their heads when they walked erect. They quickly developed the habit of walking bent over, and at the same time they learned how to get through a narrow watertight door in a hurry. But the worst thing about submarine life was the bridge watch. It lasted four hours. During this time they were not allowed to sit or lean on anything or remove the binoculars from their eyes, and they were heavy Zeiss glasses. Each of the four lookouts was responsible for a ninety-degree sector of sky, horizon, and sea. The top of a mast on the horizon, thin as a pin, had to be reported at once; and if there was more than a mast truck to be seen, the lookout could be prepared for punishment. And then there were the gulls. They had an ornery way of looking like planes, especially when they came gliding out of the sun; or else the planes looked like gulls, and gulls are to be seen all over the ocean, except that there are fewer of them on the high seas than along the coast. But even in the middle of the ocean there were enough of them to complicate life for the bridge watch.

On her way through the Bay of Biscay the sub had had to dive six times to evade planes. Twice depth charges were dropped, but the aim was poor and by the time it was improved the sub was thirty fathoms down. Sometimes there were bombs that exploded on the surface and in no way endangered the submerged boat. But there was still the noise. The sound of an explosion is five times as powerful under water as in the air, and that was something you had to get used to.

The captain expected the midshipmen on their off watch to familiarize themselves with the functioning of G7a and G7e torpedoes. The torpedoman was supposed to instruct them. But since any superfluous effort on the off watch was unheard of, they played cards in the petty officers' quarters. The torpedoman lost regularly. He soon reported to the captain that the course of instruction was complete and that the midshipmen knew what had to be known about the torpedoes. Next the captain ordered the midshipmen to supervise the men's daily cleanup details. This was for the birds, the exec confided to the midshipmen; the men were packed like sardines in the forward torpedo room; they couldn't walk erect, and had to eat and sleep on the torpedoes. They had enough to do with their mess duties, and simply couldn't be expected to clean up the whole ship every day.

The exec stood pretty high with his men. The more the captain bawled him out—and the captain tended to treat his officers like boots—the more popular the exec became. The man had a skin like an elephant. He went right on calling his men by their first names, although the skipper was much annoyed every time he heard him. The familiar tone made the men feel good, for the exec was one of the aristocracy; he was a real prince. The captain addressed him as Wittgenberg, though that was only part of his name. His subordinates addressed him as Lieutenant and sir, but it sounded as if they meant to say "your Highness." He was a fine-looking man. He had a well-shaped boyish face, jet-black hair combed straight back, full lips, and sparkling teeth; he was almost as big as Teichmann, but more slender and supple. His favorite word was *picobello.*" When he liked something, he said *"picobello,"* and when he didn't like something, he said, "That's not one bit *picobello.*" This was the most pronounced disapproval he ever expressed, for he was a very polite man.

Up until then he had supervised the cleanup from his bunk, merely saying to the leading seaman, "Give us a *picobello* cleanup now." Then he turned over and went back to sleep. He advised the midshipmen to do the same, except that they mustn't use the word *"picobello";* only he was entitled to the privilege of speaking Italian.

The midshipmen took his advice.

On the eleventh day out Stollenberg, in foggy weather, sighted a shadow, relative bearing three one zero. The shadow quickly grew. The captain gave orders to submerge.

While Winkler was maneuvering to periscope depth, the shadow, according to the sound man, crossed the sub's bows. The captain was in a fury because in his opinion Winkler was taking too long in getting to periscope depth. And when he did get there, he couldn't hold it. Twice the periscope went under. The captain threatened to have him court-martialed. When the periscope dipped a third time, the engineer asked the captain for more speed. The captain ordered full speed, and then the engineer was able to hold her at seven fathoms. But at this speed the periscope vibrated so hard the captain couldn't see anything. He cut down the speed, and the whole comedy started all over again.

Twice the engineer asked permission to speed up. When permission was granted, the shadow was no longer to be seen in the periscope. The skipper gave orders to surface.

The sub steered a course from the last sound bearings. There was nothing to be seen. Half an hour later, she dived again, took new sound bearings, surfaced again, and followed the last sound bearings at full speed.

Meanwhile a breeze had sprung up, and the light swell had turned into a choppy sea. The weather was coming from ahead, the glasses were constantly wet, and the spray lashed the faces of the bridge watch.

Shortly before midnight they sighted an object. It was a tanker, about ten thousand tons, they thought. She was doing at least eighteen knots and zigzagging wildly. It was only the zigzagging that enabled the sub with her fourteen knots maximum to regain contact. The sub ignored the zigzags, and stubbornly followed the tanker's base course of 280.

At 0300 the sub came close to the tanker. Teichmann was amazed that the tanker hadn't detected them. With the naked eye he could see the whole ship. But they seemed to be asleep; nothing was stirring, and she couldn't be more than six hundred yards away.

The captain had ordered the torpedo tubes made ready for surface fire. The fire control instruments were set: target speed 18, bearing 60, range 600. When the exec had the tanker in the TBT she was enveloped in a low-lying cloud. The attack had to be called off.

It took an hour to get back into firing position. At the last moment the tanker zigzagged off schedule, having done so only half a minute before. The attack was abandoned.

Forty minutes later the sub was back in position again. Tube one was fired. The torpedo rose to the surface and there it remained. The men stared at it. The tanker spotted it and then at last discovered the sub. The tanker turned away and fired her stern gun. The sub ran full speed out of range.

Two hours later they closed in again. But by this time the wind had risen, there was a rough sea, and that made it impossible to fire a torpedo with any accuracy. Once more the attack was abandoned.

When the sky began to grow light, the tanker sighted the sub again and opened fire with two guns.

"Do we go down, sir?" asked the exec.

"No, we'll wait for the sea to quiet down," said the captain. "With that sea they won't hit us. Those fellows can't shoot."

The sea did not quiet down. The wind rose to storm strength and piled up the long Atlantic swell into vertical walls that descended on the bridge, tearing at the belts with which the bridge watch had made themselves fast. At the approach of a wave the men on the bridge lowered their heads, clung to the bridge coaming, and humped their backs like a cat in a thunderstorm. At first Teichmann was amused, but not for long. Once he was barely able to hold his breath until the wave had passed over; it had covered the whole boat. The other waves did that too, and he wouldn't admit it to himself, but sometimes he was a bit afraid. The odds were too great: the little ship with her bridge scarcely nine feet above the surface and these monstrous masses of water. The waves approached like swiftly moving dunes, burying the four men on the bridge alive. You had to learn how to breathe on time but not too soon, and hold your breath just long enough. You were always in water, but when the great waves buried you, you were way down under like a high diver. Once when the boat got away from the helmsman and broached, the sea came from aft, wrenched the machine gun out of its mount, and poured into the bridge, piling up against the closed gunwales and hurling the four men overboard. All four dangled helplessly from their safety straps. With great difficulty they clambered back onto the bridge, and at that moment a mountain of water fell on them. Teichmann thought he was going to suffocate; he had forgotten to take a deep breath. At the last moment the sub shook herself free and Teichmann could go on living. When he was relieved, conditions were even worse. Everyone had forgotten about the tanker; she was gone for good.

At noon Teichmann came on watch again. The storm had not abated. Twice he had been rolled out of his bunk although he had taken great care to wedge himself into an almost intolerable position. Sleep was out of the question; you couldn't even put on dry clothing. Half the crew were seasick and vomiting all over the place. The stench alone could make you seasick.

The captain stood in comparative dryness in the hatchway, peering out to see that the helmsman kept on course, and in such weather that was quite a trick. Then Teichmann closed his eyes and pressed against the bridge coaming, because the ship had got away from the helmsman again, and a mountainous sea was coming on from abeam. The belt of the port after lookout let go; the man was picked up by the sea, flung high, and dashed against the bridge coaming. And then the bridge was submerged. When Teichmann could see again, the man was wedged between the forward deflecting wire and the bridge. He had been very lucky. Teichmann hauled him in. It was Michels, a seaman first-class. He was the smallest man in the crew, but now he was heavy, he seemed to weigh about five hundred pounds. With the help of the exec he lowered him carefully into the control room. They hoped that he was only unconscious.

The captain ordered the hatch closed only when so much water had been shipped that the bilges in the engine room were running over. Now and then he opened that hatch and asked the exec if there were any signs of the tanker. At first the exec answered him. But as the storm increased it became harder to hear, and the captain had to ask two or three times before the exec replied that there was nothing to be seen. Sometimes the exec purposely failed to hear the questions. After a while the captain began to be annoyed. He called up to the exec to turn the boat into the wind and let him know when the bridge was clear; he'd have a look at the situation for himself. "Aye aye, sir," called the exec, and as an immense wave was approaching he called down into the tower, "All clear." The captain climbed through the hatch, Teichmann had to count nineteen before he could breathe again, and after that no one looked out any more. They heard the auxiliaryman bellowing up at the bridge, would they tell him what ass-hole had left the hatch open. "That'll keep him quiet," said the exec, winking a reddened eye at Teichmann. It took more than that to keep the skipper quiet, but at least he stopped opening the hatch. He changed his clothes and now he was back in the control room; he had upped the periscope a couple of feet and surveyed the sea that way.

The bridge watch was gradually getting its fill. The towels wound around their necks under their sou'westers were soaked through. Their rubber wristlets were not tight enough; when they were tight, they stopped the circulation, and you couldn't hold your binoculars steady because your hands were trembling. Only your own skin was waterproof, and that was wet from head to toe.

Michels lay in the forward torpedo room, strapped into his bunk. An arm and a leg were broken. That much had been determined by the radioman, who was doctor on board, having once taken a three-day medical course. He managed to set the leg. The arm was set by the motor machinist's mate; it was a compound fracture and the radioman said he couldn't stand the sight of blood. While the leg was being set, Michels recovered consciousness and set up such a yell that the captain sent the chief quartermaster to see how he was getting along.

At dusk, the boat dived. The exec forgot to close the speaking tube on the bridge, and when the bridge went under, a stream of water flowed inside. Hell broke loose in the control room. The auxiliary man employed a few expressions that did not suit the skipper and was put on report. Perhaps the captain remembered his question when the water had streamed in through the open hatch. After supper, in any case, the man reported and was given three days in the brig, to be served in port.

The sub spent the whole night submerged. Thirty fathoms down all was quiet; the storm was imperceptible.

And then for a long time—for two whole weeks—nothing happened. The ship remained in the field of operations ordered by Submarine Command, waiting for ships that did not materialize. Along with other U-boats, she searched the sea at a snail's pace and her crew was bored. The only pleasure in life was the good food, but even that grew tedious. The shipboard routine turned to mere meaningless motion because nothing happened; there were not even any planes to be seen. Now and then the sub passed through thick fog. It was like a Turkish bath; from bridge you couldn't even make out the bow or stern of the boat. And then suddenly everything changed. One afternoon the fog lifted and at the same time a convoy was reported.

When Teichmann was awakened at midnight, he heard the engines running at high speed. He drank his coffee in the control room. The mere smell of this wonderful aromatic liquid roused his animal spirits and made him curious to see what was doing on the bridge: the engines wouldn't be running that fast for the mere fun of it; the oil reserve was low. Meanwhile he had become reconciled to life on board, even to the watches; you could get used to anything. His chief sorrow now was that Stollenberg was on the first lieutenant's watch, but there was absolutely nothing to be done about it. Two midshipmen could not be on watch at the same time, and that was that.

While Teichmann was sipping his coffee, the exec told him they would hit the convoy in four hours if the convoy stuck to its course, and if the sub that had made contact had indicated the position correctly.

The convoy must have zigzagged; at 0400 there was no sign of it. Toward 0500 a light mist arose. At 0525 the sub did an emergency dive but was only fifty feet down when the bomb fell from the air. Engel, the first lieutenant, got such a fierce bawling out from the captain that the midshipmen fully expected him to hang himself.

The induction valve had sprung a leak; the boat had to surface. The plane had gone on its way. After two hours' work the engineer announced that the valve was tight. But the ballast tank leaked and had to be blown out every half hour.

At 1400 they sighted columns of smoke. It was the convoy. A Sunderland flying boat was circling over the ships. The sub was able to keep track of the convoy by means of the plane, without attracting the attention of the destroyers.

When five subs had made contact with the convoy, ComSub gave the order to attack. The ships closed in on the convoy and attempted to circle around in order to attack from ahead. The plane did not bother them greatly. When it came too close, the captain gave the order to slow down, to reduce the froth of the wake, and that was enough. Everybody seemed to be asleep on the plane with the possible exception of the pilot.

Lüttke was first to dive for the attack.

Teichmann had his battle station in the forward torpedo room and looked on as the torpedoman got the tubes ready. Water was let in and the outer doors were opened. Teichmann heard the ships circling overhead; this he did not take very seriously, supposing it to be a normal part of the game. Even when they told him it was a destroyer, it struck him as perfectly normal. He could hear only indistinctly what was being said in the control room. But he heard clearly when the skipper suddenly said, "Depth forty meters," and the engineer said, "Full dive!" and the captain, "All ahead full."

The sound of the destroyer's screws came rapidly closer. Then they were directly overhead; the destroyer was running over the sub. The men looked up as if there could be something to see. Teichmann was startled by the terror in these men's faces. Maybe the situation wasn't so normal after all. He too looked up. Then everyone had to hold fast to keep from sliding; the sub was tilting heavily forward. The depth gauge in the forward room read fifty meters. Somewhere a dish locker had opened; plates fell crashing to the deck; an empty brass coffeepot rolled as far as the forward bulkhead. "Diving fast," said the engineer. A moment later he said over the loud-speaker system, "Lay aft to the bulkheads." Teichmann was sitting near the bulkhead and only had to

273

slip back a little to obey the command. The other men in the forward room were sitting on the deck or on the torpedoes. As they all stood up, to move aft, a crash of thunder knocked their legs out from under them. Teichmann sat paralyzed. Everything seemed to collapse inside him; his guts were in a tangle, twitching and quivering; it amazed him to find that he was still able to breathe. He looked through the open watertight doors: the men in the control room were visibly trembling; the machinists in the after room were trembling still more; they looked blurred as in a fuzzy photograph. The whole boat seemed like a string that had been stretched to the breaking point.

But then suddenly everything was back to normal. No more depth charges were dropped. A few glasses and light bulbs had been broken in the control room; otherwise, there was no damage. "That was just to put the fear of God into us," Teichmann heard one of the men with the frightened faces saying. But he had his own ideas on the subject.

The depth gauge read seventy meters. The torpedoman and his helpers jumped up and began to close the outer doors of the tubes. The operation took a minute or two.

While they were working the skipper came into the forward torpedo room.

"Is this when you decide to close those doors?"

The torpedoman and his men kept on cranking.

The captain repeated the question. Then the torpedoman answered.

Two red spots appeared under the captain's cheekbones. He turned round and went back to the control room. Here he announced, "Dinner." The exec said through the loudspeaker system, "Attack discontinued. Secure from battle stations." The engineer set the depth at thirty fathoms.

A few depth charges went off in the distance. Later the sound men reported sounds of breaking bulkheads as in sinking ships. The cook called forward, "Come and get it," and the skipper ordered the crew to table. There was nothing more to be heard of the convoy.

Supper passed in silence. No one had much of an appetite. Dr. Timmler, the war correspondent, ate nothing at all. His stomach was out of order, he said. Maybe that ash can had fallen on his stomach, said the exec. No one laughed and Timmler said nothing.

At table Teichman asked the chief quartermaster why the attack had been called off. At first the chief quartermaster said nothing, then he grumbled, "Dumb question. Because the torpedo tube outer doors were still open at seventy meters."

"How do you expect me to guess that?" said Teichmann sullenly. "I'm new to all this."

The door between the wardroom and the chiefs' room was open and the captain overheard this exchange. "Send me the torpedoman," he said.

The order was passed to the control room and from there to the petty officers' room. The torpedoman wasn't there. The order was then passed from the chiefs' room to the forward torpedo room.

The torpedoman was a quiet, well-balanced man, but not a pussyfoot. He had five missions behind him. But when he went into the wardroom he was white as a sheet. "Someone's going to be slaughtered," whispered the chief quartermaster with malicious glee.

The torpedoman reported to the captain.

"Do you know why the torpedo tube outer doors have to be closed when the boat goes below thirty meters?"

"Yes, sir."

"Why?"

"Because the steering mechanism of the torpedoes must not be exposed to higher water pressure, or it won't steer the course that has been set. But, sir, it was impossible for me to . . ."

"I did not ask you why the doors were not closed; I asked you if you knew why they should be closed, and that you have already told me. Why did you neglect to mention this in instructing the midshipmen?"

"I forgot, sir."

"Very well. You reported to me that the midshipmen had been checked out on torpedoes. That was a lie. You will report to me at nine o'clock tomorrow morning for punishment. Dismissed."

. "The dirty dog," said the chief quartermaster after dinner when the captain was out of hearing. "The whole thing was the old man's own fault. He should have given the order to close those doors. And the exec could have thought of it too. He's torpedo officer. So what happened? The man with the lowest rank gets it in the neck."

Later the motor machinist's mate warned the midshipmen to be leery of the chief quartermaster; he had ambitions to be an officer and Lüttke had told him that as long as he was skipper no petty officer risen from the ranks would be recommended for a commission.

The midshipmen felt sorry about the torpedoman. It was their fault, after all, if he had told the captain a falsehood. "Hell, that was nothing," he said. "I thought he was going to have me courtmartialed for leaving those doors open."

The four torpedoes in the tubes had to be removed. The screaming Michels was moved to the chiefs' quarters, and everything possible was taken out of the forward torpedo room. But there still wasn't space enough. The captain gave the order to fire two torpedoes from the tubes. There was then room enough to unload and adjust the other two.

When the sub surfaced the following morning, the convoy, or what was left of it, was so far off that pursuit was hopeless. Reports of the other boats' successes were piled high in the radio room, and the Army newscast spoke of them too.

The torpedoman was given five days of arrest, to be served in port. For which offense he was not told.

The boat waited three weeks for another convoy. When none came, it received orders from ComSub to take on fuel in mid-ocean from a submarine of the IX-D type, which was returning home because of engine trouble.

With great difficulty they transferred Michels to the homeward-bound vessel. He was in great pain and suffered agonies while they were taking him out through the tower. The men were able to send mail. All letters had to be submitted to the captain for censorship. Teichmann provided him with

276

no reading matter; Stollenberg wrote his parents a postcard.

By nightfall they were finished fueling. The hoses were removed, and the IX-D made off at full speed eastward to fuel another submarine. In two days she was to meet Lüttke again to give him torpedoes.

The captain ordered the rubber raft brought out. Teichmann climbed in with a paddle and signal flags. The idea was for the sub to dive and circle round the raft. Teichmann was to signal with his flags when he could no longer see traces of the oil spilled on deck. Stollenberg gave him a pack of cigarettes, tropical packing, to kill the time.

The sub moved off a few hundred yards and dived. Teichmann stretched out and lit a cigarette. For the next few minutes there would be nothing to do. The sun was still a bare hand's breadth above the horizon. The sky was blue and cloudless; in the west the blue was fading into a delicate pink. The sea was calm and immensely wide. The long light Atlantic swell lifted the raft up gently and let it down just as gently. He felt as though nothing could ever happen to him, as if a storm could never ruffle this tranquil surface, never dig chasms in it in which to bury ships. Teichmann felt almost happy in his little raft, and for a moment when he managed to expel all thoughts from his mind, he was completely happy. He threw his cigarette butt away, but he didn't light a fresh one. This was no place for cigarettes, it seemed to him. A moment later something kicked him in the behind.

At first he thought nothing; he was only surprised. Then it occurred to him that perhaps it was the submarine; maybe the captain had poked him with the periscope as a joke. But he quickly rejected this notion. The captain never made jokes, and besides there was the periscope three hundred yards away. The sub had described a semicircle and was running at high speed, the periscope leaving a broad strip of foam. Otherwise, there was nothing to be seen, and that made Teichmann uneasy. It hadn't been a very powerful kick, but who should be kicking him in the first place? It might have been a fish, he reflected, but an ordinary fish doesn't do that kind of thing, or at least he had never heard of it. Maybe he *would* light a cigarette now. As he was taking one from the box, he received another kick, more powerful this time, and when he looked around for the culprit, he saw a fish. No whale; a little fish, about the size of a hogfish, only thinner. He knew the hogfish well; they were merry playmates, the way they raced back and forth across the bow of the submarine, tempting you to lower your binoculars and let the war take care of itself.

Well, then it's a hogfish. He stuck to the idea even when several fish came shooting toward his raft like rockets, dived under, and butted against the floor. They want to play with me, he thought. But then he was compelled to change his mind. Just before reaching the raft the fish turned over on their backs. He saw that the new fish were much larger than the first ones and that they had triangular tail fins.

He had never had any dealings with sharks, except for a few small dogfish. He was not prepared to make their acquaintance. He now realized why they turned over on their backs; he also realized that they had sharp teeth, that the raft was made of rubber, that the sharks were presumably hungry, and that if the game went on for too long it couldn't turn out very well for him. Here in their native habitat they were even prettier than in the zoology books. But then one of them bumped him so hard that it almost threw him overboard. There was nothing Teichmann could do to defend himself. His paddle was ridiculously small, and his signal flags were even smaller.

He could have told the sharks—there were six or seven of them—how to go about it. All they had to do was come up close and sink their teeth into the side of the raft. One little hole, and all the air would shoot out. Well, I won't suggest it to them, he thought, not even for the humor of the thing. He was beginning to feel very uneasy. The sharks had a hard tail fin, and they no longer turned on their backs to attack. They rubbed their dorsal fins against the bottom of the raft, and the raft was made of rubber, and the rubber was not very strong.

He could no longer observe them closely; there were too many of them. They came from all different directions at once. Apparently they were very hungry. He wished they would bash each other's skulls in under the raft, but they wouldn't oblige him: each time they emerged in fine fettle. Before the attack a shark would show its tail about twenty yards off, and then bring it down on the water as a swimmer kicks the wall of the pool in turning. Then it made a beeline for Teichmann. Each time he sucked his belly in, and with each fresh start the sharks grew more furious. He knew that he had every reason to be afraid, and he was afraid, but not as much as the situation warranted. He was still too much surprised, and when the surprise wore off he had no time to be afraid. The worst of it was that he couldn't hold on to anything. He didn't dare to clutch the line running round the raft, for fear the sharks would saw his hand off.

He had no very clear idea what he was doing when he took up the signal flags and began to wave them. But he did know that the sharks weren't playing with him, and that the flag-waving might help.

For a moment he saw the periscope. It was raised a few feet above the water, but the captain was paying no attention to him; Teichmann could see the back of the 'scope; the skipper was searching the part of the sea where Teichmann wasn't. The guy is acting like God, he thought, and cursed aloud and lay down on the floor of the raft. He had only been able to wave for a moment. That wasn't enough time, he couldn't see me, but he must know I'm here; he's got to come looking for me sometime; I'll wave again later on. If it isn't too late. If they haven't eaten me up in the meantime, I'll wave again. He took both flags in his right hand and waved them.

The assaults of the sharks abated. He saw that only little ones were left. Then they were gone too. Ten yards off the captain showed his periscope. He didn't need to be in that much of a hurry, thought Teichmann. The sub must have passed under me; that must have been something new for the sharks.

The periscope turned a slow circle and was retracted. A few seconds later the bow shot out of the water, then the bridge, and then the whole deck. The captain's white cap appeared on the bridge and beside it the exec's blue cap. Teichmann heard Wittgenberg calling down into the tower; "Blow her out with the Diesels." The engines started, but the port engine smoked a little, which immediately provoked the captain's displeasure. The sub turned toward Teichmann. The raft was pulled alongside with the boat hook. Teichmann jumped up on deck. The raft was brought on board and the air was let out. Then they folded it up and put it away.

"You're nuts," said Stollenberg when Teichmann told him the cigarettes had fallen overboard and the sharks were to blame. From the deck of the sub Teichmann saw that there was no sign of oil. But neither were there any sharks to be seen, and that griped him. Now they'd be perfectly welcome, and if they don't show up no one will believe my story.

Two days later Lüttke's sub surfaced again beside the IX-D. Her captain was apparently a lieutenant commander. Lüttke spoke to him very deferentially and even said "if you please, sir," when he wanted something; in his mouth the words sounded like some foreign language.

The sea was no longer calm and smooth. The sailors had stripped and stood on deck ready to take on torpedoes. The captain, the chief quartermaster, and a seaman stood watch on the bridge; Timmler was there too, but he didn't count; he was taking pictures.

Teichmann informed the exec that he had seen sharks two days before. "I'll be damned," said the exec. "Maybe we're in for some excitement. Report that to the old man." Teichmann went up to the bridge and reported it to the captain.

"Little fish," said the captain, and ordered the off-watch firemen to stand on deck with tommy guns and fire if the little fishes should feel like biting off somebody's leg. Then he leaned over and told the sailors that if any sharks showed up, they should put their heads in the water and yell; that would chase the sharks away, and if it didn't the fireman would shoot at them.

"At whom are they going to shoot?" Stollenberg asked Teichmann. The captain concluded his remarks with: "Have you got everything straight?" "Yes, sir," cried the sailors. Then they jumped overboard and swam over to the IX-D.

The distance was about thirty yards. Each of them had on a yellow life jacket but it was not inflated, because you swam better that way. They'd have to come back without the life jackets anyway.

The men on the IX-D had hauled a torpedo up on deck through the forward hatch. The men from Lüttke's sub shoved their life jackets under the torpedo and blew them up. The hatch was closed, and the captain flooded his forward ballast tanks, submerging the bow. The torpedo floated on the lifejackets. The men from Lüttke's boat took it between them, gripping the life jacket with one hand and swimming with the other.

The wind had shifted. Lüttke's boat was to windward; it took them fifteen minutes before they could tie up the torpedo alongside. Then they rested for a few minutes on deck. As a sign that the break was over, Lüttke flooded his forward ballast tanks; the men lay in the water. They cursed softly, furious that the captain hadn't even seen fit to announce that he was flooding the tanks. When the torpedo was floating over the deck, the tanks were blown out again, the deck emerged from the water, and on top of it lay the torpedo. They lowered it through the hatch into the forward torpedo room.

At noon the wind came in gusts, and the sea roughened. The sailors were given a cup of bouillon and no more; the captain said you can't swim with a full stomach, and he was right.

It took them an hour and a half to transfer a second torpedo. Now they had their full complement of twelve torpedoes below and two in the reserve. When the exec reported the deck clear for diving, Lüttke steered a course toward Central America, and the IX-D started for home. "Heil and victory and good hunting," cried its captain. "Thank you, sir," Lüttke called back.

For three weeks they combed the Caribbean Sea from Puerto Rico to Trinidad without getting anything to aim their tubes at. The whole time the sea was as calm as if it had gone to sleep, and when it did move it looked like a molten mass of lead. The sky looked milky and lazy. Here and there a few clouds hung as still as barrage balloons. The sun was coppery brown and beat down mercilessly on the bridge watch. It blazed for fourteen hours a day, and most of the time it stood vertically over the four men on watch. Its rays fell in a concentric bundle as though to melt the steel hull of the boat. The searing heat destroyed every bit of energy, killed every thought, and sucked the last drop of life out of the men. They stood bareheaded; there was no defense against the sun. Their craving for liquid became a raging torment. Around them they saw the endless watery waste, glittering like a tin roof, and they had next to nothing to drink. Fatigue weighted them down, and from hour to hour their limbs grew heavier. The temptation to lower the glasses, to close their weary eyes, to doze, to sleep, to sleep on watch, was almost overpowering. But still they stared through the glasses. Now and then their eyelids closed from exhaustion, but only for a few seconds. Then they rubbed their eyes, and at noon, when the sun was so hellishly hot that they grew dizzy, they bent far forward to stimulate the circulation in their brain. If that didn't help they had a bucket of sea water poured over them. But now and then one of the watch would collapse and have to be let down into the control room.

Inside the boat it was like a Turkish bath. The average temperature was 120°. For inexplicable reasons the distilling plant had stopped working, and there was even less to drink than usual. A bottle of warm pop had to do three men for twenty-four hours. Hardly anything was eaten. The bread was moldy, the butter was liquid and rancid; and when occasionally the men were hungry and cans of meat were opened, they were half empty and mysteriously mixed with sand.

The firemen had oil boils, some all over their body; the rest of the crew had skin rashes; corroded by the salt water and baked by the sun, their faces pealed like dried potato skins. Huge pimples formed on their dirty necks, under their beards. Everyone lived with a dull, throbbing headache. The leather of the bunks was slippery with sweat; the whole boat oozed with sweat—and stank of it. No one could sleep in the heat and in this miasma of oil, damp leather, sweaty clothes, rotten lemons, and the body vapors of fifty men.

The submarine was a torrid, cigar-shaped prison. Day after day the men saw iron, steel, wheels, levers, valves, and always the same sleepless faces with the black rings under the eyes. There was no sleep but only an apathetic somnolence that brings no repose and leaves the nerves jagged.

After their watch the firemen smoked a cigarette under the "village linden tree," as they called the spot by the periscope. They saw the sky through the open hatch, and this was all they ever saw of it. Enemy planes were frequent, and no one was allowed on the bridge except for the watch and the captain. The temperature was 150° in the engine room.

In the Caribbean the boat dived eleven times when planes were sighted. This was all that happened. Everything else was daily routine, and part of the routine was the disgust that the men felt for each other, the irritability that sent them into frightful rages at the slightest provocation. Somehow they managed to keep from fighting among themselves, and this was no mean accomplishment.

The books in the ship's library had all been read dozens of times; the library didn't amount to much. The book most in demand was Nansen's *In Night and Ice*. Sexy items were also popular, and in general sex was the chief subject of conversation. There was no more saltpeter in the food, and besides a good many eggs were eaten: they were about the easiest thing to get down in the heat. The lockers were adorned with the most alluring pictures of movie stars. Timmler said they took turns sleeping with their director and the Minister of Culture, and if the war were lost they would oblige the victors with almost the same enthusiasm. They were always on the side of the winners, and that was how you could tell a whore.

Dr. Timmler must have known; he wrote film scenarios. One, he related, had almost been used; one of those whores with her intrigues had been to blame that nothing came of it. Timmler's story smacked of sour grapes, and didn't fit in with his philosophical system. The officers called him the "ship philosopher," because he took himself for one.

He made his debut as ship philosopher in the chiefs' room with a lecture on the officers' brothels. The only pleasant thing about his appointment as war correspondent, he said, was that it conferred the right to use the officers' brothels. But even in this domain he had been disillusioned by the officer caste. Oh yes, the houses were clean, they were hygienic, but at the expense of atmosphere. They were institutions for the cure of excess virility. And he concluded his remarks with the observation that the enlisted men would be missing nothing if they remained what they were.

His next philosophical talk was delivered in the wardroom. The door to the chiefs' room remained open and the midshipmen were able to listen. In line with the prevailing fashion, he began by saying that as an educated man he did not, of course, believe in God or any such nonsense. Timmler was willing to discuss religion at the drop of a hat—even when he was cold sober. He was a nihilist, he now announced; he despised people who ran off to church because they were afraid to take the consequences of thinking, that is, afraid to think. People who did not think but just lived did not exist as far as he was concerned. He didn't think much of politics either. The Germans had no gift for art, because they were not superficial enough; they could not compromise; they had to do a thing radically or not at all; they were immoderate in good and evil. Right now, to be sure, they were having a good period. Biopolitically—he was very given to this word; he had created it, as he never wearied of pointing out—biopolitically speaking, Germany was the only dynamic nation left in the Western world. The other nations had long since passed their prime. He knew all about the war too, and like a true philosopher he spoke with the pathos of the dilettante about bravery and honor. . . .

"Aren't you hungry?" Teichmann heard the captain ask.

"Why, of course, sir. Man doesn't live by his mind alone, ha-ha-ha—but if I may be permitted to say so, the spirit comes first, even before the soup pot."

"Then you go on with your spirit, and in the meantime we'll eat your portion," said the captain, and had Timmler's plate removed. That was the first and last time that Timmler philosophized in the presence of the captain.

There wasn't much to his nihilism. He was brave only with his mouth and he secretly hoped to be rewarded someday for his knowledge, which, as he freely admitted, brought him so much suffering. All in all, he was just an unsuccessful writer who was piqued because the sailors, despite his vast intellectual gifts, didn't take him seriously. With his sterile intellectualism he persuaded himself that he had a right to look down on his companions, and if a depth charge destroyed his appetite, he claimed it was because he had more sensitive nerves than the others.

For the sailors Timmler was a clown, a harmless lunatic. They tolerated him until the tropic "woobles" got him and he became dangerous. It developed that for him the same sex was the other sex, and that created a stink among the crew. He grew violent and they had to tie him in his bunk. Then his madness took a new form: an irresistible urge to read his works to anyone who came near him.

The trouble had begun with the War Diary. Now and then the captain made penciled entries in a little notebook—this was his War Diary. When there was nothing else to do the first lieutenant was asked to edit his text and type it. Timmler helped him. This was his only work on board; it brought out the pedant in him, and he kept carping at Engel.

One day he undertook to enlighten Engel on the fine points of German grammar. The world "while," he maintained, "may be employed only when two actions run parallel in point of time." Engel could not write, "While in the tropical heat the distilling plant ceased to function," because the heat was not an action. As an example of the correct use of "while" one might say, "While I unbutton my fly with one hand, with the other I take the condom from my pocket."

"The only difference between a pig and you," said Engel, "is that you have only two feet."

Timmler jumped up and ran to the control room. There he raced back and forth in great agitation and in the course of his peregrinations ran across a bottle of pop. He put the bottle to his lips and drained it. As he was putting it down, the auxiliaryman saw what had happened to his pop. He took the empty bottle and applied it to the philosopher's head. He later apologized to the engineer for his action, saying that he hadn't known a man could keel over so easily.

When Timmler revived, he reported the incident to the captain. Winkler spoke up in favor of the auxiliaryman. "The poor bird!" he said. "Swindled out of the pop he'd been saving up for three days; why, he acted under emotional stress— like a husband who catches his wife's lover in the act."

In view of the extenuating circumstances the auxiliaryman received seven days' arrest, to be served in port. That meant he could say good-by to his next leave. Timmler wanted the incident reported in writing, but this the captain refused to do on the ground that Timmler was not military personnel.

Next day Timmler went into the control room and struck the auxiliaryman in the face. When Winkler came in, alerted by the noise, Timmler boxed him on the ear. Timmler was obviously off his rocker. The engineer, the chief quartermaster, and Teichmann conveyed him to his bunk.

On the way the philosopher kicked and struggled, and the strap of Teichmann's watch parted. He now wore it when off duty and even on the bridge in dry weather. The captain had never mentioned it again. When Teichmann had received the watch, a piece of leather had been pasted over the back. In the heat of the last few weeks, the glue had softened and the leather had come off. The jeweled inscription and the date were still there. It's still valuable, Teichmann thought, and hid it in the farthest corner of his locker.

He had received it back as a present. Frau Wegener had written him in Flensburg, asking him to stop by and see them in Berlin before going to the front—her husband would be very much pleased. Teichmann made a detour to Berlin and caught up with the special ComSub train in Cologne. His stay in Berlin was very brief. He arrived at noon and went straight out to Dahlem. In the garden a young man was busy raking the gravel path. He had on a green gardener's apron. Not a bad-looking fellow, Teichmann thought, and wondered how he had managed to keep out of the Army. The young man was very friendly and opened the garden gate for him. The maid came out and showed him up to the second floor, where he had to wait for a few minutes in a little pink sitting room.

Frau Wegener came in. She had on a simple dress and was carrying a blanket which she threw over her legs as she sat down. She gave him her hand and bade him sit down again and said she was glad he had come; her husband was taking a nap, but he would be out in fifteen minutes or so. Teichmann asked how he was and she said "Well." Before he had time to realize how long fifteen minutes can be if you have to fill them with conventional small talk, she said, "Let's not play-act this time. I know I'm opening wounds that I caused, and that may have healed in the meantime. Or perhaps . . . well, never mind that. You—you love me, don't you?"

Teichmann heard a clock striking in the next room. It struck three times with a bright silvery sound like a music box. He looked at the wall behind Frau Wegener. The wallpaper was pink with a linear design. On it hung an oil painting representing a girl of fourteen, Frau Wegener as a child. He looked into the girl's eyes and said "Yes."

"And you know too that you mustn't?"

"Yes."

"I can't forbid you. But you shouldn't have done that."

"Yes."

"I know it's awful for you to sit there saying yes, but it will be over in a minute. Will you promise me never again to do anything that I will have to forbid?"

Teichmann didn't answer.

"It's flattering to me as a woman that you take your time about answering. But now it's been long enough. Will you please say yes just once more?"

"Yes."

Although he was perfectly serious, the whole thing struck him as a bad play in which a part had been forced on him, and he felt that once again she had got the better of him.

"Thank you. And I promise you never again to be wicked

and torture you. I did torture you, I know it, but I won't tell you why—I can't tell you. You just have to believe that I didn't enjoy doing it. It wasn't what you might think, what you might . . ."

He had upset the ash tray. His cuff button had got caught in the fringe of the tablecloth, and the ash tray that stood on the little table between them had fallen to the floor. But before he could pick it up, Frau Wegener bent over and put it back on the table. She had done this without reflection and her face was very red, her self-assurance gone. She put her hands on the blanket before her, like a child in school, and contemplated them. It was as though she didn't know what to say next, as though it took all her courage to tell him she was going to be a mother. A look of helplessness had come into her face; her smile seemed embarrassed and false. But then she took hold of herself, and looked at him as she said, "Otherwise I couldn't have spoken about all that. And you saved my husband and . . ."

"I saved your . . ."

"I know you just saved one of your comrades, but it happened to be my husband. I know you would have done the same for anyone else—we won't argue about that. But I know too that you were aware the whole time—on the raft and in the boat—that it was *my* husband." There was a barely perceptible note of triumph in her voice as she said this. He blushed in embarrassment. She looked back at her hands and then said very calmly, almost as though in passing, "I'll never forget that. My husband is going to give you his wrist watch; you've worn it before. Please accept it. And now tell me a little about your friends. . . ."

Two hundred and fifty nautical miles southeast of Trinidad they sighted a freighter. She was faster than the submarine, and the chase would have been hopeless if she had not, for no apparent reason, changed her course seventy degrees. That gave the sub a chance.

The sub dived. The captain ordered battle stations and had the tubes made ready for underwater firing. "Hook up tubes one, three, and four for a spread." Then he gave out the data: target speed one six, bearing eight zero, range one thousand. Engel fed the readings into the fire control instruments. The sounds of the ship's screws could now be heard by everyone. "Tubes ready," the exec reported. The outer doors were opened, the captain corrected the target position a last time, and said, "All ready." And a moment later, "Fire spread. Make ready tube two."

From the forward torpedo room the torpedoman reported, "Spread fired electrically; tube two ready."

The stop watches ran—one with the captain in the conning tower, one with the chief quartermaster in the control room, and a third with the torpedoman in the forward room. Total silence. The men crouched motionless and listened. It was as though a swift-running film had suddenly been stopped.

When two minutes had passed, the men looked as though hypnotized at the hand of the stop watch. It quivered like a spider's leg, but advanced at an even pace over the black marks on the dial. To the men it seemed to be racing. The torpedo crew wiped the sweat from their faces; the torpedoman frowned and cast a swift glance at the torpedo tubes as though to convince himself that the torpedoes had really left them.

"We'll hit him all right," whispered one of the sailors. "The old man never misses," muttered the torpedoman, "and certainly not with a spread." The stop watch in his hand trembled. "Just the same, a mistake of one knot in the target speed would . . ."

"Stow that."

When two and a half minutes had passed, the men sitting in the far end of the room stood up and gathered round the stop watch, waiting for the explosion. Then simultaneously, and in almost the same quiet, impersonal tone, the torpedoman in the forward room and the chief quartermaster in the control room announced, "Time's up." Three minutes had passed. The men didn't dare to look at one another.

In the conning tower a heated exchange began between

the captain and the first lieutenant. It turned out that Engel had forgotten to throw the blue switch after the captain's last correction; the new data had not gone into the steering mechanisms of the torpedoes.

"Stand by to surface. Prepare for surface battle," said the captain.

In the control room the vents were checked. In the passage between the captain's room and the radio shack the deck plates were lifted. The ammunition chamber was opened and a number of shells were passed out.

"Boat is ready to surface," reported the engineer. "Full rise," said the captain, and went up into the conning tower. "Let her blow," Winkler ordered, and the auxiliaryman opened the main blower. The compressed air shot into the ballast tanks, and the boat rose. "Tower hatch clear," the engineer called to the captain. "Tower hatch opened," the exec called down into the control room. "Equalize pressure," called the engineer.

The gun crew scrambled up. When Teichmann came out on the bridge he heard Engel report, "Gun ready." Even before the captain gave the command to fire, the freighter let loose. "They must have their pants full," said the chief quartermaster. "They must have seen those torpedoes," said the exec.

The ship had two guns, one fore and one aft. Both were of larger caliber than the sub's; the geysers their shells sent up were pretty tall.

The enemy's first shots were long. The sub's first shot was short, but not much. "Up four. Fire," cried Engel to the gunner. The second shot was long. "Down one. Fire." Engel commanded.

His calm was impressive. He had just got hell from the captain for forgetting to throw that switch, and now he stood there, as calmly as if he were firing at a practice target. His fourth shot struck the after deck, only a few yards abaft the superstructure. "Three shots rapid fire," he called, and a moment later the ship's stack collapsed.

The freighter was still fighting, but her marksmanship was

poor. Her best shots were at least a hundred yards from the sub.

For the submarine crew it was a party. As far as they were concerned the duel could go on for hours. To them it was like the Battle of Skagerak. The periscopes were raised a bit; the off-watch firemen stood looking through them in the conning tower and the control room, and those who were on watch or passing ammunition were relieved for a few moments so they could have a look at the battle too. Among the spectators there were men who had been on five or six missions without ever having seen the enemy face to face. And now they saw him. They were delighted. At every shot they howled like Indians. To them it was a football game; they were the audience and their team was out on top. At every hit they cheered as if their team had scored.

Actually, the captain had no business getting into this kind of battle. He kept changing the sub's course, but a single hit would have made her diving apparatus inoperable, and his ship would have been finished. But Engel was in fine form; neither the cheering from the sidelines nor the freighter's two guns could rattle him. He had nothing but his eyes and his binoculars, not even a rangefinder, but his shots hit the mark. It's hard enough to shoot accurately when your own ship keeps changing course, and now the freighter was zig-zagging too. But nothing could cramp his style. He scored hit after hit.

"Engel, take a break for a minute," said the skipper.

"What's that, sir?" Engel was dismayed; he had been right in the groove, and now he was expected to stop. The men on the bridge stared at the captain; they thought they had heard wrong. The captain stood leaning nonchalantly against the bridge coaming; he didn't even find it necessary to raise his binoculars to his eyes.

"Engel, I just want you to watch the way those fellows are shooting."

"Aye aye, sir."

"If I ever catch you shooting like that, I'll break you to seaman second-class."

"Yes, sir."

"Very well. And now finish him off. It's revolting not to be able to shoot any better than that."

"Aye aye, sir."

The captain examined his fingernails. His features revealed such contempt for the incompetent gunnery of *his* enemy that the exec suggested signaling over the submarine's latitude and longitude. The captain gave no answer. He sniffed in distaste, perhaps at the unpleasant smell of the gun smoke, and went on looking at his fingernails, which were well manicured and trimmed to a point.

With the twelfth hit Engel knocked out the freighter's stern gun. That was the end of the battle. The ship's only hope lay in flight. But to make a run for it, she would have to turn her stern to the sub and her forward gun would be useless.

Dense clouds of smoke went up from the freighter. That meant she was driving her engines and would try to get away. Engel chalked up seven more hits; the seventh got the boiler. The ship stopped and put out lifeboats, while a great mushroom of smoke formed over her. The submarine approached.

The ship was called the *Hudson,* an American vessel of sixteen thousand tons. The *Hudson*'s lifeboats—there were four of them—were ordered alongside the sub. In one sat the captain, rather elderly and visibly unnerved. Lüttke spoke to him in English. Four wounded seamen were moved to the submarine, where they received first aid. The dead— three in number—had been left aboard the *Hudson.* The submariners gave the men in the lifeboats a few cans of butter and sausage and bread, and a little fresh water. Lüttke showed the American captain his position on the chart and indicated the course to Trinidad. The sub moved a thousand yards off from the *Hudson* and sank her with a torpedo from the after tube. Lüttke sent out an English radio message in the clear, stating the position of the lifeboats. Then the sub dived and headed east.

At the end of November the submarine pulled into the underground submarine pen at La Pallice. On the return voyage they had sighted two convoys but were too short on oil to risk operation at high speed.

Teichmann and Stollenberg lodged with the crew in the Prien Compound on the outskirts of La Rochelle.

The captain and the officers stayed in Schepke House in the city. The captain, the engineer, the first lieutenant, and those married seamen who had no time in the brig to serve went on leave in the first shore party. The vessel was taken into drydock, and the rest of the crew went on watch. The midshipmen and the chief quartermaster took turns as chief of the watch.

The watches, like everything else connected with this shipyard, were a pure horror. The chief of the watch had to spend twenty-four hours on end in a boat that was half torn apart, but which had lost none of its sickening smell. The hammering never ceased. Day and night the air was filled with the clatter of the riveters, the hissing of blowtorches, the buzzing of pneumatic drills. You had to bellow to make yourself understood. Outside lay the twilight gloom of the great concrete pen, beclouded with oil smoke and dust. Impossible to take a step without stumbling over rails, cables, rolls of wire, or getting in the way of the great trucks. And at the outer entrance to the pen, swathed in smoke and barely visible on sunless days, lay the surface vessels with their spots of red lead, like leprous animals, with workmen swarming over them like maggots.

While on watch you could do nothing—neither read, nor write, nor sleep. You could only wait in dull discouragement for the twenty-four hours to be over.

When the midshipmen were off watch, they ate lunch in Schepke House, and that they liked. The food was excellent, and they enjoyed the company of the officers—all regular Navy men, lean, wiry, thin-hipped, weather-beaten, moving with the easy grace that was peculiar to professional Navy officers. They could all drink—and hold—stupendous quantities of liquor. And they seemed remarkably well balanced, going about their business in a quiet, good-natured way, without waste motion, useless talk, or heroics. Perhaps this was the only way in which it was possible to do their kind of work. In the newspapers, in the movies, and over the radio they were praised, flattered, cheered—but these men whose names filled the enemy with dread seemed, when you got to know them, to have lost all interest in the newspapers and the radio. Once when a group of them went to the movies, a submerged submarine was shown in the newsreel. "Ping, ping," came over the sound track, and the commentator explained, "Those were depth charges." The submariners got up and walked out, wondering what would happen if that audience should be subjected to the noise that a depth charge really makes when it goes off fifty yards from your sub.

They did not talk about the war. But when it was absolutely unavoidable or when liquor loosened their tongues, they spoke about *their* war in witty and rather cynical terms. By this time two or three out of every ten submarines that put out to sea were failing to come back. They took the losses quietly, without fuss, just as they took the victories. They kept their spirits up and twitted death as best they could. They were the elite of the Navy, and all through the war they bore themselves as such—when success smiled on them and when they had become little more than cattle going to slaughter.

Mail came for the midshipmen. A letter from Heyne related the details of his life in his usual disdainful style. The letter was from Pillau. After his first mission, he had been sent to Submarine School for special training. His friends took a dim view of what would happen if one of Heyne's letters should fall into the hands of the censors. There was also a letter from Bülow, who informed them that he was married. How he had managed that, he did not say. He seemed to be pleased with his new status; he wrote like a man at peace with the world. Even Stollenberg thought the letter seemed a bit too smug and settled for a chap like Bülow.

Teichmann received a letter from Berlin, in which Frau

Wegener announced the birth of a son. If Teichmann should have nothing better to do at Christmas, she and her husband would be delighted to see him; he was cordially invited.

Stollenberg undertook to answer Heyne and Bülow. He liked to write letters. Teichmann watched him, as slowly and deliberately he wrote letter after letter in his legible, graceful hand. They sat in their room, facing each other across the table. Teichmann smoked a cigar and Stollenberg, immersed in his labors, held his cold pipe between his teeth, shifting it now and then from one corner of his mouth to the other. From time to time he frowned, and ran his fingers through his blond, unruly hair as he pondered what else he could write. When he had hit on something, his blue eyes lit up, and again he bent over his letter. He is good nature personified, thought Teichmann as he watched him writing. Suddenly he felt such a surge of affection that he came close to telling him what a good fellow he was.

Teichmann himself had to write the letter to Berlin. He wrote as if he were telling an old friend from the mine-sweepers something frightfully important about submarine warfare. She'll be bored when she reads this, he thought.

In mid-December the first group came back from leave; the captain and the engineer stayed away for Christmas. Teichmann decided not to go back to Gemany, and Stollenberg said that he wouldn't know what to do at home. After the second wave had gone off, the two of them led a quiet life. They went to Biarritz once and twice to Royan, where they spent Christmas. They drank a good deal; it was all rather dreary, but with the help of liquor they got through it pretty well—very well, in fact, for their Christmas celebration went on for three days.

After Christmas a package came from Berlin, for which Teichmann had to write a thank-you letter. Then they spent three days in Paris and went to the opera, where they heard *Rheingold,* which pleased them enormously, and passed their night in amorous company.

In mid-January the submarine put out again. The crew

was the same except for the first lieutenant, who had been transferred to another boat as exec. Müller, his replacement, was a reserve officer and father of several children; it was his first combat mission.

The farewell ceremonies were as stirring as ever. The day before sailing there was a medical examination. This was a serious business. Anyone who had got himself a dose could expect a court martial for sabotage and conspiracy to avoid combat duty. At sea a case of VD would have been a catastrophe for the whole crew. Only one head was available; the other was piled high with canned goods. Lüttke's crew came through the medical all right. The captain was exempted.

That night there was a big drinking party in the mess. Next day the men packed all their private belongings into trunks with the required last will and testament on top. Then the trunks were locked and sealed and left in charge of the flotilla administrative officer. The crew boarded a bus and rode from the Prien Compound to Schepke House. Here the captain and the officers got in. The bus continued on to La Pallice and stopped outside the submarine pen. The crew stowed their gear in the boat and fell in on deck. The chief engineer and the exec saluted the captain and reported their sections present. The flotilla commander appeared with a large retinue, including newsreel men—"Smile now!"—and Red Cross nurses who passed out flowers—"All the best of luck"—and liaison officers from the Army and the Air Force, and gentlemen from the civil administration—"Fine boys, the lot of them!"—and shipyard executives whispering, "There's an old wreck that won't take many more depth charges," and officers from other submarines. After the captain's report the flotilla commander, standing on the pier, delivered a mercifully brief speech. Then he stepped down to the deck and shook hands with every man in the crew.

At this point the air-raid alarm was sounded. That was something you could count on whenever a sub put to sea. It was not very difficult for the French intelligence agents to keep tabs on the movements of the subs: they got their information through the brothels. The arrival or departure of a sub was immediately reflected in the volume of business.

The exec blew his whistle and the lines were cast off. The first watch went to their sea stations and the rest of the crew remained in formation on deck. The fore and after lines and the springs were taken in, and the sub backed slowly out of the pen on her motors. The flotilla commander and his retinue shouted hurrah, hurrah, hurrah. The men on deck followed suit. Out in the basin the sub turned about, and the engines went into action. As she was turning, a small rowboat, caught between the submarine and the pier, was bashed in and sank. Embarrassed because of the onlookers, the captain sandpapered the exec. Wittgenberg went to the radio shack and put on the record of "We're Setting Sail for England." While it blared over the loud-speaker, he came out and, with a total deadpan, announced the first sinking of the expedition. The captain turned red as a lobster and said that such jokes were entirely out of order.

Twice the men on deck were called to attention, in answer to the salutes of an Italian submarine and of a German torpedo boat flotilla. Then the sub passed the breakwater and ran out to the rendezvous point in the wake of a patrol boat.

The deck was made ready for diving. There was a nervousness in the voices of the officers as they gave their orders to the men on deck: the Bay of Biscay lay ahead, and it always took a few days to get back into harness. The bollards had to be lowered, the boat hooks lashed tight. The lines were stowed under the deck and everything movable had to be made fast to avoid the slightest sound of rattling or rubbing when running submerged. Wearing an ornate pullover and a blue silk scarf bearing his family crest, the exec came down from the bridge and inspected the men's work. He supervised the test firing of the 20-millimeter and the machine guns. Then the machine guns were stowed below, Wittgenberg said *"Picobello"* to his men, and they climbed down the hatch. The exec went to the captain and reported, "Deck ready for diving, sir." Shortly afterward the engineer reported that all was ready below.

At the rendezvous point the patrol boat turned about, signaling good-by and good luck, and headed back to port. The submarine ran a few miles on the surface and then submerged.

13

The mission began well. Five days from shore they sighted a six-thousand-ton freighter in the dusk, alone but running at gratifyingly low speed. Two hours after the first sighting a torpedo struck the freighter amidships. The ship stopped, but there was no discernible list. The captain ordered the exec to fire a second torpedo. Just then the radio room announced that the freighter had sent a message on the six-hundred-meter band: "SOS torpedoed by German submarine sinking fast"—with an indication of position. The captain said to hold the *coup de grâce*. He had no sooner spoken than the freighter rolled over on her port side, lay flat for a few seconds, and went down.

The sub spent the following weeks prowling the North Atlantic, but nothing turned up. ComSub had picked the North Altantic as her field of operations, so there they remained, waiting and freezing. For weeks the sea swept at storm strength over the bridge watch while the bitter wind lashed their faces. The inside of the sub was at water temperature. At midnight and at 0400, when the relieved watch went down into the control room, their faces were frozen masks, covered with ice crystals. Their beards froze fast to the collars of their leather gear; the leather itself had congealed into armor. The men could scarcely move. In the dim light of the control room they looked like gnomes from another world. It was half an hour before the feeling came back into their hands. Their boots were damp on the inside and frozen on the outside, and they would not come off. Even their underwear was wet; they would wring it out and hung up what they could in the electric motor room. If they left it anywhere else it would be frozen stiff when they had to put it on again.

It was dismal, but better than the tropic heat. Just once the sun peered out of the clouds for a while. Teichmann, who was on watch, sent a message to Stollenberg to come up on the bridge with an empty tin can and collect vitamins. But just as Stollenberg was heading for the bridge, the captain went up. Lüttke stayed until the sun was gone, and Stollenberg remained below. He stood under the "village linden," smoking his pipe. Suddenly the first lieutenant called, "Alarm!"

Teichmann and the two after lookouts dropped down the tower hatch. Müller, the first lieutenant, shouted "Flood" even before the control room had reported ready. Müller tried to hold on to the hatch cover as he was climbing down, but the cover was no longer secured and fell shut. Müller roared with pain. His fingers were mashed between frame and cover. He could not get them out, and for that reason the cover would not shut tight. The sub was bow-heavy and dived steeply.

Stollenberg had seen it all. He was sick with fear, incapable of any thought. In his excitement Müller had lost his footing on the ladder. He clutched the hatch wheel with his free hand, supporting his whole weight with his right arm. The fingers of his left hand were still wedged in. "Open the hatch," shouted Stollenberg.

The sea poured over the hatch. Water drove through the crack between cover and frame. Stollenberg seized Müller's feet and set them on a rung of the ladder. Müller shoved his shoulder against the hatch cover, and opened it enough to release his fingers. And then his rings—a wedding ring and a heavy seal ring—got stuck in the catch. Stollenberg heard the hatch cover fall into place, and that was the main thing. But water still poured in, because Müller could not turn the hatch wheel with his left hand. The water gushed through room. The men in the control room lost their heads; they thought Müller still had his fingers in the hatch and that this was what prevented the cover from closing. And they didn't want to drown on account of a couple of fingers. It was dark in the tower; they couldn't see that the cover was closed and that Müller was merely hanging from the catch, too bewildered to work it loose. One of the control-room men pushed his feet off the ladder, clutched them, and pulled with all his might. Others did the same—there was a sound of cracking and tearing—and Müller fell into the the conning tower and splashed on the deck of the control control room.

Stollenberg climbed up the ladder and tightened the hatch. When he came down again he stepped on Müller, who lay on the floor. Between the middle finger and little finger of his left hand, there was a long triangular gap extending almost to the wrist.

"What's the matter, Stollenberg old boy?" asked the exec. "Why?"

"Your face is bloody," said Teichmann.

"There's a finger hanging up there," said Stollenberg. It had dangled in his face as he was turning the hatch wheel.

"I never want to see that damn fool again," said the captain. Müller didn't hear him; he had lost consciousness. "And the same goes for that washerwoman in pants."

That was Timmler, who lay huddled in a corner of the control room. They picked him up and carried him, none too gently, to his bunk. On the way he came to.

The sub had gone down to forty fathoms before the engineer could stop her. The negative tanks had been blown out too late. The men who normally did that had been busy tugging at the first lieutenant.

"Will you kindly bring us back to periscope depth," said the captain. "What did you take us down for anyway?"

"On account of a plane, sir," said Teichmann.

"Must have been a sea gull," said the captain.

"Sir," said Stollenberg, "could I have a glass of schnapps, please?" The captain kept the schnapps under lock and key, and brought it out only on special occasions. It seemed to Stollenberg that this was a special occasion.

"What for?"

"I feel a little faint, sir."

"Nonsense," said the captain, but he went to his cabin, opened the schnapps locker, and poured Stollenberg half a tiny glassful. Stollenberg bolted it down; it was scarcely better than nothing. "Wash the dirt off your face," said the captain, putting an end to Stollenberg's drinking bout.

They carried the first lieutenant to his bunk. He screamed a few times but in the main he was quiet, because he lost consciousness again. The radio doc gave him a tetanus shot and passed out, because he couldn't stand the sight of blood. The motor machinist's mate had to come and bandage Müller's hand. It gave him pleasure to say "Shut your trap" to the first lieutenant when he groaned. When he had finished, the machinist's mate got a gigantic bawling out from the captain for leaving his submerged station without permission.

After a look-around through the periscope, the captain ordered Winkler to surface. Then he began to fume because the finger was still hanging from the catch. The helmsman had to take it down and throw it into the control room. Now it was the engineer's turn to bellow. "My control room isn't a garbage pail." When the boat shot out of the water, Lüttke began to rage again, because he couldn't get the hatch open. This time Stollenberg was the biggest idiot on board. Teichmann climbed up the tower and brought all his strength to bear, but the hatch wheel wouldn't budge.

"Winkler, submerge to twenty meters," said the captain. It was easy to see what had happened: when Stollenberg had closed the hatch the water pressure on the cover had enabled him to give the wheel one or two more turns than usual.

At a depth of ten fathoms the captain gave the wheel a few turns. When the boat surfaced, he fumed some more because he got wet, though it was his own fault for releasing the wheel too much at ten fathoms.

At lunch the exec gave a little lecture on the perils of marriage in general and for submariners in particular, or how a wedding ring can endanger the lives of fifty men. If Müller had not been wearing a wedding ring, he would still be in possession of his ten fingers. When the engineer called it to his attention that the seal ring and not the wedding ring had been to blame for the loss of the finger, the exec replied that the first lieutenant had only worn the seal ring to lessen the temptation to remove his wedding ring. Then the engineer took a pair of pliers, picked up the finger with the rings still on it, and set it down on Müller's chest. "When he wakes up, that'll send him right back to sleep again," said Winkler. "Cheaper than morphine—and better." After a few more malicious remarks at the expense of the first lieutenant and a dirty joke or two, the incident was closed.

Thus began one of the last battles with convoys before the Götterdämmerung of the German submarine fleet. The plane came back. It did not attack the submarine but turned away and disappeared below the horizon. Within an hour this happened four times. The second time the plane came quite close. It was a carrier plane. And carrier at that time meant convoy.

When Teichmann went on watch at 1600, the light was already failing. The wind had died down; the sea was relatively calm and coal black. Slowly the night rolled out of the east.

The first stars appeared, glittering uncommonly bright, and soon the sky was filled with them. It was bitter cold.

A quivering glow was seen in the north and the air seemed to crackle with electricity. In places the sea turned dark green. The bow stirred up the phosphorescent plankton as though plowing a field of golden sand. Little by little the hesitant glow in the north turned to flashes as of lightning. And when all the stars that Teichmann had ever seen were in the sky, the northern lights flared across the heavens like glittering spears.

The radiomen cursed; the northern lights made for bad reception. At 1900 they decoded a garbled message from a sub reporting a convoy.

The captain came up on the bridge, set a new course, and ordered both Diesels on "full." Teichmann went down to dinner; he and Stollenberg divided the first lieutenant's watch between them. Slowly and thoughtfully Teichmann ate his beans with smoked pork and mashed potatoes. Thus fortified, he relieved Stollenberg on the bridge.

At 2030 a radio message came in from ComSub: eight

subs, including Lüttke's, were directed to make for the convoy at high speed.

At 2310 they sighted a destroyer. The captain ordered the combat bridge watch aloft. It consisted of the exec, the two midshipmen, and the quartermaster. The chief quartermaster sat over the charts in the control room, plotting the course.

The destroyer did not concern itself with the sub, or perhaps did not see it. Lüttke was able to keep on his course. Then black shadows appeared on the horizon and their presence was reported to ComSub. The shadows grew larger; they were making directly for the sub. The captain ordered a slight change in course.

Shortly before midnight there was another radio message from ComSub. Lüttke was ordered to keep contact and direct other subs to the convoy. The homing device was rigged and signals were sent to give the other subs a bearing.

At 0100 the bridge watch sighted a German sub on the port quarter. At the same time the radio room announced that two other subs had contact with the convoy.

At 0120 a message came if from ComSub: "Go to it."

"Torpedo battle stations," said the captain, and the order was passed on over the loud-speaker system.

Tubes one to five were prepared for surface fire and set to fire a salvo. The chief quartermaster had computed the target's course and the captain estimated its speed at nine knots. The sub ran ahead of the convoy at full speed; the captain planned to fire on a bearing of forty-five degrees.

At bearing ten he reduced speed in order to cut down his wake and slowly, showing the enemy his narrow silhouette, he edged up to the leading ships of the convoy. The northern lights prevented him from getting very close. Even so, the men on the bridge could not make out why the enemy failed to see the submarine. Two British destroyers of the latest design were circling around at the head of the convoy but they did not detect the sub. One of them, sending up a great wave of phosphorescent foam, came to within five hundred yards.

"Destroyer bearing zero, sir," said the exec.

"A little accuracy, if you please. That bearing is five."

Despite the cold, the men were beginning to feel warm. As Teichmann and Stollenberg searched their sectors through their glasses, they heard the words that were spoken on the bridge. To them it seemed that the destroyer was practically alongside.

"Range still about eight hundred yards, sir," said the exec.

"You *are* so well informed."

Now it seemed to the midshipmen that they could hear the destroyer rushing toward them. Teichmann cast a glance toward it and started as though he had been pricked with a red-hot needle. With its lofty superstructure, the destroyer looked like a small skyscraper, and it was heading straight at him.

"Bearing five; range seven zero zero, sir," said the exec.

"I'm glad you've finally got that bearing right. But your range is off. You will please make your observations more accurate. That range is six zero zero."

"Yes, sir. Do we dive?"

"Hell, no. Those fellows are sound asleep."

And so it seemed. The destroyer turned off again and ran back to the convoy.

When the sub was still some twelve hundred yards from the right column of the convoy, the captain ordered the exec to fire. "If you miss, I'll throw you overboard," he added.

Two big tankers were observed on the outside of the starboard column. This was unusual; as a rule the most valuable ships were kept in the middle for protection.

But then the captain discovered an aircraft carrier where the tankers would ordinarily have been. There was no chance of getting at the carrier.

"We're going to get the tankers and the two ships behind them."

"Aye aye, sir."

"Aim for the forward edge of the bridge. Amidships too if you feel like it."

"Aye aye, sir."

"Have you got a clear view?"

SHARKS AND LITTLE FISH

"Yes, sir."

"Lenses clear on the TBT?"

"Yes, sir."

"How many degrees to go?"

"About twenty."

"Good. I'll swing her around. Watch out that they don't go by." And he called down the tower to the helmsman, "Ten to port. Starboard ahead one-third. Port ahead dead slow."

Silently the torpedoes left the tubes.

"Tubes one to four fired electrically."

"Make ready tube five," ordered the exec.

"Tube five is ready."

"Thank you," said the exec.

"I'm turning off. It's too late for an aimed shot. And one of those fish costs seventy thousand marks."

"Yes, sir."

The sub turned off at right angles to the convoy. The helmsman in the tower was reporting the new course when the first explosion was heard. A column of water arose from the first tanker. Even before the geyser fell, there was a second explosion, and then at regular intervals the last two torpedoes hit the ships further astern.

The first tanker exploded, flinging up burning oil like a volcano. The second tanker began to burn and fell apart like cardboard, spreading its oil over the sea.

A few seconds later all was still except for the seething and bubbling of the oil. The men on the bridge could hear the oil bubbles bursting dully as they came into contact with the oxygen of the air and caught fire.

And then the fireworks began. The ships shot red flares into the air and their sirens wailed. The destroyers replied with green flares and more wailing of sirens and explored the sea with their searchlights. Now there were three destroyers on hand, signaling one another. Here and there a rocket went up from one of the ships. It was like New Year's Eve, an impressive sight with the northern lights in the background.

A few minutes later three or four more detonations were heard from the left column of the convoy. That was the

other subs. Then *bam* at the head of the convoy. Then again
to starboard.

The right column scattered. One of the destroyers dropped
a series of depth charges. They seemed to have been dropped
at random, presumably to keep the subs at a distance.

The oil spread like a red carpet unrolled by invisible arms
and pursued the fleeing ships. As the carpet overtook a ship,
tongues of flame leapt up the side, higher and higher, until
the whole vessel was ablaze. Ships rammed each other in
their frantic efforts to escape. The air was foul with burning
oil and seemed almost sultry.

The six men on the bridge of the sub looked on. They
had no need of their binoculars; they could see men in the
water, living torches, and now and then they could hear
screams. They saw them struggling and splashing; they could
hear them howling; and they could smell the burning flesh.

"Eyes to port. Get them used to the darkness. I will watch
the convoy and no one else."

"Yes, sir."

But it was impossible to look away from this inferno. It
cast beams out into the night; tatters of light fluttered past
like great white sails. The smell of death crept over the
water like a hideous monster. The screams of the burning
sailors rang in the ears of the submariners while the flames
rose crackling to the sky, where the hosts of pallid stars
trembled with the cold in this icy night despite the searing
flames beneath them.

Down below the men were in high spirits. The men on
the bridge could hear that too, and they knew that the
German radio would be splitting the air with Liszt fanfares
and making a special announcement to the effect that so
and so many thousand tons of shipping had been sent to
the bottom. *Shipping*—only that word was needed to make
the inferno complete.

Teichmann stared into the water and followed it with his
eyes as it flew whishing and whirling past the side. He took
off one glove and set his hand on the bridge coaming, but
the iron was too cold; he was afraid that his skin would
stick to it. Now he too felt the cold, and suddenly he was

filled with rage. He did not know against whom or how it had come. A cold, inarticulate fury had settled within him, tearing open all the wounds that four years of war had covered over. The wounds bled within him, and burned, and ate at his nerves.

When it was over and the rage had died down, he felt empty and lonely, as though he were the only human being at the edge of this sea of flames, as if he alone had set the sea on fire. The loneliness was worse than the fear of death; it was the end of everything. Down below, the men were whooping it up.

"It's horrible," he heard Stollenberg whisper. He had come close to Teichmann and spoken into his ear, and the loneliness was gone. What remained was a dull, oppressive sadness that made him weary and indifferent. We have a right to send the enemy to hell, he argued with himself. Those fellows down there didn't see it or hear it. But the sadness remained.

"Looks as if you've given them a cooking, eh?"

Teichmann turned and saw a head in the tower hatch. Under the head shoulders appeared, and then the whole man was standing there. "Terrific sight, eh?"

From time to time a scream could still be heard—strangely protracted, like the whistle of a locomotive that is running out of steam.

"No misplaced sympathy, gentlemen; don't forget that those pirates starved our women and children in the last war. . . ."

"You keep your trap shut," added the exec, who was a very polite man.

"It's the truth, though. England was first to make war on the civilian population. . . ."

"Make yourself scarce," said the captain, and Timmler faded away like a lowered backdrop.

After a while he popped up again. "Just want to take a few pictures. A scene like this—got to preserve it for posterity; it's my job, sir. Hey, down there, hand up that camera."

By the time he had the camera, everything was covered

with dense black smoke that settled over the flames like a black shroud.

"Balls," said Timmler.

Now there was nothing more to be heard, nothing human was left. There were only the elements raging against each other—fire and water. The sea won out, but it took a long long time.

The sub dived. The forward torpedo tubes were reloaded. This was done in the record time of fourteen minutes. Then the boat surfaced again and ran along behind the convoy. Suddenly they saw the destroyer—as if it had sprung up out of the sea. The smoke had concealed it. Sending up an immense wave, it came racing toward the sub.

"Dive! Emergency!" cried the captain. The helmsman threw on the alarm bell. Sixteen seconds later the boat was under water. The destroyer ran over her, but dropped no bombs.

The men in the sub could distinctly hear detonations from the direction of the convoy. The other subs had sunk their teeth in the convoy and refused to let loose; the men in the sub thought the destroyer would have no time to waste on them but would go back to drive the other wolves from the flock. But the destroyer remained near by.

The captain had the stern tube made ready for submerged firing. Then he showed the destroyer his periscope. When the destroyer started for the periscope, the captain retracted it, ordered both electric engines on flank speed, and turned off at right angles to the destroyer's course. When he reached bearing forty, he fired.

The torpedo struck forward. The destroyer's bow was blown off, and she began to settle forward. The bulkheads burst and, still advancing at high speed, she sank. In less than thirty seconds she was gone.

This technique of sinking destroyers was one of Lüttke's daredevil tricks. Not one in twenty submarine commanders would have attempted it. And the captain said not one word about the maneuver to his crew.

Before the sub had time to surface, a second destroyer was on the scene. Lüttke decided to attack.

"There's a bit of sea," said the captain to the engineer. "Watch what you're doing."

"Aye aye, sir."

The attack went off according to plan. Once, when the periscope dipped, the captain had a few harsh words for the engineer, but he kept his wrath within bounds. Again he tried to fire on bearing forty-five, because he could not accurately determine the target speed. The estimate was correct, but the torpedo ran along the surface. The destroyer had no difficulty in getting out of the way.

"Stand by to fire spread of three," said the captain.

Some depth charges exploded. They sounded abominably loud but they were badly placed. They had been dropped only to keep the sub at a distance.

While the captain was trying to get fire data for the spread, the periscope dipped. Teichmann could tell by the Papenberg gauge. The engineer and the others in the control room saw it too. The captain's voice trembled with rage as he told the engineer what he thought of him. The captain's thundering made the engineer jittery. He ordered full climb on both planes, and asked for more speed.

"All ahead two-thirds," commanded the captain.

"All ahead two-thirds, sir," came the response.

Slowly, with icy politeness, the captain asked the engineer, "Do you think you can get us back to fourteen meters before the day is out?"

"I've set both planes on full climb, sir."

"Who the hell cares what you've done?"

"Screw sounds are getting louder," the radioman announced from the sound room.

Then, perhaps ten seconds later, the engineer reported, "Periscope clear."

"Couldn't you tell me that on time?"

"Thirteen point five meters. We're rising, sir. . . ."

"Get down to forty meters quick. All ahead, full. Get down there or he'll ram us." The captain spoke quietly and distinctly as he always did, but faster than usual.

"Lay forward to the bulkheads," cried the engineer.

When that failed to depress the bow, he cried, "All hands forward."

The men rushed forward as fast as they could. The bow shot down like a plummet.

"The stern's out of water," said the captain. His voice was a trifle hoarse. He was in the conning tower, at the periscope. Unable to see him, the men paid close attention to the sound of his voice. It wasn't a very expressive voice. But this time they heard something.

"Submerged stations," the engineer called.

The bow was still heavy. The men slipped on the deck plates, and it took them quite some time to get back to their stations.

"Do you know what happens when the acid runs out of the batteries?" the captain asked the engineer. He seemed to take a perverse pleasure in the engineer's mistakes. The captain climbed down to the control room and stood behind the engineer. Holding on to the cable of the lookout periscope with his left hand, he set one foot on the chest where the engineer was sitting.

The boat dived. The men heard the destroyer coming closer. She was coming on fast. The sound swelled and diminished and swelled again like a powerful drill working unevenly. When the destroyer was overhead, the men looked up and began to count. A depth charge sinks four meters a second. . . .

Boom! Boom! Boom!

The light bulbs shattered; the darkness was complete. The men could feel the trembling of the hull, and it gave them a queasy feeling. They were too frightened to think much.

"Take her down slow to one two zero meters," Teichmann heard the captain saying. His voice sounded cool and indifferent, and absolutely self-confident. Teichmann was filled with admiration. He knew that if fear got into the skipper they were all done for.

The captain switched on his flashlight and directed it at the depth gauge. Eighty meters.

"Do we pump, sir?" asked the chief engineer.

"Yes," said the captain.

"Start main bilge pump," said Winkler to the auxiliary-man.

Someone called for the extra fuses. The planes were put on hand operation.

"Pump-in operation," said a voice.

The emergency light over the charts had come on. The auxiliaryman had put in a new bulb. It was not a strong bulb, and the light was very dismal. The men at the pump behind the gyro worked silently, moving like shadows in the gloom. The pump made a little hissing sound.

When the depth gauge showed one hundred meters, the engineer had the boat back on an even keel. But it was still too heavy and kept sinking.

The destroyer was again approaching.

"Give me a sound bearing," said the captain.

"Sound bearing three three zero," said the radioman.

"Right full rudder, course six zero," the captain called up to the conning tower. As he repeated the command, the helmsman sounded as if he had high fever. His breathing could be heard in the control room.

The needle of the depth gauge stood at 120 meters. Suddenly it jumped—four times.

"Engine room shipping water," shouted the machinist.

The four depth charges had been close. They had pushed the stern down, bending the hull like a bow. The crash was indescribable. "Winkler, go aft and take a look," said the captain. "I'll take the wheel till you get back."

"Yes, sir."

Only the captain's flashlight was still burning. The emergency light over the charts had been smashed. The pump had stopped working. The auxiliaryman was tinkering with it in the darkness.

The engineer came back. "The induction valve is leaking, sir. Just a trickle. We can fix it."

"Send me that machinist."

The order was passed on to the engine room.

The machinist came in panting. "We can't go much deeper, sir, or . . ."

"Who are you?"

"What?"

"I asked you who you are. Have you got dirt in your ears?"

"Machinist First-Class Hübler reporting, sir."

"Sounds better, eh?"

"Yes, sir."

"If you come up with any more false information, I'll have you court-martialed."

"Yes, sir."

"Right here on board. Half an hour later you'll be feeding the fishes."

"Yes, sir."

"What comes to your mind when you talk about 'shipping water?' An accurate report would be 'slight trickle from induction valve'. Do you understand?"

"Yes, sir."

"You can't report a waterfall every time you take a leak."

"No, sir."

"And now get back to the engine room and stop that leak."

"Aye aye, sir." On his way back the machinist slipped on the glass splinters and hit his head against the watertight door. "God damn it," he said, but very softly.

The sound room reported that the destroyer had stopped.

"I want absolute quiet," said the captain. "If you haven't got anything to do, hit the sack and go to sleep." He ordered the port motor stopped and the starboard motor ahead one-third.

In the officers' quarters Müller began to moan. Aft, the firemen could be heard working feverishly but very quietly. Then a wrench clattered on the deck plates.

"Those ass-holes," the engineer muttered. He was thoroughly unnerved.

"Winkler!" said the captain. "You will watch your language."

"I beg your pardon, sir. It just slipped out."

"They call it a *lapsus linguae*, Winkler, old man," said the exec. "It can happen to the best of us." There was something wonderfully refreshing about those Latin words here at the bottom of the sea in a situation halfway between life and death. Teichmann found himself admiring the exec more than ever.

The needle of the depth gauge indicated 116 meters. Both planes were on full climb. The sub was going down more slowly, but it was still going down. If the main pump isn't fixed, we'll go right on sinking, thought Teichmann.

"*Tok.*"

The men cowered as though a whip had struck them in the face.

And then again: "*Tok.*"

Then it stopped. Teichmann could hear the others breathing.

"*Tok.*" And a pause.

"*Tok, tok, tok.*"

Silence.

Then a sound as if someone had thrown a handful of pebbles against the side.

"We're in the destroyer's sonar beam," said the radioman in the sound room.

"Correct," said Lüttke, and gave orders to the helmsman.

He tried to turn his stern toward the destroyer to make location more difficult. But the sub was making too little headway and did not react to the rudder.

"Destroyer headed this way," said the radioman.

"Let her come," said the captain.

"Bearing one two zero. Coming in fast," said the radioman.

"Always in a hurry, those tin cans," said the captain. And then he did some quick reckoning: his own course, target course, evasion course—if he reckoned wrong, he would run into the depth charges. The men knew that and kept their eyes on him.

"Right full rudder; port ahead full," said the captain.

The screw sounds grew louder. Suddenly the destroyer was straight overhead. The screw sounds swelled to a roar. . . .

Wait.

Wait and see what happens.

Wait—

Two crashes of thunder. But much louder than thunder. Teichmann fell into the potato crate. He felt rust and flakes of paint down his neck. It's all over, he thought, or rather he thought nothing, and just had the feeling that it was all over. But it was far from over.

When he was back on his feet, a knife cut into his face. The cut burned like fire. At the same time the engineer said, "The water gauge is leaking."

"Fix it," said the captain.

"Destroyer sounds moving away," said the radioman.

The captain stopped one engine and put the other on "dead slow."

There was no sound except for the hissing stream from the manometer, higher, lower, higher, and finally settling down to a steady soprano. The depth gauge read 160 meters. The captain switched off his flashlight. Timmler was whimpering.

"Have we a baby on board?" the captain asked.

"Not that I know of, sir," said the exec.

Timmler kept on whimpering. His teeth could be heard chattering in the darkness.

"Herr Doktor Timmler: The moment we surface you will read Seneca. He's in our library. That is an order. In three days at the latest you will bring me an essay at least twenty pages long entitled 'What I Have Learned from Seneca.' Do you understand?"

They heard the destroyer slowing down. Timmler did not reply, but at least he stopped whimpering.

"Have I failed to express myself clearly, Herr Doktor Timmler? Or does it strike you speechless to hear the name of a philosopher out of *my* mouth?"

The destroyer had stopped. They heard nothing more and knew she was looking for them.

"Oh, God," Timmler moaned.

Lüttke headed the sub into the last sound bearing. It was deathly still, both inside and out in the water. The men began to take hope: maybe the tin can wouldn't find them.

"No need to address me as God. Respect me as the devil, that's good enough for me, Herr Doktor Timmler."

"Yes . . ."

"I beg your pardon?"

"Yes, sir."

"Very good, Herr Doktor. In time perhaps I'll teach you, Herr Doktor."

The silence lasted a long time. Maybe he's lost us, Teichmann thought. He was alone. This night each man was alone with his fear. This fear was something you had to take care of all by yourself. Teichmann closed his eyes and listened into the night. And all the men listened; only their sense of hearing remained alert. But hearing gives no notion of time; no one had any idea how long the silence lasted. And then it was over. *Tok.* Someone was knocking on the side.

For the first time in his life Teichmann heard a man— Timmler didn't count—crying. Maybe the auxiliaryman, he thought. The crying was contagious.

Tok.

And after a few seconds: "*tok.*" Then the pauses, during which the sound beam missed the steel hull, grew shorter. And then came the shower of pebbles. The destroyer's screws began to turn, faster and faster, nearer and louder. The destroyer was coming; the men in the submarine could hear it all: the destroyer passing overhead, the ash cans splashing in the water. And automatically they began to count.

As the destroyer made off full speed to keep from being torn apart by her own depth charges, Teichmann was weak with fear. He sat huddled on the deck, his head on his knees, his arms around his ears, his hands folded over his head. They're set for deeper, he thought; that's why they're taking longer. But the deeper they explode, the greater their effect. The water is harder. Those Tommies are no beginners. They're not going to waste their ash cans. I shouldn't think, he thought, or I ought to think of something else. Just wipe that destroyer out of the picture. He knew that he was surrounded by his comrades, but he felt very lonely and wretched, like a pig waiting to be stuck. But the comparison didn't appeal to him. Unfortunately, he thought, he wasn't dumb enough for a pig. Just to be thinking something, he cast about for another animal, and hit on a rat drowned in its hole. But they give it a good shaking first, to torture it; and they let it drown nice and slowly, to be sure it knows what's going on. He felt that he had turned coward; he felt all his manhood seeping out of him—his manhood that he had made so much of on certain occasions. A single *tok* and there was nothing left of it. The destroyer dropped ten depth charges.

A few of the men screamed. Masses of water had been parted by the detonations and now fell thundering back. The charges had gone off in quick succession over the submarine and had driven it still deeper.

The captain lit his flashlight and turned it on the depth gauge. The needle stood at the end of the scale. Then he flashed it through the control room. The cone of light passed over the men's faces. They were standing by the control-room bulkheads. They were holding their escape lungs. Some had opened the zipper bags. And they were six hundred feet below the surface of the sea.

The destroyer made off.

The captain was in no hurry to turn off his light and did so only when the destroyer stopped. The engineer's voice: "Do we blow out ballast, sir?"

"No." Then: "I don't remember telling anybody to leave his submerged station."

Teichmann heard the men getting back to their stations.

"We're going down," said the engineer.

"Is that bilge pump going to be working soon?"

"Can't see anything, sir," said someone from the direction of the pump.

"Get the emergency light on."

"Working on it, sir."

Then a new fear seized them. The hull creaked and groaned under the pressure. Eerie sounds that went right through you. And they never stopped. The pressure hull was taking its maximum load. The engineer estimated the depth at 690 feet.

The emergency lighting system flashed on; the sounds in the pressure hull grew louder—as though the steel cylinder were being slowly bent out of shape. A report was heard aft, hard and dry as a pistol shot. Someone screamed and then was still. The cry was followed by a loud, even sound like the buzzing of a circular saw.

The motor machinist's mate stuck his head through the controlroom bulkhead and said, "Water in the engine room."

"Teichmann, go see what's up."

"Aye aye, sir."

The machinist's mate went ahead of Teichmann with his flashlight. A fine, almost invisible stream, thin and white as the E string of a violin, passed through the middle of the engine room. It went from the deck plates, which had been bent by its impact, up to the overhead deck. On the deck plates lay a man. Who it was Teichmann could not see. The machinist's mate said it was Carls, one of the firemen. His severed left hand lay beside him. A rivet had sprung from the pressure hull, bashed in his skull, and gone through the deck plates. As the man fell, the jet of water had hit his left wrist.

Teichmann went back to the control room and reported to the captain.

"Can they fix it?"

"Not at this depth, sir."

"Request permission to blow tanks," said the engineer.

"No."

Teichmann went back to the chart table.

"Close after bulkhead," said the captain. The watertight door was closed. The men in the engine room and the motor room were shut in. The stream of water could still be heard in the control room.

"Winkler," said the captain, "get us up to one five zero meters."

"Request more speed, sir."

"All ahead two-thirds."

"All ahead two-thirds," the helmsman repeated.

The engineer had both planes on "full rise," but the needle of the depth gauge didn't budge. The engineer tapped the gauge, but it still didn't move.

"We're not reacting to the planes, sir," said the engineer. *Tok.*

318

"All ahead dead slow," said the captain.

"All ahead . . ."

Tok.

"Tongue been cut off?"

"All ahead . . ."

Tok.

". . . dead slow."

Pebbles beat against the side.

The destroyer came on, passed overhead, and dropped six depth charges.

"Sir, she can't rise on power. . . ."

"I know it."

Silence.

And then again tapping against the side. The intervals between the taps were longer than before, but more regular. The beam struck every thirty seconds on the dot. The destroyer didn't move; she was taking her time. She held the submarine as a spider holds a fly. The sound beam was her web. It was only a question of time—a little example in arithmetic: when would the sub's batteries run down? To maneuver away from depth charges, you need high speed, and high speed takes current. Low speeds use up the current too, but more slowly. It could all be worked out. You could also figure out when the oxygen in the sub would be used up. The only thing you couldn't figure out was when the sub would be crushed by the water pressure; that was a matter of experience, and once you'd found out you were in no position to tell others. But at a depth of 120 to 140 fathoms, it could happen any minute. Or if the ash cans were well placed . . .

After every *tok* the men began to hope that there would not be another. A childish hope. When they had counted to thirty, it came again.

The destroyer started a run.

"We'll give it another try," said the captain to the engineer.

Radioman Striker Bolz appeared in the forward passageway. He was a pleasant fellow, a bit shy, but otherwise all right. He didn't talk much; but there was no harm in that.

And there was no harm in it if he carried a little Bible around with him, and read it in his bunk or in the radio room when there was nothing else to do. Now he read aloud. Something about the dark vale of tears in which we live. He's got something there, thought Teichmann, must be a Psalm or something; anyway, it takes his mind off his troubles. For the moment he seems to have forgotten all about those ash cans.

When the destroyer dropped her charges, he had to stop reading; he was only human. But a moment later he started in again, reading very fast, as though afraid that he might not get to the end of his chapter.

Teichmann had a feeling that the depth charges weren't so close this time; the emergency lights had not been smashed. If it goes on like this, he thought, I might get religion. The destroyer moved off. The man went on reading.

"That's enough now, man of God," said the captain.

"We're rising," said the engineer.

"Why, Winkler, you notice everything."

Bolz read to the end of his chapter, then thrust the Bible into his back pocket like a wallet—without a trace of embarrassment.

"See here, who gave you permission to kick up all that fuss?"

Bolz fell from the clouds.

"My orders were that anybody who had nothing to do should hit the sack. And you come in with your big mouth. Do you think this is a reading circle?"

"No, sir."

"And you left your submerged station without orders. What exactly did you have in mind?"

Bolz had no reply.

"At that rate anybody could come in here and start telling fairy tales. What do you suppose would have happened if I began reading potboilers instead of thinking about that destroyer? I'm the one who decides what's to be done on this boat, and no one else. Remember that. When we get back home, I'll put you into a good kindergarten. Then you'll be able to tell all the fairy tales you please, you clown, you.

320

SHARKS AND LITTLE FISH

I've a good mind to lock you up for a few weeks first. God Almighty, what a menagerie I've got here! Well, before our next trip, I'm going to do a little housecleaning—you can count on that. Now what do you want?"

"Nothing, sir."

"Then don't stand around. Shove off. And by tomorrow 1200 I want you to write a hundred times, 'The captain and no one else decides what is to be done on board.' I will . . ."

"The main pump is fixed, sir," said the control chief.

"You are not to interrupt me when I'm speaking."

"I'm sorry, sir," said the control chief.

"What did I tell you to write?"

"The captain and no one else decides what is to be done on board."

The men too had judged Bolz. The higher the boat rose the more severe became the verdict. He shouldn't have brought out that Bible, the men felt; it had been tactless and improper. He had found a source of help that was not available to the others—even if they had wanted it. That was uncomradely. If he had read softly at least. . . . Yes, they thought, the skipper was perfectly right; if he had read softly, nothing would have happened to him, but as it was—

When the depth gauge read 120 meters, the control chief said Bolz ought to be a missionary, a German war vessel was no place for him.

"I didn't ask for your opinion, you cry-baby," said the captain. And again he was right, the crew thought. That settled the control chief.

Tok. Tok. Only twice. Then the destroyer was overhead, and as it receded there were ten detonations. . . .

At every explosion the men screamed. They were all desperate. It was worse than the first time. Again it was pitch-black all around them.

"Close all watertight doors," said the captain.

The forward section was closed off. The Papenberg gauge sent a broad stream of water into the control room. The sound of the water streaming into the engine room grew louder. The boat was going down fast.

"Get that bilge pump going," said the captain.

"The pump is functioning, sir," came the answer.

At 200 meters the needle of the depth gauge came to a halt.

"The destroyer has stopped," said the radioman. "New screw sounds farther away, coming closer. Bearing two two zero."

That was the end. The destroyer had called in reinforcements.

"How many revolutions?"

"Can't tell yet, sir."

"We can't hold this depth," said the engineer. "My estimate is two hundred and fifty meters."

The captain took the microphone of the loud-speaker system. "All hands: open watertight doors. Prepare for surface battle. We fight until we run out of ammunition. When the seamen are knocked out, the firemen will man the gun."

That was a relief. It was sheer madness to attack two destroyers with one gun, but at the moment no one thought of that.

"Quartermaster, stand by to destroy all secret material."

"Aye aye, sir."

"Winkler, blow all tanks. Watch your pressure compensation."

"Aye aye, sir."

"All men with flashlights to the control room."

The men passed on the order. The control chief put on his work gloves; his hands trembled, but a glimmer of joy came into his tearful, terror-stricken face as he manned the air manifold. The ammunition ready box was opened. An intermittent *tok* was heard, and pebbles beat against the side, but no one noticed. That was old stuff. With an immense din, as though to drown out the sounds of the destroyer, the men hauled shells into the control room. Teichmann saw Stollenberg; he saw him consciously for the first time since the first depth charges. And Stollenberg's convulsed face broke into a crooked but well-meant grin.

"Wittgenberg," said the captain, "you will take Müller's place as gunnery officer."

322

"Yes, sir."

The destroyer started her run.

"We'll wait this one out," said the skipper.

The destroyer was coming on at high speed. The men in the submarine groaned. They wanted to die topside, at the gun, in active combat, and as the destroyer came racing toward them they feared that even this death would be denied them. Then *boom*—but the destroyer hadn't reached them yet. Then the sound of cracking bulkheads. The destroyer's screws seemed to have slowed down.

"Sounds of ship sinking," said the radioman.

"Where?"

"Bearing two four zero. Close aboard."

"Can you still hear that tin can's screws?"

"No, sir."

"He can't have sunk himself."

"Sir, I hear screw sounds on bearing two zero zero. Sounds like Diesel engines . . ." The radioman could say no more. He was like a small child speechless over an unexpected present.

"Out with it. You know what that means. It means another sub has knocked him off. Winkler, stand by to surface."

Teichmann climbed up on the bridge with the first watch. Starry sky. Cold. Faint, bluish northern lights. No sign of the destroyer.

"Hand up the searchlight."

The helmsman handed it up. Blinker communication was established with the other German submarine. A few minutes later the two boats were within calling distance.

"That fellow was making it pretty hot for us," Lüttke shouted over.

"That's what it looked like," the other captain replied. "He was so busy he didn't see me coming."

"Did you attack as soon as you saw him?"

"Hell, no. He was good enough to stop dead ahead of my torpedo tubes. I don't pick fights with any destroyer."

"Well, good hunting."

"Same to you."

Down in the conning tower little red dots appeared. The men on the off watch were standing under the "village linden tree," smoking their cigarettes. They lent a hand when Carls, tied up like a package, was pulled up through the hatch and thrown overboard. The chief quartermaster made a cross on the chart, wrote in the latitude and longitude, the date and the clock time. "Three hours under depth charge attack," wrote the captain in his War Diary.

The outer door of tube four refused to open. They worked on it in three shifts: the exec and the boatswain's mate; the two midshipmen; the torpedo man and the leading seaman.

The water was like ice. But the stretch across the deck was worse. The first time the naked men thought the cold would simply kill them in the couple of yards from the tower to the bow. They found it hard to lift their knees, and when they had gone halfway they would just as soon have stopped and let themselves freeze to the spot; they absolutely rejected the idea of crossing that ice-covered deck with bare feet. But on the bridge stood the captain. They felt his eyes on their backs, and one thing they didn't want was one of his remarks. The eyes were bad enough.

The water was a relief at first; it was warmer than the air. But after a few seconds they felt its full iciness, and if it hadn't been for the captain up there, looking at his watch, they would have stopped working and jumped right out again. As it was, they worked with a mounting frenzy because they knew that the torture would go on until they got that door open.

None of them could stand it more than four minutes. They had a line around their waists, and at one-minute intervals the men on deck gave the line five short jerks, which meant are you all right down there? If the diver didn't answer immediately with five jerks on the line, he was pulled right up. That was a painful business; the line cut into his flesh, and afterwards, as he worked, it kept scraping the same spot, which never stopped bleeding.

The worst part was the way back. Panting, shivering, and exhausted, they crossed the deck, but before going below they had to report to the captain and tell him that the door could still not be opened and why not. There was no beating around the bush; the captain knew exactly what a torpedo tube outer door looked like and how it worked. Of course he could have taken this report down below, but he had his reasons for doing so in the open. The men knew his reasons and complied. In the control room they were rubbed down until their skin was lobster red, and they drank their extra schnapps ration. Then it was time to start in again.

On their third dive Teichmann and Stollenberg succeeded in opening the door. A plump hogfish, a good three feet long, had been looking on and immediately stuck his head into the tube. Teichmann smacked him on the tail fin and he shot out of the tube like a bat out of hell. It was a comical sight. Teichmann and Stollenberg couldn't help laughing, and they both got a mouthful. Stollenberg lost the mouthpiece of his diving mask and had to surface in a hurry.

Lüttke was trying to make up for lost time.

"That convoy isn't going to wait for us," he had said, and ordered both engines on "full." Other submarines had contact with the convoy and had radioed its position and course.

The wind rose. When Teichmann went up on the bridge that night there was a No. 8 sea. In the course of the night the storm reached hurricane strength. The bridge watch waited for the order to submerge. But it didn't come. Instead, the captain appeared on the bridge and shouted to the exec, "Hold to your course and speed." He stationed himself by the periscope standard, and there he remained for fifty-two hours.

There was nothing to be seen. Mountainous waves rolled in from abeam, and when the heads of the men emerged from the water, the wind lashed into their faces as though to tear off their skin. The ship rolled eighty degrees on both sides. The men knew it could not capsize, that the lead keel would always right it, but they did not know how long they themselves could take the punishment. They fully expected to be crushed by the masses of water or washed overboard. They strapped themselves tight, but they knew that straps can part. The icy water seemed warm to them, but the wind that swept over their drenched leather gear cut like a knife and howled like a fortissimo from a thousand organ pipes. The men's arms were as stiff as if they had become a part of the boat. And the captain stood there like a second periscope standard.

The night was black and impenetrable, and only the foam at the crest of the waves glittered like white sugar, strewn over a wild black mountain range whose summits were flung high by a continuous earthquake. In their berserk fury the wind and sea had singled out this little low bridge as their victim.

The tower hatch had been closed. The captain and the four men of the watch were all alone in their fight with the hurricane. As far as the men were concerned, it was a senseless fight. They cursed their captain as though he were the devil in person. They cursed him out loud, for no one could hear them. The voices were swallowed up in the howling of the wind and the thunder of the sea.

At the end of three hours, there were only four men on the bridge. The disappearance of the port after lookout had gone unnoticed. Then the captain shouted into Teichmann's ear to ask through the speaking tube if the man had possibly gone below.

The question was a pure formality, but Teichmann shouted into the speaking tube just the same. It was impossible to understand what they shouted back, and Teichmann managed to get that over to the captain. As they emerged from an avalanche of water that had submerged them for twenty seconds, the captain told Teichmann to take a look down below. It seemed odd to Teichmann that the captain should take an interest in such things.

When the bridge was clear of water for a moment, Teichmann tore open the hatch cover and climbed down into the conning tower. He closed the hatch immediately. The helmsman in the conning tower looked at him as if he were a ghost, held his head over the control-room hatch, and threw up with a groan. "Get me relieved," he said to Teichmann. "I can't hold a course; the compass needle is driving me crazy." Teichmann looked into the man's eyes and believed him. Then he went down into the control room, and while he was still under the hatch the helmsman vomited on his head as though to prove that he was really going crazy. Teichmann was too tired to do anything but shake his head in disgust.

"Is the old man nuts?" cried the auxiliaryman. His hands over his head, he held fast to the valve wheels, and when the boat heaved hard it looked as if he were walking on his hands.

"You ask him."

"The dirty dog. The God-damned dog. The dirty bastard. . . ." The last words sounded so shrill that Teichmann, who was already halfway through the forward watertight door, turned back, thinking the man had gone mad. But then he saw that the auxiliaryman had only screamed that way because at that moment he was standing more on his hands than his feet.

At first Teichmann saw nothing in the forward torpedo room. When his eyes had partly accustomed themselves to the darkness, he picked out details: a boot, a loaf of bread, a sailor lying on his back with his feet up in the air as if he were doing gymnastics. Everything was hurtling from side to side. Some of the straps supporting the bunks had torn and the men didn't know where to stow themselves. It was a mystery to Teichmann how they could stand being tossed about like this hour after hour. He saw a few injured men, with bleeding hands and faces. The head of one was all red with blood on one side; he looked like a woman who had started to dye her hair a rusty brown and had been interrupted in the middle. But Teichmann stood watching only for the barest moment, and then the whole room was turned on its head.

He had forgotten what he had come for, but then the torn straps on the bunks reminded him of the captain's order.

The missing lookout was not there.

On the way back Teichmann looked into the petty officers' room to see how Stollenberg was doing. He lay awake, wedged in between the wall and the rough-weather slat of his bunk, and started with fright when Teichmann touched him.

"How you doing, Emil?"

"Rotten."

"Seasick?"

"No, I just feel rotten. There's something wrong with me. I feel terrible, and I don't know why." He looked bad, too. Teichmann had never seen him so dejected. He seemed a stranger, his boyish face grown suddenly old.

"I guess your stomach isn't used to this roller-coaster."

"It isn't my stomach, Hans—I want to tell you something. It's no good what the captain's doing, it's going to end badly. I know why he's doing it. It's because he hates the English. Winkler told me. We were talking about it. I asked him why the skipper is that way and he told me. On his first mission—it was off Gibraltar—he looked on through the periscope while two English corvettes were shooting up the crew of a damaged German sub that had to surface. It seems the captain was sick for two days. And he's been this way ever since."

"You mustn't forget that those corvette officers aren't professional sailors. Think of Pauli . . ."

"Yes—but even so. He ought to dive. In this weather the convoy is going to have to change course anyway. I feel bad, Hans; I can't help it. I tell you frankly I wish we were back home. This whole damned war makes me . . ."

"Herr Teichmann, sir. The captain's asking what's become of you."

"I'm coming."

So the man had been washed overboard; that was definite. Teichmann shouted his report in the captain's face. He would have liked to throw more in his face than that.

The weather was unchanged. Teichmann was filled with impotent rage. He caught himself repeating the words of the control chief—to himself. Why they should be up here on the bridge was more than he could see. The light of the foaming sea, snowy and cold, was all that could be seen in this darkness. All right, he thought; in a pinch I can understand that the captain wouldn't want to dive. Under water we can do only three or four knots; now we're doing about ten. But why does he need five men on the bridge? Then the relief came: the chief quartermaster, Stollenberg, the coxswain, and a seaman first-class. The captain stayed where he was.

Teichmann tried to undress. In an attempt to get a boot off, he stood on one foot and toppled over. When he tried it lying on his back, he rolled around like a barrel. When he tried to squirm out of his leather jacket, which was wringing wet and as heavy as a dozen winter overcoats, his head flew into the case of the fathometer with such force that he said to himself, Something busted; if it's not the fathometer, it must be my head. Then little by little, carefully allowing for the laws of gravity, he managed to get out of his jacket. He even succeeded in pulling off his wet sweater and wringing it out. But that was all.

With chattering teeth, he sat on the deck of the control room, sliding from one corner to another, and the exec slid with him. Teichmann could see what a struggle it was for him to keep his good manners under these conditions. When a board came out of the potato crate and the potatoes tumbled over his chest, even he couldn't help uttering a pretty respectable curse. "You're learning, sir," Teichmann shouted at him. "Hell," Wittgenberg shouted back, "I'm sick of this sleigh-riding. If I could only get some sleep . . ." And at that moment both of them collided with the bilge pump.

Time seemed to stand still, and the torture went on and on. The men in the boat cursed and yelled; their state of mind oscillated between rage and despair, between rebellious fury and dull resignation. The cold was bitter. The steel sides seemed like walls of ice. The men felt that they were slowly congealing, and perhaps they would have congealed if the sea hadn't kept them in motion. There was nothing to eat and nothing to drink, either.

Someone called down through the hatch, "Man overboard."

Teichmann heard the words and his mind was a blank. Then . . .

"Who is it?"

"They didn't say."

"Helmsman, I want to know who it was. Right away."

"They didn't say, sir."

There was Wittgenberg, climbing up into the tower. Teichmann heard the hatch cover opening and he heard shouting. Then he saw the exec's boots. Then he saw his pants, and then the whole exec, thoroughly drenched again and looking like a swimmer coming out of the water. Then he saw the exec slip on the dock plates where the helmsman had vomited, and fall. And then he saw the exec's face—and looked away.

The exec had not said a word.

Teichmann looked around the control room. He examined it slowly and thoroughly. The wheels and levers that governed the vents of the five diving tanks: one, two, three on both sides, four and five. Tank five was forward. Tank one was aft. Both had wheels. Three had levers. Beside him he saw the distilling plant. He noted that it was actually working. He saw the fathometer. The chart table. The potato crate. The instrument panel. The two hydroplane handles. The depth gauges, the big one and the little one. The wheels of the air manifold. And then he started all over again.

And again.

And again.

Then the control room began to spin around in his head.

And then he started in again, listing everything that his eyes showed him. . . .

When the bridge watch was relieved, three men came down. The captain had stayed up top.

"You're not looking so good yourself, Hans, you . . ."

"I thought—the exec said you'd gone overboard."

"Me? No, it was Schmidt, the coxswain."

"They told me it was the forward lookout, the one next to the chief quartermaster," said Wittgenberg.

330

"That was Schmidt. I was aft this time, because the captain . . ."

The exec and Stollenberg turned away and busied themselves with something. Teichmann wondered if he should say something about the way the salt water burned a fellow's eyes.

In the morning the first watch returned to the bridge, hungry, frozen, and dead-tired. It was still dark. The storm was still raging. They put on their clothes sopping wet, but it was all one, they reflected, as the seas swept over them. Again the water was like ice, yet warmer than the wind.

By 1000 there was a bit of dawn in the sky. A pale cold light dragged itself over the horizon, and turned the world a dirty gray. The sea was covered with flaky foam, but it no longer sparkled snowy white. Even the foam seemed dirty—like a thin gruel. There was something strangely depressing about this dingy light. It sapped your strength and courage until you didn't care whether you lived or died. Toward noon a kind of sun could be made out—a pale yellow disk that sent out no rays.

When they were relieved at noon, the men were utterly tired and broken. All they could do was collapse on the deck of the control room. For an hour they lay inert, hurtling from side to side; then they tried to remove their outer clothes. But they were too tired and the leather was too heavy. They staggered into the engine room, where it was a few degrees less cold, and despite the pounding of the engines running on "full," they managed to doze a little.

In the afternoon they went back on watch, fortified by two slices of canned bread with a little butter on it, but tired, desperately sleepy, totally frozen, and in a state of mind that fluctuated between utter indifference and a fierce irritability.

On the bridge it was black again. The bedlam of the previous night was repeated. If you gave in to your weariness, you were done for; you had to control your breathing; if you forgot to breathe on time, you stood a good chance of suffocating, because when the boat heeled, it took forever to right itself. And all the while the clumsy steel hulk struggled through the raging sea like a tired whale.

Again there was nothing to be seen—not a star, not one single star. There was only the white foam on the seething sea.

The next day brought no change: nothing warm to eat or drink; no dry clothing, no rest, and always the bitter cold. Bloody welts formed on the men's necks; the frozen collars of their jackets kept scraping at the same places when the men drew in their heads before the unrushing seas and the cutting wind. Their hands had turned into red tongs. After their watch, when they tried to take their clothes off, the blood ran out from under their fingernails, and the salt cut like knives in their open wounds.

Teichmann looked aft and saw that the boat left no visible wake. His eyes grazed the captain's face—a statue of rough-hewn stone, encrusted with salt, seamed with deep furrows—and he saw two red circles as though some blood had been spattered on the stone. And then the stone face crumbled. One little question was all it took. On his way down into the tower, Teichmann turned to the helmsman, and more from habit than from any real curiosity asked him, "What course are you steering?"

"One sixty, sir."

"What's that?"

"One sixty, sir."

"Since when?"

"For the last twenty-four hours."

"I thought the course to the convoy was one sixteen."

"That's news to me, sir."

The course was one sixteen.

The captain gave the order to submerge. He put no one on report. It was impossible to read the bridge compass because of the constant darkness, and in this weather you couldn't read a compass properly anyway, because the needle oscillated fifty degrees in each direction.

For twenty-four hours no one could speak to the captain. His savage, cruel obstinacy—cruel to himself, the crew, his boat—was broken, at least for the moment. The gale had defeated him.

The First Lieutenant was up and about. From time to time, when no one was looking, he contemplated the gap where his ring finger had been. But otherwise he seemed all right, except that he had lost a little weight. He kept his rings in the breast pocket of his shirt. What he had done with his finger he told no one. The exec claimed that he had put it in alcohol. The engineer said he had thrown it into the bilges, and that was why the boat stank so. There was no doubt, in any case, that the stench was growing steadily worse. They had been at sea for eleven weeks.

In the dusk they sighted a ship traveling alone. She was very long and was doing twelve knots. When they came closer, they saw that she was an empty tanker. The ship zigzagged frequently and it took Lüttke four hours to get into position.

The exec fired a spread of three at an unusual angle, bearing one sixty. Two torpedoes hit. The tanker slowed down but kept on going.

Half an hour later they pumped another torpedo into her. The tanker settled a bit but kept on going, at a speed of five knots.

"For God's sake, let's finish her off," said the captain to the exec. "Give her one from the stern tube."

The tanker was hit four times and went right on.

"She's floating on her air bubble. We'll deflate her with the gun."

"Aye, aye, sir."

"Man the flak gun too. I'm sort of expecting a love bird."

"Aye, aye, sir."

Müller was back on duty. The two men who had been washed overboard belonged to the gun crew. Stollenberg and one of the torpedo hands took their places.

At the first shot the gun blew up. Müller had stood on one of the wooden folding seats on the bridge. His head was torn off by an iron fragment. The blood gushed like a fountain from the stump of his neck and the whole bridge was

333

red with it. Müller and the four dead men of the gun crew were thrown overboard. Stollenberg and the boatswain's mate were let down into the control room by lines, while the tanker attacked the sub with her two guns. Lüttke dived.

Stollenberg's right leg was a shapeless mass of flesh; the bone was shattered, the kneecap gone. The exec said the leg would have to be amputated.

They laid him on the table in the petty officers' quarters; it was the longest table in the boat. A tourniquet was applied below the hip; then Wittgenberg held the leg fast and Teichmann sawed through the bone. Stollenberg said he felt no pain, that he felt nothing at all, in fact. The exec said that would come later and placed clamps on the blood vessels. The captain let himself be persuaded to surface for a moment. During this time they threw Stollenberg's leg overboard and filled three buckets with sea water. They poured the water over the stump. Winkler said there was nothing like sea water for disinfecting wounds. Then they bandaged the stump and carried Stollenberg to a bunk in the chiefs' room.

The boatswain's mate was beyond all help. He had suffered internal injuries; when he coughed, he spat blood, and he coughed the whole time. He had great holes in his abdomen, which bled copiously. The blood could not be stopped. His heart was still working. But at the end of two hours there was no blood left; the heart had nothing more to do and stopped pumping. The captain gave permission to put him in an empty torpedo tube.

Müller had been to blame. In reporting the gun ready for action he had forgotten the muzzle cap. The muzzle cap was not simply inserted as in land artillery, but screwed into a thread, to keep out the sea water. The shell just hadn't been able to get out.

Stollenberg was delirious for two days. He rambled on about his school days, and when he woke up he was so convulsed with pain that he had to be held. When he was off duty, Teichmann sat beside his bunk, but there wasn't much time because nine men were missing, and there were

334

only two watches. When the boat was submerged and Teichmann sat at the hydroplane, he could hear Stollenberg. Then Winkler took his place, and he went in to Stollenberg.

On the third day the fever abated. Stollenberg was calm and fully conscious. Teichmann brought his food and tried hard to explain that he had to eat to get his strength back. But Stollenberg would not eat. Teichmann said it was stupid of him not to eat. He filched the last can of strawberries from the galley and poured sweet cream over them. He ate them before Stollenberg's eyes, but even that didn't make Stollenberg hungry. He said he'd like to sleep a bit, maybe he'd be able to eat something later on. "But there won't be any more strawberries; they're all gone," said Teichmann, though the can was still three-quarters full. "It's all one to me," said Stollenberg.

Teichmann went to his bunk in the petty officers' room. Later on the chief electrician's mate shook him awake and said the captain had no objection to their putting the midshipman in a torpedo tube too. "Give us a hand. But make it quick. It doesn't smell like roses in the chiefs' room."

On the way through the Bay of Biscay they had to dive twenty-two times to get away from planes. The return trip took twice as long as scheduled. They had to wait at the rendezvous point a day and a half for two other subs. Then they were escorted into La Pallice by a patrol boat and two minesweepers.

Before the submarine docked the captain made a speech. All the men who were not on watch stood in formation on deck, and the captain spoke for five minutes about the consequences of venereal disease. He said it was unworthy of a Navy man to set foot in a brothel; the married men should wait till they got home, and the unmarried men should practice continence and engage in athletics. No one had ever died of continence; and Frenchwomen were no good anyway; they were no fit company for a German sailor.

The captain's countenance was deadly serious, because in making this speech he was complying with the wishes of the Commanding Admiral of the Submarine Fleet. The admiral believed that captains of naval units should exert a whole-some influence on the private lives of their men. The men knew the speech; the captain made it after every mission. And they knew their captain. When he asked if they had got that straight, they had been in the service long enough to reply with a resounding "Yes, sir."

But the captain had reckoned without Special Services. A whole flock of chorus girls were on hand to welcome the returning submarines. They stood in a row, their feet flush with the edge of the pier, and put on their prettiest smiles. The flotilla's Special Services officer, a man no longer young, had dreamed up this welcome. The girls stared wide-eyed at the bearded seamen, and tossed down flowers. The men stared wide-eyed at the girls, threw them kisses, and, scru-tininzing their undergarments, guessed that it was summer here on shore. A band played, and there were cheering and speeches. The best of all was the ice-cold beer. Each man got a bottle.

Then the submarines put in to the pen. The men cleared their belongings out of the lockers and took the bus to the Prien Compound. There the flotilla commander presided over a dinner attended by the crews of all three boats. There was a good meal, with beer, speeches, and in the end cognac. Lüttke drained off a bottle of soda. It looked bad, but at least it was original. If he had heard the cracks the men made, they would all have gone on report.

After dinner Teichmann had his trunk brought to his room, which he now had all to himself, and set up house-keeping. He was able to buy what he needed in the canteen: two bottles of Hennessy, two bottles of armagnac, a bottle each of Martell and Calvados, and ten packs of cigarettes, six of which he traded for cigars. A sailor helped him to carry the bottles to his room.

Then he went to the shower room and took a generous shower—warm, cold, hot, lukewarm, then as hot as he could stand, and finally cold. He allowed himself an hour. Half the crew was assembled in the shower room, and some of the men indulged themselves still longer. They sang in the shower or groaned voluptuously as they washed away the accumulated grime of three months. Those who were not showering embarked on solemn discussions of how they would spend their time ashore, tossing out numbers that would have won the admiration of a dozen Casanovas. Emerging from the water, Teichmann wrapped his towel round his neck, slipped into bathrobe and slippers, and ran to his room. He lay down on the freshly made bed and lit up a cigarette. As he was inhaling the delicious smoke, there was a knock at the door. "Come in," he called, thinking that if it was one of the chorus girls he wouldn't turn up his nose. But it was a man, who greeted him with a crisp "Heil Hitler."

The man had excellent manners; he introduced himself as a disbursing officer, and handed Teichmann his pay, plus underwater bonus and danger bonus. He counted out the money, although Teichmann told him it wasn't necessary. It was second nature, the man said; he had been a bank director before the war. Teichmann said he was glad to make his acquaintance and reached under the bed where he had stashed away his bottles. The bank director drew a fresh white handkerchief from his pocket and unfolded it, revealing a small glass. It was a custom of the financial world, he confided; a drink or two smoothed off the rough edges, so to speak, and the gentlemen of the Navy recognized this profound truth. When he came to pay the higher ranks, he always brought his little glass along. Teichmann admired the man's sense of the social amenities.

They drank each other's health and began to chat. Teichmann apologized for drinking from the bottle; he hadn't had time to get a glass. The bank director said this manner of drinking was very becoming to Teichmann, and Teichmann thanked him for the compliment. He decided the bank director was a great fellow. And the bank director formed the same opinion of Teichmann.

They drank to the health of Teichmann's captain. When Teichmann told him his captain was a teetotaller, the bank director said that called for two toasts. Then they drank the health of the flotilla commander and the Commanding

337

Admiral of the Submarine Fleet. Then Teichmann reached under the bed and brought out a new bottle. The Führer rated a double toast because he too was a teetotaller. And they drank one or two to Goebbels because his fairy-tale hours on the radio gave them so much pleasure.

The bank director was crocked. He put his glass in his pocket and took his leave with as much formality as his condition permitted. Teichmann also did his best to observe the forms; for him it was easier, because he could do so lying down. He addressed the disbursing officer to the last as "Herr Direktor," although it had come out in the conversation that his drinking companion had run afoul of the Third Reich's currency regulations and spent a few years in the clink. In leave-taking Teichmann presented him with a bottle of Calvados. The beneficiary did not look as if he would partake of his gift in any great hurry. Teichmann was the last man to be paid that day; in fact, the disbursing officer left his payroll and money box on Teichmann's bedside table. Teichmann tossed it all under his bed for safekeeping.

Then he began to read, but it didn't quite work out. The exec had lent him the book—"very witty, something you really have to read." There was a forester in it, but Teichmann couldn't make out what the fellow wanted. The Hennessy is to blame, he said to himself. You're just plain boiled. He sat bolt upright, and commanded himself to read at least ten pages in this position, to prove that he wasn't boiled. But it was a failure. He still could not understand, and when he observed that this book contained sentences with the verb in the singular although there were several subjects, he gave up; it was too much for him. He never did find out what that forester was after, and he was sorry, because he liked foresters.

The worst part of it was that he couldn't sleep. He had lost the habit of sleeping in a bed that didn't move. There was nothing for it but to reach under the bed again.

After a while he dozed off. He was back at sea; he felt like a sea gull riding the waves, and suddenly he understood how gulls are able to sleep on the rolling sea.

14

When he woke up the sun was shining. He blinked for a while and then he read his mail.

Heyne had written from Swinemünde, where he was taking a gunnery course. On the upper left-hand corner of the envelope he had printed in block letters: "Dr. Bauernfeind's Sanatorium." It was his best deal, he wrote, since he had been in the Navy. His boss, Lieutenant Bauernfeind, was a prince of a man, and you could even learn something from him. The place was an oasis, a garden spot; unfortunately, the course was only for three weeks. Otherwise everything was the same. The letter was addressed to Teichmann and Stollenberg.

Bülow too had written. He was well and studying architecture, and when were Teichmann and Stollenberg coming to Hamburg? "To both of you, hearty greetings; from my wife too. Your friend, Bülow." "P.S. Dora would be very glad to see you. She has come up in the world and now owns a movie house."

There was a letter from Tegernsee. Wegener had dictated it to his wife. He and his family were spending their vacation here in Upper Bavaria, and it was lovely. His only regret was that he could not talk about the Navy with the native population. There was a convalescent home for submariners in Wiessee, but he didn't know anybody there.

Teichmann went without breakfast. He located the banker and returned payroll and cashbox. The officer hadn't missed them; he was still asleep. Then Teichmann rode out to the submarine pen.

The flotilla administration had provided two coffins.

"Couldn't you find cheaper one? Those things look as if they'd fall apart any minute."

339

"We aren't an undertaker's establishment."

The two yeomen from flotilla headquarters whom Teichmann had taken along just ran away. When Teichmann opened the breech locks of the torpedo tubes, they said no, they couldn't do it. They were not yet eighteen, and they looked as if their breakfasts wouldn't stay down another minute. They were sincerely apologetic. Teichmann chased them out of the torpedo room, closed the tubes, and went to the port office to telephone. The flotilla medical officer was nowhere to be found. Nor was the chief administrative officer. Finally a pharmacist's mate came to the phone and promised to be there in half an hour with the necessary equipment.

On the way back, Teichmann ran into an old friend. He recognized him from the rear: no two men walked like that, and his head was even bigger because he no longer wore his hair like stubble, but in long waves, and when he turned around Teichmann saw that he had developed a comfortable little paunch. He informed Teichmann that he was assistant administrative officer of the flotilla, and he definitely looked the part. "My boy, I've been getting ahead."

"I can see that."

"What do you mean, *see?* You'd have to hear me. But you don't know any Swahili anyway."

"But aside from that, how are you?"

"I can't complain. First-class food, first-class liquor—I must admit it, that's the way I am, I need my liquor—and women like sand on the seashore."

"And you go wading through it?"

"You're asking old Ramer? I wallow and roll in it, haha."

"Seems to agree with you."

"Just fine."

"How many missions you got?"

"Not a one, so far. Man, don't get that look on your face; I work hard. I'm knee-deep in work. Papers, papers, red tape. In addition to everything else, I'm substituting for the Deceased Property Officer, and you can't even imagine all the work that gives me. But for you I'll shut up shop. Dinner's on me."

Teichmann spoke of the job he had to do, and Ramer offered to help him. Wait till he sees, Teichmann thought.

When he saw, he felt pretty queasy but he stuck to his intention of helping, merely suggesting that they get something under their belts first, preferably a spot of liquor. Not a bad idea, said Teichmann, but before drinking he would require a bite to eat; he had had no breakfast.

Teichmann gave the dock workers a few cigarettes and received a big helping of potato soup in return. After that he drank a bottle of champagne with Ramer. An ideal combination, Ramer said. Where he had got the champagne so quickly he didn't say.

When they reached the sub, the pharmacist's mate was already there. He had brought a small saw, various knives and forceps, and an enormous instrument that looked like a chisel. "It's always the same old crap," he said. "It's a waste of breath telling submarine captains not to put stiffs in the torpedo tubes; it ain't the captains that have to get them out again." Teichmann told the man to mind his tongue. "Hell," said the pharmacist's mate. "I won't say anything against your dead buddy. All I can tell you is this: it *was* your buddy."

They began to work, speaking little. Ramer, who was working on the boatswain's mate, said, "How far have you got with yours?"

"Hell," said Teichmann. He had to laugh: there was nothing else to do when you wanted to cry like a baby. The more they worked the more they cursed; they wallowed in obscenity and listened gratefully to the cynical remarks of the pharmacist's mate, who referred to the whole business as a large-scale abortion.

When they were about half through, they washed their hands in a pail of water in order to remove their shirts. Then, bare to the waist, they worked their way deeper into the tubes. At first they were sick at their stomachs, but after they had thrown up a few times they got used to it.

341

After three hours of toil, the tubes were empty. Not clean, but empty.

Then they set out for the whorehouse. As midshipmen, they were entitled to frequent the officers' brothel. Ramer had spoken of a woman called La Jaune—a cross between a Malay and a mulatto, or maybe some kind of creole. Anyway, she wore a transparent lemon-yellow dress and nothing else; her hair was pitch-black, her bosom was painted, and . . . "That's enough," Teichmann had said. "She's just what I need."

"Hell, somebody got here ahead of us," said Ramer as they entered.

"That woman has class. Yes, she's really got class, but the character with her is my captain."

"That's Lüttke?"

"Yes. It so happens."

"Is that bad?"

"Hell, no. But we'd better come back later."

They went out again. Ramer scratched his belly and said, "Maybe you're too optimistic. She's expensive too and we're only midshipmen."

"She doesn't go for rank. I don't think so anyway."

"What does she go for?"

"Looks, maybe."

"No, that I don't believe. It's out of the question. What she goes for is money," said Ramer and scratched his belly again, more perseveringly than the first time.

"You got fleas?"

"No—but what I was saying: do you happen to have any money?"

"I can manage," said Teichmann, with a sidelong glance at Ramer.

"Can you lend me some?"

"Not for La Jaune."

"That's too bad," said Ramer. "But on the other hand, if you're right that she's not keen on money but prizes other qualities, I won't need any to make time with her. No, not I."

"I wouldn't say that for myself. I certainly need a little

342

money. She won't even look at me if I have no dough at all. So you see that I can't lend you very much. You understand, don't you?"

Ramer lit a cigarette.

"What are you going to write his parents?"

"I won't say anything about the amputation. I'll write that he was killed on deck and I'll say he died instantly." Teichmann spoke more rapidly than usual.

"What date are you going to give? I've got to know because of being D.P.O."

"The right one. I don't imagine his parents will ever see the War Diary. As long as they don't open the coffin, it'll be all right."

"I don't think they'll open it. I'd . . . Say, who's that?"

"Ah-ha, puts your eye out, eh?"

"Lord in heaven, look at the way he walks."

"That's the handsomest man in the Navy: His Excellency Ehrenfried Berthold Prinz von Wittgenberg-Weissenstein."

"How do you come to know him?"

"Our exec."

"How do I address him?"

"Not in Swahili."

The exec came striding up, every bit the prince. He wore an impeccably fitting blue uniform of the finest serge; his weatherbeaten neck was framed in a resplendent white shirt with an open collar so cut as to disclose a bit of the curly hair on his chest. He wore freshly whitened tennis shoes, almost covered by his ample trouser legs. In his left hand he held his cap like an opera hat, and in his right he swung a cane. But the most striking part of his costume was the decorations. On the left breast there was nothing. But on the right breast there was a delicate gold embroidery representing the German Cross, and the Iron Cross Second-Class dangled like a pendulum on a long black, white, and red ribbon affixed to the topmost buttonhole of his jacket. In his breast pocket he had a white silk handkerchief folded in the shape of a fan.

"No ovations, gentlemen, I know how I look. And how did you spend your first night?"

"Seriously. Reading Ernst Jünger."

"Splendid, splendid. And now, if my eyes do not deceive me, you have been frequenting a distinguished house."

"Yes, a nice place," said Teichmann. "But nothing came of it. Do you know La Jaune?"

"I have not yet had the pleasure of meeting that eminent artist. But I've heard of her."

"Our captain is having the pleasure right now."

"Really? Has he had the pleasure or is it still to come? I mean . . ."

"Still to come. He's sitting with her."

"Ah, still sitting . . . ah-ha!" The exec plucked at his chin, then he began to rub it. "I've got a kind of an idea: why don't we go and watch him?"

"He won't like it," said Ramer.

"But think of our point of view," said the exec.

"Let's make it fast, then," said Teichmann, "before they go upstairs." And they started off at a rapid pace.

On their forced march to the brothel they accidentally jostled a middle-aged Air Force major who was heading somewhat hesitantly and uncertainly in the same direction. "Damn it all, men," he cried, "where's the fire?"

"We're on our way to the brothel, sir," said Teichmann.

The major was rather taken aback. "Outrageous!" he called after them. "There's the Navy for you. It's typical."

"He would have been mighty glad to come along with us," said Wittgenberg. "He looked unhappy."

They were on time. The exec headed directly for La Jaune, made a perfect bow, mumbled part of his name, and said, *"Je suis très heureux de vous connaître, madame."*

La Jaune nodded. The exec introduced his companions. For the first time Teichmann saw his captain at a loss. For the present he merely sucked in the air very audibly through his eagle beak.

"Permettez, madame, que je m'installe à côté de vous," said the exec, and sat down beside her. *"Mais j'avais oublié de vous présenter mon capitaine."*

"What did he say?"

"He introduced you to the lady, sir," said Teichmann.

"None of your insolence, Wittgenberg," said the captain.

"I didn't mean to offend you, sir," said the exec. "But if you need an interpreter . . ."

"I do not need an interpreter."

"Mais votre prononciation est excellente," said La Jaune to the exec.

"He is one of my subordinates, madame," said the captain in English.

"Ma bouche sait encore autre chose que de parler français," said the exec.

"Je veux bien le croire," said La Jaune, looking like a lioness who has not yet made up her mind which chunk of meat to devour first.

"What did he say?"

"The executive officer said he could whistle too, sir," said Teichmann.

"What does that mean? What is he going to whistle with?"

"With my mouth of course. What did you suppose, sir?" said Wittgenberg.

This went on for an hour. The captain spoke English, the exec French; Teichmann translated, and since no one knew Swahili, Ramer just listened. La Jaune was enjoying herself immensely. They drank some sticky peppermint liqueur that La Jaune had ordered—it stimulated the conversation, and that wasn't all it stimulated. From time to time the Air Force major came over and drank their health. He was very pleased to have friends in this perilous spot, and he drank repeatedly to the Navy. Then he went back to his table, which he shared with a lady approximating his own years. The exec ordered a bottle of soda.

"Le capitaine adhère à l'abstinence, madame," said the exec.

"Qu'est-ce que cela veut dire?" asked La Jaune.

"Cela veut dire qu'il s'abstient."

"What's he saying?"

"He says that you are abstinent, sir," said Teichmann.

"From you, Wittgenberg," said the captain, "I would have expected better manners."

"De quoi s'abstient-il?" asked La Jaune.

"What's she saying?"

"She wants to know what you abstain from," said Teichmann.

"Madame, I do not . . ."

"*De tout mal, madame,*" said the exec.

"*Alors qu'est-ce qu'il fait ici?*"

"Madame, I am only drinking with you as an act of politeness."

"*Voulez-vous que je lui demande, madame?*" asked the exec.

"*S'il vous plaît.*"

"Sir," said the exec, "Madame would like to know what you are doing here."

For the second time the captain was at a loss. Finally he shouted at the exec. "What are *you* doing here?"

"I intend to rest my weary bones with this lady, sir."

"Rest—ha!"

"*Qu'est-ce qu'il dit, votre capitaine?*" asked La Jaune.

"*Il ne comprend pas que nous voulons nous reposer, madame.*"

"What's he saying?"

'He says, sir, that you fail to understand that Madame and the executive officer wish to rest," said Teichmann.

"Rest—ha!"

"*Qu'est-ce qu'il a, votre capitaine?*" asked La Jaune.

"*Il est très ardent, brûlant, chaud . . .*"

"*Je le vois,*" said La Jaune.

"Madame, he is drunk."

"Oh, I have not the impression, *mon capitaine,*" said La Jaune.

"*Capitaine* means captain, sir," said Teichmann.

"Imagine!" said Lüttke, snorting violently.

"I suggest we throw dice," said Teichmann.

"It's getting to be time for you to disappear," said the captain.

"Oh no, sir. I'm spending the night here."

"So am I," said the captain.

"*Qu'est-ce qu'il dit, votre capitaine?*" aked La Jaune.

"Il dit qu'il veut dormir, étant fatigué, madame," said the exec.

"What does he say?"

"The executive officer says you are tired and wish to go to bed, sir," said Teichmann.

"Bon soir, mon capitaine," said La Jaune.

"What—"

"Madame wishes you a very good evening and a restful night," the exec translated.

Lüttke muttered something about "bad company," took his hat, and left. He teetered slightly; the bit of alcohol he had imbibed to please La Jaune had not agreed with him.

La Jaune didn't seem entirely satisfied with this solution; she had expected the captain to take up with one of her associates.

"Gentlemen," said Wittgenberg, "this is a significant moment. It is probably the only time our captain has ever beaten a retreat. Let us raise a glass to his health and honor."

The major came back to their table and asked leave to drink the health of his good old comrade from the Navy. They permitted him to do so. The major was in seventh heaven and drank so generously to the health of the Navy that his lady had to steer him away from their table.

"Time to throw the dice," said Teichmann.

"I don't think such an important matter should be left to chance," said Ramer. "After all, it was my idea to come here in the first place." He didn't sound very convincing.

"It seems to me," said the exec, "that the dice have already fallen." Secretly Teichmann thought he was probably right, but the idea irked him, for this La Jaune seemed very desirable. Even if you hadn't spent the last three months at sea, even if you hadn't been drinking, she would have been desirable.

"You think the whole thing is settled because your captain has been eliminated," said Ramer to Wittgenberg. "But I wish to repeat that I made the suggestion, and no one else . . ."

"That's the truth, my friend, and I shall always be beholden to you for such a fine suggestion. But what can we do in view of the fact that the lady prefers me?"

Suddenly La Jaune, who had been sitting silent and seemingly bored during this dialogue, opened her mouth and spoke German: "Gentlemens, you 'ear I spik pretty well Zjerman. I 'ave learn zis *langage* in my profession, *n'est-ce pas,* and I . . ."

"Did you understand what we were just saying?" asked the exec, somewhat alarmed.

"Oh, eet was verry nice. But now it eez for me to shoose, no?"

"Why, certainly, madame," said the exec, his spirits reviving.

"*Bien,* I vood like zis one."

Wittgenberg's brown neck turned red, his face grew suddenly apoplectic, and his hands played the piano on his knees.

"Oh, do not be *offensé,* my *chéri,* you loook verry nice, and are very *charmant,* you 'ave many advantage, you speak verry goood French and many many sings—but he is strongair, *compris?*"

"*Force majeure, mon prince,*" said Teichmann.

She was a real whore, a whore for the pleasure of it—from vocation, so to speak. And she was more: she was one of those women who in all their bodily nakedness preserve a kind of secret that no man can decipher—or at least Teichmann felt that this was so. She wore nothing but a red coral neckless and a little wrist watch. Teichmann possessed her body, the slender, supple body of a dancer. Her golden bronze skin felt like a ripe peach. Her body was totally hairless and free from powder. He possessed her body, but that was all he possessed. And when he thought that she belonged to him entirely—as he did for brief moments—she slipped away from him in some inexplicable way. One of her professional tricks, Teichmann thought. In any event it was a successful trick that goaded him to conquer her over and over again, and all the surprising, wild, pleasurable discoveries that he made were mere fragments of a whole that remained unattainable. The woman remained the victor, and the more often she gave herself to him, the more manifest was her victory.

348

But it was not always the same victory: she gave it different forms.

Later she said he could spend the night with her. When he did not reply, she asked him if he accepted all distinctions so silently.

"Distinctions?"

"Zat was my Iron Cross."

"Haven't you got something better? Pour le Mérite, or something of that sort?"

"Oh, Pour le Mérite is good, verry good. I vil give you it, but only after many Iron Cross, *compris?*"

"I want the Pour le Mérite."

"Oui, but ze night is long. . . ."

But then there was a disturbing incident. Calm and relaxed, the two of them lay side by side. Meaningless questions had been asked and meaningless answers given; cigarettes had been smoked and cognac drunk. Then the woman stood up—to put on fresh perfume. Avoiding the awkward, childlike gait of naked, barefoot women who set down their whole foot at once, she walked on tiptoes. And suddenly it occurred to her to ask him for a picture of himself. He had none. In vain he poked around in his billfold. He only had the photograph in his paybook, but he couldn't give that away. This she did not understand; she wanted the picture, she said, it was all she wanted of him; he could keep his money. It struck Teichmann as funny; this was a new way of paying, and he would rather have done it with money. Finally he discovered in his billfold a group photograph taken at the boot camp. She studied the picture very attentively. She would point to one or another of his comrades and in her halting, ludicrous German make some remark about their virility. Then her long, pointed, red-laquered fingernail came to rest on a good-natured, childlike face, and Teichmann began to tremble all over. His hands clutched at the pillow and he buried his face in it, moaning softly . . .

At first the woman cried out *"Mon Dieu,"* but then she fell silent and rested her hand on his head. She sat there waiting, from time to time casting a glance at her watch.

349

When he had quieted down, she lit a cigarette, pulled his head up by the hair, and stuck the cigarette between his lips. That made it impossible for him to bury his face in the pillow. He lay on his side and through the cigarette smoke surveyed two steeply rising hills surmounted by observation towers.

"Has he long been dead?"

"No."

"Out on ze sea?"

"No. Some of him is floating around the water outside the submarine pen, and some of him is nailed up in some miserable boards."

"I am verry sorry *pour toi* and . . ."

"Who shaves you so clean anyway?"

"You 'ave not many camarades, *n'est-ce pas?*"

"Oh yes, yes . . ."

"Zen you not always all alone?"

"No, no. I'm not alone; not now, no . . ."

When he went away in the morning, he had a pleasantly empty, light feeling in his loins and a clear head. La Rochelle was asleep as he made his way home to the Prien Compound. Everything was silent and a little blurred; a spring mist hung over the city, refreshingly cool, and if the streets hadn't been so dirty it could have been a German town. But the smell was different. There was something drowsy about it, like a musky perfume; and there was the salt and rot of the sea, the pungent, cloying smell of moldering seaweed. But it was a pleasant smell. Teichmann was thinking about it when he felt a cold puff of wind in his face and a small hard object hit him in the chest. It didn't hurt particularly. And then he heard the shot.

He flung himself to the ground. It just grazed me, he said to himself. He heard steps and he heard his heart beating against the stone pavement. The stone felt like ice. His face lay flat on the ground and he saw a little eddy of dust in front of his nose as he breathed out. For a moment he was annoyed at the thought that his hands were getting dirty.

There were two men. He lay still. They moved as lightly as

cats. They ran toward him. I'm unarmed, he thought. I haven't even a knife. I'll play dead.

One of the men was over him. He reeked of liquor. When the man leaned down and belched, Teichmann noticed that it was absinth. Like a scythe cutting only a hair's breadth above the ground, he swung out and knocked the man's feet from under him. The man fell, a metallic object clanged on the cobblestones, and the man said *"Merde"* and something else that Teichmann did not understand. Without reflecting, Teichmann beat the man's head against the cobblestones—twice in quick succession. Then he ran after the other man.

The man ran very fast. But I'll last longer, Teichmann thought, and ran as fast as he could. The Frenchman was small and quick as a greyhound. He was running for his life, and that gave him extra speed. Teichmann had forgotten his night's exertions; he had a violent stitch in the side although he had only been running for two or three minutes. Besides, he had been shut up in a steel tube for three months. As he ran, he noticed that he was lost; the neighborhood was unfamiliar to him. Maybe he's drawing me into an ambush, he thought, and slowed down. The distance between them increased. He was going to give up, but then the Frenchman turned about and ran toward him, as though he suddenly felt strong enough to attack his pursuer. Teichmann stopped short. Something cold and prickly ran down his back. He held his breath and saw the Frenchman's blackjack, and for a second he saw the face, which seemed to be made of pure fear. With the thought, He's more scared than I am, he sprang.

The Frenchman swung long before Teichmann was within reach. When he raised his blackjack to strike again, Teichmann seized the upraised arm from below. It was the simplest of all judo holds; the blackjack fell to the street. The Frenchman went stiff with terror. And then Teichmann's fists struck him as though to smash his face into little pieces.

"That's enough, boy. There won't be anything left of him." Teichmann felt himself pulled away. "Excuse me, sir, what happened?"

"Oh, the night patrol! Well, it's damn nice of you to get here."

"What's that?"

"Oh hell, I'm sorry," said Teichmann, and paused for a breath.

"He came running toward us, and then he suddenly turned around and . . ."

"And ran at me," said Teichmann. "But he'd already taken a pot shot at me."

The night patrol consisted of a petty officer and a seaman first-class. He told them what had happened. They picked the Frenchman up. He looked as if he had been lying in a puddle of red ink, and they had to carry him.

The other Frenchman had not stirred. He was still on his knees with his head on the ground. Like Esch in the washroom on Christmas Eve, Teichmann thought. The man was dead.

Teichmann picked up his cap. The revolver was a little farther off. The petty officer picked it up. It was a German make; there were still five shots in it. "Some people are lucky," said the petty officer. Teichmann furnished his name, unit, and present address.

On the way to the Prien Compound he was seized by fear. Unexpectedly and for no good reason, he began to be terrified. He didn't know where the fear came from or how he was going to get rid of it. It all seemed pretty complicated, and without troubling his head any further he hastened his steps. In the end he was running. He had forgotten all about La Jaune.

He stood under the shower and examined the dark spot under his right nipple. He was rubbing it when they came for him. "Get dressed on the double and come along. It's important." They were very excited.

"A rotten business. You've been mighty lucky."

"Maybe I just had harder fists, sir."

"It's all in how you look at it."

"Well, that's how I look at it," said Teichmann without great conviction. The car stopped in front of the Kommandantur. "Anyway, you can be glad that you're still alive," said the lieutenant and got out. "I am," said Teichmann. The last to alight was the potbellied technical sergeant, who was sitting in front beside the driver. Teichmann was led to a room where an Army captain and a Navy medical officer were sitting pale and nervous on the table. The medical officer seemed rather the calmer of the two.

"Have you had breakfast?" the captain asked.

"No," said Teichmann.

"Then hold on," said the medical officer, and led Teichmann, followed by the Army captain and the Navy lieutenant and the tech sergeant, into the next room.

"Do you know any of these men?" asked the lieutenant. "Take a good look. You must know them. They were enjoying themselves in the same house as you, at the same time." "Except that they left sooner," said the medical officer. "This is exactly how we found them," said the lieutenant. "Take your time," said the tech sergeant. "And this has to happen just when I'm officer of the day," said the lieutenant. "It's disgusting," said the medical officer. The captain gnawed his fingernails and said nothing.

Teichmann didn't recognize any of them.

"Look closely. You must know them," said the lieutenant impatiently.

"That brown mess comes from acid," said the technical sergeant. "Yes, they must have used acid."

"I'll take their privates out of their mouths," said the medical officer.

"But you'll have to put them back afterwards," said the captain. "They haven't been photographed yet."

This made them no more recognizable. Only the opening that had formerly been a mouth with lips, tongue, and teeth had now become larger. There were other holes in the irregular black spheres, but the former mouth was the largest opening.

They all looked the same and smelled bad. The smallest corpse still had a little blood in it and had not yet turned black. One had corns; an oblique stripe of sunlight fell right on them. "Must have been an older fellow," said Teichmann. "Where are the uniforms?"

"Gone," said the lieutenant. "No sign of them," said the tech sergeant. He sounded as if this pleased him in some way.

They all looked at Teichmann. He looked at each of the three corpses in turn. He heard someone lighting a cigarette behind his back. That must be the driver, he thought. Outside in the street a car made a sharp turn, its tires scraping the street; the tech sergeant strode slowly to the window. Teichmann heard him say, "That fella had luck."

He moved slowly about the corpses, examining the heads from different sides. There was a bit of hair in places, and in the end he recognized Ramer's hair. It belonged to the small corpse that was still relatively fresh. He felt pretty sure it was Ramer's hair because it was so long. It looked black like dried blood.

"Well, that's one, at least," said the tech sergeant.

"Call up Schepke House," Teichmann said to the tech sergeant, "and ask if Lieutenant Prince von Wittgenberg is there."

"What's the name?"

"Wittgenberg. Prince von Wittgenberg-Weissenstein."

"What do I call him?"

"Hell, you don't have to speak to him; just ask if he's there. For God's sake, don't make such a fuss."

"I'm not taking orders from any midshipman."

"Then I'll do it myself."

"Go ahead and telephone," said the lieutenant to the sergeant, who went off grumbling. He could be heard telephoning in the adjoining room.

"Was he there too?" asked the medical officer.

"Yes, but I don't know when he left. May I open a window?"

"Of course," said the captain.

The technical sergeant stuck his head through the door and said, "The prince himself is coming to the phone—I still don't know how to address him. Won't you tell me, please?" He was greatly perturbed.

"Call him sir," said Teichmann.

The head went back to the telephone. He could be heard

354

speaking High German—he was from the Palatinate—and under other circumstances everyone would have laughed. Then he hung up and came back very much relieved, rubbing his belly with his sausagelike fingers. "The prince is very nice," he said to Teichmann. "Really nice, and so polite. Have you known him a long time?"

"Who did it?" asked Teichmann, startled at the loudness of his own voice.

"The French, of course. Who'd you think?" said the medical officer, shrugging his shoulders.

"The swine!" said Teichmann, his voice growing still louder. "That's the only way they know how to make war. I thought they had signed an armistice. Attacking at night and from behind, drinking to give themselves courage—the cowardly dogs. Ramer was a friend of mine. . . ."

"Yes, it's sad," said the captain.

"Those swine, those dirty swine. And what's going to happen to them?"

"The most we can do is shoot them," said the tech sergeant. "If we catch them," said the lieutenant.

"You ought to skin them alive, half an inch a day. And when they pass out, you stop until they come to, and . . ."

"Cigarette?"

"Hell . . . And then you begin all over again. Or you could boil them in water, and just as they're beginning to die you turn the fire out . . ."

"Don't you want a cigarette?"

"No, thank you. Listen to what I'm saying." He seized the captain by the buttons of his uniform. "You mustn't kill them right off, you promise me that. It wouldn't be right . . . the lousy murderers. They aren't soldiers, they're murderers. They're . . ."

"Yes, yes, it's terrible," said the captain and tried to free himself.

"Where's that Frenchman? Where's my Frenchman? The swine belongs to me. I'll deal with him, see. Nobody's going to take him away from me. Where is he? He's not going to be tried by any court; he's mine, I'll . . ."

"Take it easy, son. Take a vacation," said the medical

355

officer. He laid a hand on Teichmann's shoulder, releasing the captain, who sighed with relief.

Teichmann left the Kommandantur. Everything around him was like absorbent cotton. His feet walked on cotton and felt like cotton, and his throat was stopped up with a great wad of cotton that made him gag. He could think of nothing and was amazed to find himself suddenly at the Prien Compound, bathed in sweat. He went to the shower room; the shower was still running. When he left the room soon after, he heard the men laughing behind him, "Say, he must have a load." "In broad daylight." "Under the shower in full uniform." "Man, I'd like to be that boiled sometime."

La Jaune was shot four days later. She and the other girls in the house had arranged to dismiss the victims from their beds at suitable intervals so that the murderers should not have too much work at once. The first victim was the Air Force major, the corpse with the corns. His needs had been quickly satisfied. The next had been Ramer, and the third had been the engineering officer of a submarine; they were particularly keen on submariners. Teichmann was to have been the last. Lüttke and the exec had been lucky. Furious at his rebuff, Wittgenberg had gone back to Schepke House and got drunk; Lüttke was already so tight that he had barely managed to topple into his bunk. Two other whores and the Frenchman whom Teichmann had caught were also shot.

Teichmann was furious that La Jaune had only been shot. To down his rage he drank. He drank for several days, always managing to find a few companions. But Stollenberg was no longer there, and the drinking didn't help. And then there was a letter that helped.

South of the river Main the Navy was almost unknown, and a Navy officer could expect to be taken for a station-master or some kind of policeman.

It started in Munich. At the main station a colonel of the Alpine troops applied to him for information about trains to Leipzig. When he noticed his mistake, he said, "Oh, I beg your pardon, comrade." Teichmann was forewarned. All this had been a familiar joke at the Naval Academy. He didn't mind, as long as he wasn't asked to carry baggage. He made his way to the Holzkirchen station. The conductor gave him a second-class compartment, saying that officers, and captains it went without saying, were entitled to travel second class—this with a glance at the two stars on Teichmann's shoulder straps (he had meanwhile been promoted to senior midshipman). Teichmann made no attempt to disabuse him; he had no objection to the upholstered seat. As long as an admiral doesn't get in, he thought, I might just as well stay here.

He got off at Tegrensee and went to the boat dock. The boatman raised his hand to his cap and said, "Heil Hitler, Captain." Teichmann replied, "Heil, fellow mariner."

As he sat waiting for the boat to start, he decided that he had no cause for dissatisfaction at his reception in Bavaria: in less than two hours he had risen from railroad clerk to captain. Perhaps his promotion called for a cigar. He still had a black Brazil, captured goods. As he smoked it, he reflected that he might just as well have gone to Royan or Biarritz, but he was sick of being alone and always seeing the same faces, of playing ping-pong and swimming, and drinking to work up enthusiasm over the native women. It was all right to come here, he told himself; you're not intruding, you were invited, it would have been rude to refuse. And the country seems to be nice; there's even a bit of water.

It was evening. On the mountains lay the last rays of the sun, clothing the summits in flaming purple and gold. The mountains stood there like kings, and the lake, tranquil and blue, lay at their feet. In the Bay of Egern two white, pointed triangles—sails—lay still in the evening silence.

Teichmann saw it all. And when the boat was in the middle of the lake the bells of Tegernsee, Wiessee, and Rottach-Egern joined together, ringing in the Sunday. But even as they rang, he said aloud, "It's all cold coffee." He said it again to dispel any possible doubt. The whole thing is a trick, he said to himself and drew hard on his cigar; it's just the lake and the mountains with their interesting sound effects; that's all there is to it and it's damn little help to you and none at all to your dead comrades. He spat into the lake and tossed his cigar away.

When the boat tied up at Wiessee, the sun had vanished, the kings were mountains again, cold gloomy, and alien, and the bells had stopped ringing. The darkness fell quickly.

The Submariners' Hostel in Wiessee was overcrowded—not a room to be had. In Tegernsee and Rottach-Egern there were still a few rooms available for Navy men, but unfortunately, the manager of the hostel told him, he wouldn't be with his comrades.

In Tegernsee Teichmann was given a pleasant room on the lake front in one of the few hotels that were still open to civilians. He inquired where the Riederstein-Strasse was, and went to bed.

He tried to sleep, but nothing came of it. The bed was too short and too soft. In the early morning he sat by the window and watched the ferryman. The dock was only a few yards away. At the stroke of six the ferry appeared. There was not a single passenger and there was not a living soul on the dock; and on the whole lake there was no other craft afloat. Nevertheless the boatman loudly rang the prescribed signal—one long, one short—and came alongside the dock. Then he signaled again and paddled off in the direction of Wiessee. Later, when he returned from his solitary tour of the lake, he sounded his signal as though a dozen steamers were blocking his way to the dock. Then he was off again—one long, two short—still without passengers. A little after seven his first passenger appeared, a peasant woman, who was honored with the same military salute as Teichmann.

Teichmann washed and shaved. Then he put on his freshly brushed uniform and left the hotel. In a stationery store he bought the *Deutsche Allgemeine Zeitung*, a crime thriller, and some writing paper. The *DAZ* was two days old, the book was bound in such a way that the slightest false move left you with a handful of loose papers, and the stationery was like toilet tissue. But it was Sunday and he was lucky to get anything at all.

Then he went to breakfast. He had a place at the window with a view of the lake, but the breakfast was poor; the coffee reminded him of the darkest days in the boot camp. Still, there was a tablecloth that had once been white and a friendly waitress who managed to speak High German when she observed that Teichmann was unmarried and not a Bavarian. She spoke it with a slight accent that seemed calculated to encourage the tourist trade—it was the nicest thing about her.

After breakfast he wrote a few lines to Heyne and to Bülow, with a pencil because the point of his pen stuck in the paper. He was due at the Wegeners' for lunch, but he was a few minutes late; he had underestimated the distance and it took him some time to find a flower shop.

The greetings went off smoothly; the Wegeners had acquired a dog, and Teichmann made friends with him at once. Then came lunch, and after lunch the child appeared. Teichmann couldn't say whom it resembled; to him all babies looked the same, but he didn't say so. He said it was a beautiful child. "But you prefer the dog," said Frau Wegener. Her husband had artificial arms, which he handled skillfully. He could put his pipe in his mouth, though his wife or the maid had to fill it.

In the afternoon Teichmann spoke about submarines. Wegener asked many questions which Teichmann answered as precisely and exhaustively as possible. That took time, the subject was technical, and Frau Wegener could only listen. But then the topic was exhausted and at supper there was wine and champagne. Teichmann felt uneasy, for now Frau Wegener joined in the conversation and she had taken a bit too much to drink. She spoke quickly, with animation, and now and then there was an undertone of irritation in her replies to her husband. At midnight Teichmann took his leave. Frau Wegener accompanied him to the garden gate. He was glad that the dog was there. When she gave him her hand, the dog sprang between them; he bent down and stroked him. He had to hold his cap in his left hand. She called the dog, although he was at her feet. Then she went back to the house and the dog jumped up on her.

Teichmann went down the Riederstein-Strasse swinging his cap with exaggerated gusto. Back at the hotel, he went straight to bed. At six o'clock sharp the ferry arrived from Rottach-Egern.

In the afternoon they went sailing. Wegener sat in the bow, his wife and Teichmann to leeward. For a time they sat facing each other. He felt like a little boy making his first anatomical studies. He looked at Wegener.

Wegener enjoyed himself, even without eyes. He seemed to see with his nose. He turned his head in different directions, and his wife named the villages or mountains. "It must be very beautiful," said Wegener.

Once when a yawl crossed their bow, Frau Wegener said, "Who has precedence?" "They do," said Teichmann. "It's not precedence," said Wegener, "it's right of way." "I'll never learn that," said his wife.

At dinner Teichmann drank a good deal. Wegener told amusing stories about his training as a midshipman. Frau Wegener was very vivacious and drank alarmingly. With every glass she downed Teichmann felt more uncomfortable; he was afraid that she would slip out of her role, and did his best to keep the conversation on neutral subjects. He was sorry, he said, that he could not have had midshipman's training in peacetime. Yes, he said, that must have been a fine thing, and the cruises on the training schooners must have been wonderful, a fine way to see the world. Even as it was, he said, he had enjoyed his life in the boot camp—those had been carefree days; no responsibility, your head was still full of pipe dreams, that is, he meant to say . . .

"But the rough training kept the foolish ideas from getting out of hand?"

"Why, Edith, you always felt sorry for the boys in Dänholm."

"What makes you say that?"

"She won't admit it now, but at the time she called me a slavedriver just because I made you fellows sweat a little."

Teichmann looked at his watch, quite openly.

"Some of the boys in your company were delicate."

"They were in the third platoon. We weren't very hard on them," said Wegener.

"But you took it out on us of the first," said Teichmann, who felt that he ought to say something.

"If the first platoon is bad, the whole company is bad."

"So you see that someone felt sorry for you," said Frau Wegener. "That's a help, isn't it?" And it went on for a while in this tone.

She started it, thought Teichmann; she struck up this tone. No, it began with her coming down in a new dress. Still, there's nothing wrong with the dress, except that it's beautiful. But any dress is beautiful on her. Well, just the same, she would have made things easier for me by not wearing that dress. And she doesn't need to keep crossing her legs that way. And anyway, she's drunk. . . .

She was not drunk. When Teichmann neglected to fill her glass, she stood up. But before leaving the room she looked him in the eye and said to her husband, "I wish you would come up with me now."

"Yes, it's getting late," said Wegener. He stood up and followed her, cautiously holding out his artificial arms to feel his way to the door. "Thank you, my husband can find his way alone," she said when Teichmann tried to help him; and as she spoke, she looked at her blind husband with an expression that threw Teichmann out of the house. At the door she turned around and said, "Sleep well, Herr Teichmann." And her eyes mocked him. "Good-by until tomorrow," said Wegener.

Well, she's drunk. That can happen. But she's a bitch. And I'm going to take her. To hell with what happens afterward. In any case I'm the stronger. And while I'm doing it I won't think anything at all. That's the best way. Deal out the blows, don't worry who gets hit. Even if you have to take a few blows yourself. That's the price you pay. The only thing that matters is who strikes last. To hell with all the moral ballast. Chuck it overboard. If you don't you're lost. I'll take her, I'll take a cripple's wife, damn it all, I'll . . .

He mumbled on in this vein all the way back to his room.

The next morning he left. He wrote a card saying he had received a telegram recalling him to duty. He sent a boy to the Riederstein-Strasse with the card, and instructed him to buy flowers on the way, twenty-four of them, it didn't matter what kind, but there must be twenty-four and they must be red. *He'll* only be able to smell them, he thought.

The thought lingered in his mind. Then suddenly it threw him into a rage, but it was too late to run after the boy.

At noon he went to the station. He failed to salute an Army captain and answered rudely when called to account; his name was taken. Outside the station he almost knocked over an important Nazi official, but the official only swore at him.

The train was there when Teichmann pushed through the gate. The platform was full of people trying to crowd aboard.

"I knew you'd go away—even before the card came."

As the train began to move, she said, "Don't come again, please. Never again, please . . ." And she ran a few steps beside the train.

15

Timmler was not with them on the next trip. He showed everyone who crossed his path a letter from the Reich Motion Picture Bureau, to the effect that he had been ordered to Berlin to write a scenario for a picture about submarines.

Langen, the new engineering officer—the captain had got rid of the old one—was a strange man. He had a face like a lump of dough and usually kept his mouth open, and this, with his broad, yellow, equine teeth, gave him a singularly foolish look. When Teichmann met him for the first time, he took him for a longshoreman. He had on a frayed, faded pullover that didn't even reach to his waist; his head was bare, his hair mussed, and his pants legs made you think of stovepipes. When Teichmann introduced himself, the engineer held out a hand the size of a toilet seat, and nodded.

But this man, who looked as if he couldn't count to three, had managed to escape from an English prison camp, and, as his paybook revealed, he was the son of a high diplomat. Once when this bit of information was brought up at mess, he said gravely, "My mother must have been carrying on with the plumber in those days. Yes, when I look at myself in the mirror, that seems to be the only explanation. Because my father really does look like an ambassador."

An embarrassed silence followed and Teichmann said, "You have a sense of humor."

"Did you expect me to weep?" said Langen, and from that day on they knew that he was not the way he looked.

Two days before sailing, a new first lieutenant came aboard. As he was reporting for duty, Lüttke said, "Don't whisper. I didn't get your name."

"Ensign Petersen, sir."

"Damn it, speak up. I'm damned if I'll strain my ears on your account."

"I've got a splinter in my throat, sir. I can't speak any louder."

"What kind of splinter?"

"A shell splinter, sir. It's a very small one, but they can't get it out. The doctors say . . ."

"What the doctors say doesn't interest me in the least. I expect you to speak loudly and distinctly. That death rattle of yours doesn't amuse me one bit."

"Aye, aye, sir."

"That was better, but there's still room for improvement. I'll make a man of you yet. And now you have a little talk with the exec. He'll tell you how to keep out of my bad books."

Timmler came to report his departure.

"I should have been happier," said Lüttke, "if you had made that announcement the day you were assigned to my boat, Herr Timmler. I only hope that I never have to see your film. If you could manage so that no submariners appear in it, we'd all be very grateful. Regulations require me to give you an endorsement. It consists of one sentence. Here it is."

Timmler blanched as he read the sentence: "While the crew fought, Herr Doktor Timmler soiled his pants. (signed) Lüttke, Lieutenant."

"I hope, Herr Doktor, that you are satisfied with my use of the word 'while.'"

Nevertheless, Timmler was on hand when the submarine put to sea. He strode busily up and down the pier, lecturing some Red Cross nurses on submarine lore, pointing and gesticulating, and trying to say good-by to the seamen, who ignored him. As the flotilla commander shook hands with each member of the crew, ex-War Correspondent Timmler took pictures, going down on his knees to make the men look taller. When the boat turned in the harbor basin, he was still standing on the pier, waving his cap and snapping a few last pictures.

The first thing that happened was the bombing.

Teichmann saw the bomb falling and coming toward him —suddenly it was right in front of him, a round tower, immense and yellow. He heard a scream and fell flat, and then there was the clang of metal striking metal.

It struck a yard abaft the bridge. The men stood for a moment as though paralyzed. The captain was furious. He would gladly have shot the whole bridge watch on the spot. He trembled with rage, and his face was so red the men thought he would burst a blood vessel. When he could speak it was as though he forced the words through his clenched teeth: "Get that thing overboard." Then he turned his back to the bomb, as if it didn't exist.

It had grazed the bridge after rail, driven through the wooden deck covering, and left a slight dent in the pressure hull. The contact with the rail had turned it around; it had struck with the detonator upward. It was easy enough to unscrew the detonator and deactivate the bomb; but it was quite a job getting the thing overboard. The engineer directed the operation. With the help of an improvised tackle and two crowbars, they managed it in fifteen minutes. Meanwhile the second watch manned the AA guns in case the plane should return.

The captain gave the command to submerge. He ordered the engineer to take her down to eighty meters, an unusual depth when the boat was not under attack. It was as though he wished to stage the ensuing scene without interference from outside, in his own uncontested domain, so to speak.

He sat in the wardroom. Facing him stood the four men of the first watch. The doors were closed.

"From which sector did the plane come?"

"From mine, sir," said the exec.

"Bearing?"

"Thirty degrees, sir."

"The after lookouts are dismissed."

The two after lookouts departed.

"One question, Wittgenberg. An answer in the affirmative will simplify the whole proceedings. Were you asleep?"

"Sir, I respectfully request you to withdraw that question."

"What do you mean?"

"I regard that question as an insult."

"I don't give a good God damn how you regard it. I want an answer."

"Then I respectfully request that you bring charges against me and . . ."

"You needn't worry. I'll bring charges and you will be court-martialed. You may regard the present proceedings as a preliminary hearing. I now ask you for the last time: Were you asleep? Yes or no?"

"No."

"What is your explanation, then?"

"I have no explanation, sir."

Thus far the captain had been speaking in his usual, slightly contemptuous tone as if this hearing were a pure matter of form and an outrageous imposition on his patience; he was certain that the bridge watch was to blame. But now he changed his tone. Softly, cautiously, as though waiting for his adversary to fall into a trap, he said, "Visibility?"

"Four to five miles, sir."

"Atmospheric condition?"

"Hazy. Streaks of mist, sir."

"Elevation of clouds?"

"Three to four thousand feet, sir."

"Very well," The captain's voice grew loud again: "Supposing the plane had attacked by the shortest route. I must say that strikes me as impossible. It would have shown up in the ECM. But just supposing, with the weather conditions you have just described, you would have seen a plane at a distance of seven to eight thousand yards and an altitude of at least three thousand feet. Is that clear?"

"Yes, sir. But the plane was not flying horizontally. It dived and came out of the clouds about five hundred yards ahead, dropped its bomb, and went back into the clouds."

"If that's the truth, the plane must have been piloted by the Holy Ghost."

"I have no explanation to offer, sir."

The captain took his hands out of his pockets and sat up straight. He leaned forward, placed his elbows on the table, and rested his chin on his hands. He glanced for a moment at the exec, as though seeing him for the first time. And then he spoke calmly, in the tone one might take to reassure an upset child: "Wittgenberg, there's more at stake than your person or mine or my boat. I've got to know how such an attack could have been possible."

The silence was broken by the opening of the door to the chiefs' room. "The new watch requests permission to pass."

"Refused."

"Aye aye, sir."

The door closed. The men could be heard returning to the forward room.

"You must have heard the sound of engines?"

"Only as the plane was leaving, sir. Not on the approach."

The captain looked at Teichmann. If you want to know what I heard, Teichmann thought, you can ask me; just looking at me won't do it; hell no.

"Did you hear the sound of engines?"

"Yes, sir." Teichmann paused dramatically. He wanted to torture the captain a bit. And then, just as Lüttke was going to open his mouth, he said, "But only after the bomb had been dropped. Up till then the engines were turned off."

"That is nonsense. How would you know the engines were dead? If you insist you may say, I, So-and-So, Senior Midshipman, heard no sound of engines—but I forbid such unwarranted assertions as you have just made. Do you understand?"

"Yes, sir."

"Send me the two after lookouts."

When they had come, the captain asked about engine sounds. Their reply was the same as the exec's. They were dismissed. The radioman thrust his head in and said, "Cook to Captain: Lunch is ready."

"Not interested."

"Request permission to serve, sir."

"No. And if anybody else bothers me there's going to be trouble." Turning to the exec, he said, "I will report this incident to ComSub. You will take the consequences."

"I will take them, sir."

367

Suddenly Lüttke began to scream, "You—you—you! What you take or don't take doesn't matter in the least. You don't seem to realize what this means." He jumped up and sprang at the exec, roaring, "If what you say is true, we can all report to the Army for KP. The war's over as far as submarines are concerned. Don't you fools understand that?"

The door to the control room opened; the engineering officer mumbled " 'Scuse me" and passed through to the forward room.

"Damn it all, didn't I say that I don't want to be disturbed?"

"That last oil check was wrong," Langen said to the men in the forward room. "Better put more chalk on the stick." Then he went back through the wardroom. Such insolence left the captain speechless. Langen saw this and said in passing, "That was important."

"I decide what is important on this boat, and never forget it."

The engineering officer bared his equine teeth—it was hard to tell whether he was grinning or only startled—and said, "Then please decide what's to be done about lunch. It's getting cold." With that he closed the door. He's really a diplomat, thought Teichmann, and what a sunny disposition. With him we'll topple the old man off his high horse. But when he saw the captain's face, frozen in despair, he stopped thinking. . . .

"Dismissed. Lunch will be served. Rise to periscope depth. Stand by to surface."

The words fell slowly and mechanically; the captain's thoughts were far away. He went into his room and sat down on his bunk. When lunch was served, he stood up and drew the curtain.

After lunch Langen brought the boat up to periscope depth. He sent his report to the captain, but nothing happened. The captain gave no answer. A little while later Teichmann went into the captain's room, drew back the curtain, and said, "The boat is ready to surface, sir."

The captain was still sitting on his bunk, rigid as a

statue, pondering the problem that he could not solve. He had not heard Teichmann.

"The boat is ready to surface, sir."

The captain started up, almost knocking Teichmann over, and dashed into the wardroom. "Wittenberg," he roared, "you were asleep. All the rest is nonsense. That's a lot of bilge you were giving me. I'm going to have you court-martialed, you . . ."

They had never seen him so excited. He was wild with rage. It looked as if he wanted to kill the exec. Suddenly, aware that he had forgotten himself, he said matter-of-factly, "And how do you account for the fact that the plane didn't come back?"

"Maybe it was out of bombs," said the engineering officer, who was tinkering with something in the sound room behind the captain's back.

"Why does he hate me so?" the exec asked Teichmann at supper. "I can't tell him any more than the truth."

"He doesn't hate you, he hates somebody else. . . ."

"The English?"

"I think he hates the men who sent him into this war. In spite of everything, he's a good sailor. Those fellows back home could hardly hope for a better one."

"I don't get it."

"I don't either. It's more a matter of feeling. I don't like him, but sometimes I think that for him this battle of his has become a cult, the only justification of his life. He doesn't know how to do anything else, so he fights as hard and as bravely as he can. Maybe he doesn't ask why; maybe he thinks what matters is *how* you fight and not *why*—he's a professional warrior. What else can he do to keep his self-respect?"

"Sometimes I have the feeling that he doesn't think much of the men who sent him into this fight. But he's never said a word."

"Do you expect a butcher to lecture about the advantages of vegetarianism—if he wants to keep his knife?"

"I'd be very glad if he'd put his knife away."

When the exec came off watch at midnight and the radio

book was given him to countersign, he saw that a secret radio message had been sent out, and in the Secret Book he read, "Request courtmartial proceedings against Lieutenant (j.g.) Ehrenfried B. Prince von Wittgenberg-Weissenstein for misconduct while on watch. Lüttke."

The exec made his mark in the book.

When they had passed out of the Bay of Biscay, they steered a course a little north of west. Intelligence had reported that a convoy was forming in Boston Harbor.

Six days later ComSub reported the departure of the convoy and assigned seven subs, including Lüttke's, to attack it. The submarines reconnoitered off Boston, searching for their prey. Then an unusual radio message arrived.

Teichmann had had the evening watch. Shortly after midnight he was awakened by the chief engineer and summoned to the control room. The exec and the first lieutenant were sitting there, studying a secret radio message. It was addressed to all submarines in the zone and ordered them to discontinue all attacks on escorted convoys in the North Atlantic and to shift to the Middle Atlantic. Petersen, who had decoded the message, showed it to the exec, assuring him that there was no possible error in decoding. Then the four of them sat there, trying to decide what to do. The captain was asleep. But when the radioman brought in an urgent message from a submarine that had sighted the convoy, there was no further room for discussion; they had to wake the captain.

Lüttke came in immediately and sat down at the chart table. The control room hands broke off their whispered conversation, as they always did when the captain entered. The auxiliaryman cast imploring looks around him and said quite loudly, "Quiet, the captain's working."

The captain had before him the two radio messages and the chart. He took the protractor and drew lines. His pencil point broke. He threw the pencil on the floor and was perfectly aware that one of the men bent down, picked it up, sharpened it, and then, as inconspicuously as possible, put it back on the table.

"All ahead full, course two one one."

The helmsman in the conning tower repeated the order; the captain went back into his room.

"Well, that's that," said Teichmann. "As far as he is concerned, there's no such thing as an escorted convoy."

"What did you expect?" said Langen, and took a deck of cards out of his pocket. "Do we play once around or are you gentlemen tired?"

They played until nearly four o'clock. The engineering officer won spectacularly. The exec played distraughtly and lost. That was no wonder. Almost everyone felt rather edgy when the engines were on "full." But it seemed to Teichmann that since his words with the captain the exec had lost his old poise.

The four-o'clock watch gathered earlier than usual in the control room. They talked in muffled tones with the control-room hands as they cleaned their binoculars. One of them cracked a joke; the ensuing laughter was repressed and brief. The boatswain's mate came up to the exec, saluted sharply, and said, "It's fifteen fifty-five, sir."

"Thank you," said the exec.

They played the hand out; the exec and Teichmann stood up. None of them were green hands, and all had been through more than one attack on a convoy. And yet a shudder ran through every last one of them when the chief quartermaster reported, "Shadows bearing two four zero."

"Here we go," said Langen, baring his teeth.

The first watch went up. The third watch was relieved. A moment later the captain went up top.

The shadows were moving in Teichmann's sector. They couldn't be distinguished singly. The distance was about four thousand yards. The convoy looked like a row of overlapping briquettes. The ships could be discerned only by their color, which was blacker than the night sea.

"Battle stations," the captain called down the tower. Down below the command was passed along, louder and faster than other commands, and a moment later the compliance reports of the chief mates could be heard.

"Motor room manned and ready."

"Engine room manned and ready."

"Control room manned and ready."

Half a minute had passed since the captain's order when the engineering officer called up to the bridge, "All ready below."

A few seconds later the exec reported, "Torpedoes ready."

Then came a new batch of orders from the captain: "All ahead flank, course one two zero. Tubes one to five, stand by for surface fire. Radio room: send this message to Com Sub: Convoy sighted, course two one zero, speed eight knots. Am attacking. Chief quartermaster: request target bearing."

What happened now had happened in innumerable battles and drills. Each man knew exactly what he had to do, and he did it calmly and precisely, as though it were the most natural thing in the world. Each man was practicing his trade.

The boat flew through the water. The lazy whale had turned into an intricate and fierce war machine that cut through the water like a knife. The men on the bridge could feel the change: the wind whistled louder, spray fell on their binoculars, the deck trembled beneath their feet. The Diesels seemed to have gone mad—"If they keep on like that, the engines will jump up on deck," said the quartermaster. The bow wave rose high, the foam took on a lighter color, and the forward section of the boat seemed to rise. And all this gave the men a glorious feeling that nothing could diminish—not even the knowledge that death was possible if not probable. The captain gave the order to head for the target, and down below the order was passed on. A few minutes later the exec reported "On target," and the captain said, "Fire at will." The hearts of the bridge watch pounded like hammers; their eyes bored into the night; their breath came in jerks, more in than out, and for seconds—when they thought, Now he's sighted us—they stopped breathing altogether and hot shudders ran through them. With every moment the tension mounted. They felt an unknown force gathering within them, breaking down all normal barriers, sweeping away the little habits, the little fears, the little desires and feelings of everyday life. It was as though they had suddenly awakened to real life, to a higher, stronger, fuller life.

"Break off the attack," said the captain. "Secure from battle stations below. Bridge watch stand by."

The convoy had zigzagged. The ships no longer formed an indistinct mass; they were still black, but now they had outlines, and before them rose little white hills. As usual at night, the ships looked bigger than they were. Then suddenly the little white hills vanished, and the flat black rectangles became squares: the convoy was on its new course.

The men cursed. The exec swore as he stood at the TBT and thought aloud, "All they had to do was to hold their course for twenty seconds more—that wasn't nice of them." Teichmann said, "They heard our Diesels and they didn't like the noise." "I didn't ask you for your opinion," said the captain, and all was quiet.

The sub moved forward again. The sky was growing light. They had to hurry if they were to attack on the surface.

Since changing its course, the convoy had slowed down; the submarine quickly maneuvered into position. Shortly before 0600 the captain ordered battle stations below, and just then the engineer appeared on the bridge with a pot of hot, wonderfully aromatic coffee. "Want some?" he asked.

"What are you talking about?" said the captain.

"Coffee, sir."

"I'd like a cup," said Teichmann.

"I ordered battle stations, not a tea party," said the captain furiously. But Teichmann got his cup. Langen poured it out calmly and handed it to him. Then he vanished. From below he called up, "To captain: Battle stations manned below."

Meanwhile the sea had risen. White crowns danced on the short, choppy waves; the sea came from ahead. The binoculars of the forward lookout kept getting wet and had to be handed down into the tower to be dried. This was not without its dangers, for the lookouts on the ships guarding the convoy were sheltered; their glasses were dry and clear.

So far they had made out a destroyer and three corvettes.

The corvettes were at the head of the convoy. The destroyer circled around it like a sheep dog guarding its flock.

The sub set a course toward the target.

"We can't go much closer," said the captain to the exec. "It's getting too light."

"Yes, sir."

"Hey, you up there, hurry up if you want some hot coffee," Langen called up to the bridge.

"What do you mean 'hey'? You can say 'hey' to your mother-in-law. In four years on this boat, I've never seen anything as unmilitary as you. Pretty soon you'll be saying 'yoo-hoo' when you want to ask me something." The captain shouted all this down into the tower. Actually, he was not very angry; he seemed impressed by Langen's beer-hall tranquility.

"I didn't mean you, sir. But if you don't want any, we'll just have to drink it ourselves."

They were not able to fire. The convoy had speeded up again, and by the time the correction was fed into the torpedoes the target bearing exceeded one hundred forty degrees and the range had increased.

"Secure from battle stations. We move up again and attack submerged," said the captain.

"Aye aye, sir," the exec replied.

There was no more cursing. The intoxication was over. The men felt disappointed, weary, let down. And their nerves were on edge.

A few minutes after nine the boat submerged.

The engineering officer trimmed the boat and went to periscope depth. The speed with which he did this so impressed the captain that he said nothing. Then they heard the ships. They were approaching quickly. The sub lay exactly on their course.

First the corvettes passed over, and the high whirring of their speeding screws could be heard. Then came the lumbering freighters. Their propellers turned slowly and a trifle irregularly; the tone was an octave lower than that of the corvettes. But before they could pass over, Lüttke fired.

The stop watches were set in motion. A dozen eyes were

glued to each of them. Those who could not see a watch counted softly, and at fifty-two there were four explosions in quick succession. The men exchanged looks and nodded as though to say, That's Lüttke's precision work.

The ships had been hit.

"They must be pretty mad up there," said Langen.

"You'd be mad too," said Teichmann.

"What's going on?" Lüttke called down from the conning tower. Langen stepped over to the hatch and called up, "Would you like some coffee now? It's still warm."

"What's that?"

"Coffee."

"See here, Langen, you're driving me crazy with your damn-fool coffee."

"I meant the helmsman, sir."

The captain grumbled something that no one could understand. Then he said, "Say, Langen, what's your depth?"

"On the line."

"What?"

"On the line, sir. Periscope depth."

And he was right. The sea was good and choppy, but he was right, seven fathoms on the line. With the best of intentions the captain could find no fault with him.

"Keep awake, Langen. I'm going down in a minute. I'm going to dive under the convoy."

"I always keep awake, sir."

The screws of the freighters turned as though nothing had happened, no faster and no slower than before. But they grew louder. Here and there there were sounds of breaking bulkheads. The sound room reported sinking noises.

"Depth thirty meters. Retract periscope," said the captain, and left the conning tower, where now only the helmsman remained.

The convoy passed overhead, ship after ship, a gigantic armada. It seemed endless. As long as there were freighters overhead, the warships could do nothing to the sub. The men knew that. But even so the grinding of the propellers over them was unpleasant and disturbing. Bright of the captain to dive under the convoy, the men thought. It was the

only thing he could do; there was no other possibility. But
the men didn't think of necessity; they preferred to dwell on
their captain's intelligence. That buoyed them up a bit. At
this point they needed someone to believe in. Their lives
were in the captain's hands; they had to believe in him.

Without warning the first depth charge struck, with a
devastating roar and a shock as though a volcano had
erupted beneath the boat.

It was not too close, but it was bad enough. The men's
faces were distorted. All life had gone out of them. Dead
faces, faces cut in stone. It was a long while before those
faces relaxed and some, chiefly among the older men, remained frozen for the duration of the attack. The men
stared at the deck of the control room and waited. Aside
from the captain, the engineer, the radioman, and the helms-
men, they had nothing to do. That was the worst part of it.
"They just dropped that one for the hell of it," said Langen.
But this was not true, and they all knew it. The "sweeper"—
that was what they called the destroyer astern of the convoy—must have located them. And a moment later the finger
was on them. They had been expecting it, yet secretly hoping
that it would not come, that it might spare them just this
once, that it would pass them by, perhaps by some technical
failure or human error—a little carelessness. For every man
in the submarine knew that that innocent tapping on the
side was as good as a death sentence.

"Sound beam," cried the radioman from the sound room.
They had all heard it. They all cowered as though death in
person had knocked as a sign that he wished to come in.
And ahead of him came terror like a great eagle, holding
them in its clutches, digging its claws deep into their flesh.
The men gritted their teeth, but still they groaned. They
had ceased to be fighting men; they were superfluous; there
was absolutely nothing they could do. They felt like guinea
pigs, whose life was being expended for a scientific experi-
ment. Imprisoned in a steel tube.

"Take her down slow to eighty meters," said the captain.

"Down to eighty meters," the engineering officer repeated. Then he went on talking. The men could not believe

eir ears. He gave the planemen their orders and in be-
een chatted with the exec and Teichmann. "They seem
be in an awful hurry up there." When they heard the
stroyer starting on a run, he said to Teichmann, "Do you
now this one?" And told a joke. He told it so well that the
ptain said nothing and the men listened and didn't look
until the destroyer was over them.

This time the explosions were close by. Eight depth
arges.

The boat was thoroughly shaken up. Everything that was
ade of glass smashed. Water seeped in through the hatches.
ach detonation was followed by a thrust. All the lights
ent out. The men too were shaken up—except for a very
w who stood up to the shock—and differed from corpses
ily in degree. They were finished, they had wound up all
eir business on earth, and only their hearts were still
nctioning. Their ears had been subjected to noises louder
an human ears can bear. The pressure hull saved their
rdrums, but not their nerves.

"Do you know this one?" asked Langen. "A professor in
edical school asks a girl student what part of the human
ody can, under certain conditions, swell up to thirty times
s normal size."

The destroyer had them in its beam and was knocking
gain.

"The girl blushes to the roots of her hair and says, 'No,
at part is unknown to me.' "

The destroyer started on its run. The captain ordered hard
ght rudder and both engines ahead emergency. He gave
e helmsman the new course. The submarine was now fifty-
ve fathoms down.

" 'That's too bad,' said the professor."

The destroyer was coming on at high speed, making di-
ectly for the men. Its screws spun furiously.

And then it was over them. They heard whole bundles of
epth charges splashing in the water. Each bundle had ten or
fteen times the effective range of a single charge. The
nen heard very clearly, and they crawled into themselves,

making themselves very small, but not small enough
elude the horror that was coming at them.

"The girl stood up and began to flounce out of the le
ture hall. The professor stopped her and said, 'Don't delu
yourself, young lady. I am referring to the pupil of the ey
That was . . .'"

Twenty-one depth charges went off.

The explosions lasted half a minute. The men had turn
to inert matter, fusing with the sub. The boat was goi
down. Several rivets had sprung in the engine room. Wat
spurted hissing on the hot engines. In the black darkne
the sounds were two or three times as loud as by dayligl
Steam spread through the boat. The hull began to stra
groaning as though expanding and contracting by fits a
starts.

They were going down quickly. Six hundred feet of wat
was now weighing on the hull. That was what made tho
hideous sounds. The sound beam moved back and fort
searching the sea; then the destroyer started on its ru
Huddled on deck, the men whimpered. And then the
screamed, hoping perhaps to drown out the sound of tl
destroyer's screws. But the sound persisted. And still tl
sound beam prodded here and there, as though to locate
fugitive hidden in a hayloft.

It was an unequal contest. The destroyer was in ever
way superior: it was faster and more heavily armed; it h
plenty of time, and it had an unfailing technical eye. Again
such odds bravery was useless. The men up there on tl
surface were hunters with spyglasses, pursuing a blind dee
They needed only to stand by and wait.

All this passed through Teichmann's head as he sat
panic fear on the deck plates of the control room, waiti
for the bombs. And then came hate. There was nothing l
could do to dispel it. It was a loathsome animal that s
down beside him and grew steadily bigger. He didn't wa
it. He was a sailor and a fighting man; he had never hat
the enemy. No one on board ever expressed feelings
hatred. They were sailors and those men up above we
sailors, and if they had to kill they did a good profession

job of it, because it was their trade. They had nothing in common with the men who sat home preaching hate because they lived on it. When the clubfooted Jesuit who directed the Propaganda Ministry shouted his songs of hate over the ether, they merely felt contempt for him, or shame because he was using their mother tongue.

Your hatred is childish, Teichmann said to himself. But the game was nasty and unfair. And it never stopped. The men screamed with fear, and they screamed with rage at their helplessness. The water around them was harder than steel. Explosive charges were being dropped into it, and when they exploded, something had to give way—either the water or the boat.

"They're just trying to win a medal," said the captain after lighting up the depth gauge and noting that the needle had stopped at its lowest point. "They're mad up there," said Langen. "They're mad because we go to sea without asking them for permission." "Arrogant bastards," said Petersen as loud as he could. "They think the Atlantic is an orchard and the Germans are naughty boys that steal cherries."

When the ship was overhead, some of the men vomited and urinated, and muttered unintelligible words as though imploring the destroyer to turn aside. The captain reckoned. He had to try for an evasion course at right angles to the destroyer's course, and to do so he had to get a pretty good idea of the destroyer's course. He reckoned without interruption. Everything could be reckoned. If you wanted to survive in sea warfare, you had to know your mathematics; and you had to be able to apply your knowledge even when depth charges were going off all around you. You had to do mental arithmetic in the middle of hellfire. And you had to know how to be alone. The captain of a submerged submarine was the loneliest of all soldiers, and a single mistake in his reckoning meant the life of his crew. And supposing several warships attacked him at once, no superior officer would tell him what evasion course to give the helmsman. No superior officer would tell him, for there was none.

Yet for Lüttke there always seemed to be one. With the

precision of an automaton he called out the course through the blackness of the control room.

More and more water was pouring in, and the engineer struggled to keep the boat from sinking any further. Seven hundred and fifty feet was the limit if the crew was to remain alive.

The chief quartermaster counted two hundred and eighteen depth charges; then he gave up because the desk top was all covered with lines. There were three ships on the surface now, destroyers or corvettes, circling around, dropping their depth charges.

The first to crack under the strain was the control chief. Langen had managed to raise the boat by pumping; she lay eighty fathoms below the surface when twenty depth charges went off at intervals of three seconds, and hurled her down again. Water drove through the valves. The pressure hull creaked. A number of rivets sprang. The steel tube writhed like a trampled worm. Everything that was movable inside the boat was thoroughly shaken up. And when the crashes had ceased and the hull stopped quaking, there was a sound that still went on. At first the men thought that the helmsman had fallen out of the conning tower. But the sound continued. It was as though someone were throwing cabbages into the control room. A dull thudding sound. Flashlights snapped on. It was the control chief banging his head against the floor.

The lights went out immediately. For a moment the darkness was comforting. At least you couldn't see what was happening. But the thudding went on. Someone shouted, "Stop it!" Another cried, "Oh God—" and fell silent, realizing that it would take more than prayers to quiet a madman. In the end the captain had to give an order.

Nothing happened. Not a hand stirred. No one felt that he had been spoken to; it was pitch-dark. A handful of pebbles was thrown against the side. The beam moved crackling along the hull. The skull was still pounding on the deck plates. The boat was sinking. Again the pressure hull was groaning. . . .

"Since when do I have to give an order twice?"

They reached for him. First the exec, though he wasn't at all cut out for such operations. The chief quartermaster gave him a hand. They tried to get hold of him, but he flailed around; he just wanted to go on banging his head against the iron floor. The sounds of struggle could be heard through the darkness. Petersen flashed on his light. Teichmann joined in. The control chief began to bellow. They couldn't understand what he was saying, but it ended with "heaven." Teichmann tried to pull his pants down to keep him from kicking. He couldn't bend the man's arm back to tie him. The only thing he could do was hit him.

The man was quiet. They carried him to the petty officers' room and tried to lay him on one of the bunks, but as they were lifting him up an explosion knocked their feet out from under them, and they dropped him. He came to and began to bellow again, "I want to go to heaven," and to flail around him. They seized him and dragged him aft and locked him in the head. The screams continued, but now they were less audible.

The boat was going down. The pressure hull was straining, creaking, and occasionally popping. Then the sounds became regular. The popping became constant: rat—tat—tat—tat—tat.

Down. Down. The sounds of the hull grew louder, loud enough to hurt the ears. The men no longer dared to breathe. If it would only happen quickly, they thought. This business of dying. If it would only end . . .

But the end did not come. The pressure hull held. They had passed the 125-fathom mark. The hull went rat-tat-tat like a machine gun firing slowly. "Langen," said the captain, "you'll have to bring her up a bit." "Aye aye, sir." And the thin hard jets of water pouring into the boat whistled shrilly, as though sawing the hull into pieces.

The radioman cracked. It might have happened a good deal sooner; he had been on duty in the sound room, and the strain on his ears was unbearable. He screamed a few times instead of reporting the sound bearings; then he burst out sobbing; he tore off his earphones and lay down in the passageway outside the sound room. The exec took up the

381

phones. It went on and on. The boat rose—she actually rose to seventy fathoms; then there were twelve depth charges that drove her down to one hundred; then she rose again to eighty-five and nine ash cans sent her back to ninety-five. Then she rose to seventy-five and sixteen depth charges flung her back to one hundred. Several other men cracked up, but no one noticed, for they were not needed. Then she rose again, and then five well-placed charges sent her back to one hundred. The boat stood almost on her head, the men had to cling to bars, levers, wheels, valves, then she rose again, and then she hurtled down again. . . .

This up and down went on for eleven hours and forty minutes. Then the batteries were spent.

"All hands: Stand by for surface battle. There are three warships up there. We are going to sink them one after the other."

"Which one do we take on first, sir?" asked Langen.

"Whichever is the biggest. The destroyer, probably."

"Which gun opens fire first, sir?" asked Petersen, speaking as loud as he could.

"That depends on the situation. But go easy on your heavy ammo."

"Yes, sir. First I'll cover those tin cans with the twenty-millimeter."

"And if they put about, shoot their ass off with the gun," said the engineering officer.

Flashlights snapped on. The ammunition ready box was opened, and mechanically the men passed up the shells. They sweated in the sultry air; their clothes were wringing wet and clung to their bodies. They were weary and listless and no one spoke. The steaming air weighed on their lungs and made it hard to breathe. There was hardly any oxygen left in the air, and every movement seemed to drain their last remaining will power. Anyway, the whole thing was senseless. They knew that this time there was no help. A miracle only happens once, and they had had theirs.

Some of the men, particularly the older ones, were beside themselves with rage at all this banter. They didn't understand the officers and their cynical bravado. In the midst of

382

the preparations for the last battle someone threw up. The men heard the splashing; they heard the liquid sloshing on the deck of the sound room. And in the beam of a flashlight they saw it. They watched with a mixture of disgust and satisfaction. The flashlight stayed on. It had caught the exec, and it held him fast until he had vomited the last drop. Then Teichmann knocked the flashlight out of the man's hand. The chief quartermaster put on the earphones.

"Prepare to destroy secret material. Open food lockers. Anybody can eat what he likes," said the captain. But the food lockers were not opened; no one seemed to be hungry. Someone gave a nasty laugh. It was the same man—a fireman—who had flashed his light on the vomiting exec. Teichmann hated him.

"You could open up, at least."

"Teichmann again! Always Teichmann," Langen chortled.

"Poor bird never gets enough to eat."

Again that nasty laugh.

"If those lockers aren't opened this minute, there's going to be trouble," said Teichmann; there was murder in his voice.

"The chief quartermaster has the keys."

Teichmann went to the sound room, got the keys, and opened the food lockers. From one he took a can of applesauce. "Who's got a can opener, hey?"

Five depth charges went off close to the side. The boat seemed to spin around. The cans fell to the floor and rolled about between the men's legs, pounding on the floor like a whole company of men with hobnailed boots. The crew screamed with terror and cursed with rage—louder and louder, more and more furious, as if they had all been waiting for someone to kill with their tongues. The fireman with the flashlight roared at least half a dozen times, "Does the bastard have to eat now?"

There was nothing Teichmann could do. He was furious with himself because he had lost his can of applesauce in the explosion. At least he tried to tell himself that that was why he was furious.

"Silence!" cried the captain. When quiet was restored and

only the sound beam could be heard tapping here and there, he asked, "Taste good, Teichmann?"

"There's some canned peaches in the periscope well," said the engineer.

"You'll have to wait till after the battle," said the captain. "We're going up now."

Langen blew out the ballast slowly and cautiously, alternating between tanks. Slowly the boat staggered upward.

"First, I'm going to take a little look around," said Lüttke, and added, "If it can be done."

"I'll take her to periscope depth, sir," said Langen.

"Make it as fast as you can."

They were up to forty fathoms. The higher they rose, the easier it was for the ships above them to aim their bombs. The eyes of the men in the control room were glued to the needle of the depth gauge, which rose in jerks and quivered after every leap. From time to time the hand of the first lieutenant, who held the flashlight, trembled slightly; then Langen tapped the dial and the needle jumped. The men looked on open-mouthed. Their breathing was loud and almost in unison, as if they were inhaling and exhaling on command. One man slipped and fell down. The others cursed bitterly for a moment, then their attention went back to the needle beneath the splintered, cloudy glass. Slowly, slowly it rose. And fear gnawed at their entrails.

The first part of the miracle was that nothing was stirring up above. The crew became aware of it only when the captain called for the sound bearing and received the answer, "The enemy is not moving."

"But I hear his engines," the captain replied.

"Yes, sir, but the bearing doesn't change."

"He can't stand still with his engines running," said Langen.

"Oh yes, he can," said the captain. "You don't know about those things."

"Either those fellows have got us for sure," came Petersen's death rattle, "or they haven't got us for sure."

"If there were a medal for funny ways of putting things, you'd get it," said Lüttke.

"Thank you, sir."

When the boat had risen to twenty fathoms, the whole miracle became clear. The boat rolled—gently, almost imperceptibly at first. The captain said to the engineering officer, "Langen, do you notice anything?"

At ninety feet they all noticed: the boat was rolling slowly from side to side.

"Don't go any higher. Try to hold us where we are. Maybe a storm's blowing up. When it's dark up there, we'll surface."

"Yes, sir."

Something passed through the boat. It went from stern to bow, and no one could say what it was. It was as though something had come to life in every compartment of the boat, as though the men had crawled out of their frozen masks and begun to live again. No order was given, but slowly the men picked up the cans and piled them up in the lockers. Teichmann locked up and took the keys to the chief quartermaster.

Langen tried to keep the boat in trim by pumping, and in the main he succeeded. In the next two hours the boat went down only sixteen fathoms, and in the same time only twenty-seven depth charges were dropped. Some of them were not very close.

Then for thirty-five minutes nothing happened at all, except that the sound beam touched the side a few times as though to make sure the sub was still there. After another half hour Lüttke went up to periscope depth.

They tossed and bobbed in the storm, but the engineer kept his trim by moving the crew around. The captain took a look and muttered, "It's black night." He looked through the lookout periscope and said, "They're still there, but they've hove to. We surface."

When the men of the first watch were on the bridge and their eyes had grown accustomed to the darkness, they saw a destroyer lying hove to some three hundred yards away. They could see it only when it rose on the crest of a wave. In this weather the slender destroyer was for practical purposes unmaneuverable; she had to attend to her own business to keep from capsizing.

The storm raged over the waves, carrying off their tops, as though to plane the sea smooth. The visibility was no more than half a mile. The men on the bridge clung fast and held their faces into the storm, and laughed when the sea broke over them. They loved the sea.

Lüttke ran away from the destroyer and charged up his batteries. When they were full, he dived.

"I'd sooner sink the old bucket than content myself with a couple of lousy Liberty ships," said Lüttke when the engineering officer said something about the alarming psychological state of the crew. He headed for the Middle Atlantic convoy routes. The nerves of some of the crew were shattered.

The machinists were in the worst state. They jumped at the slightest unexpected sound, swore at each other, wept hysterically, and made mistakes in performing the simplest operations. Their condition showed in their eyes, which protruded enormously, and their pupils flickered restlessly like candles in the wind. Two key men had to be relieved of their duties. The radioman's hands trembled so he couldn't hold a pencil, and the captain said, "You, with your shakes, maybe you could dry the binoculars at least." And the auxiliaryman talked incoherent nonsense that no one could understand.

That night the gyro compass went out. Teichmann woke up the chief electrician's mate, who set to work. Without the gyro it was impossible to navigate for any length of time; the magnetic compass in the control room was hard to read and registered considerable deviation. The gyro compass was indispensable for any offensive activity.

By the time the morning watch went on duty, the gyro compass had been repaired. Forty-eight hours later, again at night, the helmsman in the conning tower reported that it was gyrating back and forth like mad and that he couldn't hold a course. The exec, who was officer of the watch, ordered him to steer by the magnetic compass in the control room. Then he had the chief electrician's mate awakened.

The captain was awake and sandpapered the electrician's mate so furiously that he got the shakes and couldn't do the delicate work needed to repair the compass. But he recovered in time and by noon the gyro was functioning again.

Schofer was a member of the control-room crew, a quiet, polite young fellow who never attracted attention except perhaps by his height: he was six feet four. He had flax-blond hair that was a good deal longer than it had to be even though there was no barber on board, and blue eyes, and all in all a pleasing face. But the following night Teichmann caught him meddling with the gyro and struck that face with the flat of his hand. Schofer went sailing through the control room and landed with a crash. He lay still for a couple of seconds; then, still half dazed, he pulled himself up by the wheel of one of the diving tanks. Suddenly he cowered as if he had received another blow, this time a fatal one. He knew that Teichmann's slap was nothing compared to what was awaiting him now: before him stood the captain.

Teichmann hadn't seen him, and Schofer hadn't seen him; no one in the control room had seen him—it was midnight and no one could have imagined that the captain would be awake. The control room was dark except for the blackout light over the chart table—the captain was standing by the forward bulkhead.

He said nothing. His face gave no sign of what he was thinking. It was cold and smooth as always. His eyes were cold and distant, two balls of tempered blue steel. If they revealed anything, it was the usual mocking contempt.

He went to the chart table, took a drafting compass, stuck the point in the chart. Before drawing the circle, he spoke over his shoulder, without perceptibly turning his head, "Well, Schofer, it looks as if you stumbled."

When no answer came, the captain set down the compass and turned around, facing him. Then he said slowly, as though it made him sick to talk to Schofer, "In case you didn't stumble, you'll be dead in fifteen minutes. I will convene a summary court martial; after that you will stand up on deck and one of the men will fire the twenty-millimeter and . . ."

"I stumbled, sir."

As far as the captain was concerned, Schofer was no longer there. He busied himself with the chart. After that the gyro compass behaved.

When Teichmann passed by the captain's quarters on his way to the chiefs' room for breakfast, he saluted silently as he did every morning. And then something unheard-of happened: the captain said "Morning." He had really said "Morning." It sounded more like a subdued clearing of the throat, but even so the word had been there; Teichmann's ears hadn't deceived him. But if Lüttke imagined that Teichmann would respond, he was very much mistaken. Teichmann continued to salute him in silence, raising his hand to the vizor of his cap. The captain continued to say "Morning." This went on for four days; then it was Lüttke's birthday.

As the senior petty officer, the chief quartermaster opened the congratulation ceremonies. He presented the captain with a reading lamp that the chief electrician's mate had manufactured out of materials available on board. The captain said thank you and shook hands with the chiefs.

The other petty officers were represented by the boatswain's mate, who extended a bunch of roses. The flowers were made of toilet paper colored with red and blue ink and yellow water color; the stems were wire wrapped in more toilet paper dipped in green water color. The captain took his bouquet and held it awkwardly. He obviously didn't know what to do with it. Finally a painful "thank you" slipped between his teeth. So much for the petty officers.

Then a middle-aged Seaman First-Class whom Lüttke had repeatedly locked up for unmilitary behavior stepped forward in behalf of the nonrated men. The seaman said nothing. He merely placed a good-luck pig on the table in the captain's room; that is, he put it down on the War

Diary—a classified document, accessible only to officers—which happened to be lying open on the table. And then the two of them, captain and sailor, contemplated the pig. It apparently never occurred to the captain to close the book. The pig felt quite at home and slid back and forth as though skating.

"That pig doesn't know how to stand still. . . ."

"It's the sea, sir; he ain't got his sea legs."

"He's got to have his sea legs if he wants to sail on my boat."

"Yes, sir."

The captain took the potato and pressed the four matches that served as legs deeper into it. Then he put the pig back on his feet, and he stayed put.

"Why has he got red eyes?"

"Pigs mostly have red eyes, sir; reddish-brown. And we've only got red pins on board, sir."

"Oh."

"He stands good now," said the seaman, overwhelmed by his captain's dexterity.

"His belly droops a bit, but that doesn't matter."

"Oh no, sir. Fact is, it's a brood sow."

"What? You mean she's going to have porkers?"

"Yes, sir."

"Well, let's hope so. It wouldn't be bad if our good-luck pig had little ones."

"No, sir."

The captain held out his hand. The seaman pondered whether to take it. He pondered a bit too long; the captain withdrew his hand and nodded. And there the matter ended.

The officers presented no gifts, but each congratulated the captain personally.

When Teichmann had to pass by the captain's room, he saluted as usual and passed by. Next morning, when he saluted, the captain said, "Morning, Teichmann." Teichmann was a bit startled; he stopped, gave the captain a questioning look, and when the captain looked away he said, "Morning, sir."

They kept to this ritual; Teichmann remained the only man

on board whom the captain addressed by name except in matters of duty.

That night a man began to scream. The boat was submerged and it sounded terrifyingly loud. The sleepers jumped out of their bunks but didn't know what to do. Some went over to the screaming man, who had meanwhile quieted down; he had drunk hydrochloric acid.

The firemen had put the bottle on the stove in the galley, and the cook had thought it was something to drink. They poured milk into him, but his tongue remained as big as a beef tongue and he could only drool. The captain gave the motor machinist's mate five days' arrest because there was no label on the bottle.

The crew wasn't good for much, and in the Middle Atlantic no convoys turned up, but there were plenty of planes. The whole day was spent in emergency diving. Once the sub remained on the surface and hit a Sunderland flying boat with the 20-millimeter, but the shells bounced off the armor like peas off a windowpane, and in departing the tail gunner wounded two seamen. The captain said a submarine wasn't an antiaircraft installation and ordered the officers of the watch to dive whenever they sighted a plane.

After cruising the Middle Atlantic for two weeks, the submarine made for Gibraltar and hung around the entrance to the Mediterranean for nine days without sighting anything to attack. At three o'clock in the morning on the tenth day—the exec, Teichmann, and one of the slightly wounded seamen had the watch, and the night was still black—a light suddenly flashed on them. It was so white and blinding that they closed their eyes and listened to the bullets whistling through the air and striking the hull. When that stopped, something exploded with a gigantic roar and threw them against the bridge coaming. A waterfall descended. Then it was night again. The whole thing hadn't taken ten seconds.

Teichmann noticed that the exec was no longer beside him. He felt for him but his hands reached into the void. His foot struck something soft, and that was the exec. "Dive!" he heard the captain shout below, and the engineering officer answered, "Ready to dive."

390

"Get in there," Teichmann said to the after lookout. Then he seized the exec under the armpits, dragged him to the hatch, and dropped him. "Flood!" he cried, closed the hatch, and dogged it down. The air was expelled from the diving tanks; he heard the water rushing in and felt the boat tip forward and dive. Then came the monstrous din of the negative tanks being blown out, and suddenly he realized that they had had luck again. His knees began to tremble, his head reeled, and he collapsed on the periscope seat. He closed his eyes except for a tiny crack through which he could see the helmsman's compass. But he didn't see the numbers. He stared at the back seam of the helmsman's salt-encrusted leather jacket, and followed it up and down a few times. Then he was himself again.

The boat started for home. There was nothing else to do. Too many of the men were out of commission. The captain's wishes were beside the point. He no longer said a word to anyone. After Teichmann had described the attack, the captain sent for a radio message blank and wrote, "Withdraw petition for court-martial proceedings against Lieutenant (j.g.) Prince von Wittgenberg. Lüttke." He gave the message to the exec to countersign.

The exec had been hit in the legs; the bullets had passed clean through, and his wounds were not serious. But his head was affected. His features were convulsed; his mouth remained crooked; he was unable to close it, and try as he would, he couldn't eat. The spoon slipped out of his hand; his fingers trembled like those of the radioman, and when he sat up in his bunk the spittle ran down his chin. He could no longer relieve himself alone; two men had to hold him. He was unable to countersign the radio message.

Two days before reaching port the electrician's mate died of appendicitis. For a couple of days they had treated him with hot compresses; when that did no good they had tried cold ones, and then lukewarm ones. When these didn't help they gave him a small dose of morphine to ease the pain, and after that all they could do, for want of a doctor, was to increase the dose.

When the boat tied up at La Pallice, there was a crowd

on the pier. It had become a rarity for a German submarine to put into its home port. Out of ten subs that put out to sea, eight were lost.

There was even a movie actress, and a very good-looking one at that, on hand to welcome them. But she had tact enough to keep quiet. When the captain didn't take her bunch of flowers, she went on deck, broke it apart, and gave each man a flower. There were not enough flowers to go around, but still it was nice of her. The men loved her as one loves a sister, which was how it was intended. Then a war correspondent came on board; he wore both Iron Crosses and the Submarine Insignia and behaved accordingly. He could be perfectly sure that his reports would be suppressed by the Propaganda Ministry.

The dead electrician's mate was carried out. A doctor took the auxiliaryman and the radioman in hand. The crew cleared their moldering belongings out of their lockers and carried them under their arms to the bus that was waiting outside the pen.

When the crew had left the boat, Teichmann went back on board to get the exec. The captain was standing by his bunk. He looked at Teichmann as if he were a burglar. "What are you looking for?"

"The exec. I want to . . ."

"Clear out. You will please attend to your own affairs."

The swine, Teichmann thought on his way to the bus. The swine. As he was lighting a cigarette on his way out of the pen, he saw the captain carrying the exec ashore.

SHAKE-HAND'S LAST TRIP

16

"Make yourself at home. We're all alone. Molly's working in a munitions plant, my old man is dead, and I'm going to sea the day after tomorrow."

They fried potatoes in the kitchen with the butter from Teichmann's travel ration. Then they went down in the cellar and brought up a few bottles of Château Rothschild Lafitte. They put the bottles in the open fireplace in the living room and brought up easy chairs. Heyne produced glasses; then he went into the garden and looked to see if the windows were properly blacked out.

Teichmann disliked the room. It was crammed full of books and plaster busts. Or maybe they were marble; he didn't touch them to find out. There were the Zeus of Otricoli and Socrates; the other heads were unknown to him. Over the mantelpiece there were two crossed sabers. Below them hung the picture of a student; to the left of the sabers hung Bismarck, to the right old Kaiser Wilhelm.

It took a bottle and a half before Heyne was able to say what he had saved up for this night: "You're the only one I can talk to, and you certainly didn't come here to discuss submarine warfare." As to submarine warfare, it had taken them only a few minutes to agree that it was absurd to go on with it, and that any new submarines that were built would be too late. "And so—well, they took my father away last fall. I didn't want to write you about it, because the mail is censored and it wouldn't have done you or me or my father any good. It would only have got you in trouble, corresponding with the son of a traitor, and so on, and . . ."

"Just the same, I would have liked to . . ."

"I know. But why make trouble for you when you couldn't

393

help? And that's the truth. You couldn't have done a damn thing. They're not exactly consistent, you know. They have no objection to letting the son of a criminal—yes, for them my father was a criminal—serve on a German submarine. Anyway, I was right. It's best to keep such things to yourself—as long as you can."

The last words had slipped out of him. He quickly drained his glass. Then he poured himself another and leaned back comfortably in his armchair. The worn leather smelled of lavender, and that went well with the heavy ruby-red wine that they drank in silence.

"I wasn't very close to my old man, you know that. But even so, if they lock up washerwomen for criticizing the High Command or the government and creating defeatism, I have no objection, even if their criticism happens to be right. Because there are some people in whose mouths even the truth becomes a lie. . . ."

"Still, a government that has to fear the criticism of washerwomen . . ."

"All right. All right. I didn't mean to start in on washerwomen. All I wanted to bring out was that, unlike them, my father, as a professor of history, was entitled—he thought so, at least—to open his mouth. And he did. The reaction of the authorities was just what you might have expected; it was nothing new. Don't imagine that I'm trying to defend anybody—I'm not. I'm not interested in externals like politics, the conduct of the war, the Gestapo, and so on—I used to be, but I'm not any more. It's the human aspect that interests me. You used to call me a cynic. You were perfectly right. My fellow men have made me cynical. That's right. No one is born a cynic. The whole thing was like a bad play. Not a tragedy. There was no bigness about it; nothing but stupidity or weakness. Believe me, it's stupidity that brought evil into this world, and if our planet is a pigsty, it's because of the stupidity of its inhabitants—anyway, the overwhelming majority of them."

"I don't agree with you."

"Yes, I know. I was an adolescent once myself. I fell for all their irrational rot: the national myth, the profundity of

394

the primordial soul, and all the rest of it. I even talked about the leaven in the dough. Do you know what it boils down to? Mental laziness."

"I know the tune."

"Good. Prost. When the Germans are in a mess, it's always the fault of their emotional life, not of their minds. When they think, they can't be beaten. When they indulge their feelings, any idiot can lead them around by the nose. But that's not what I wanted to talk about. After my first mission I had a two weeks' leave. I went to town for a bit of fun; I went to see Dora; and on the way back I passed by the church where I was confirmed. I went in. It was a kind of joke, I suppose; anyway, I went in. Sometimes I like to listen to the organ. Pastor Diebold was preaching. I listened to his drivel; I had to if I wanted to hear the music. They've got a good organ, and with all the air raids you never know how much longer you'll be able to listen to it.

"Good. A few days later Diebold comes to see us and begins sounding me out about religion and so on. For him the Führer is some kind of Antichrist; that's his present position, at any rate; earlier, no, he had different ideas. Anyway, I defended the Führer; believe me, against my better judgment. Why? Probably to dissociate myself from my father and Diebold. In the course of the discussion my father brought out a big pile of manuscripts that he called his reckoning with the present regime; yes, that was how he put it, I think. Only a few of his friends knew about it, he said, and one of them was Pastor Diebold. Because, he said, only what was written today behind locked doors would be worth reading later on. I said, 'The dead won't be able to read your book; as far as they are concerned, you are wasting your time.' My father replied, 'It's diabolical to force men to die for a lie. The man is a monumental fiend.' 'A big fiend isn't so bad,' I said. 'I prefer the big devils to the little ones. There's something admirable about any form of bigness.' My father got pretty excited. 'Phrases,' he said. 'You say you prefer a big devil to a little one. You prefer a big scoundrel to a little one. Supposing a burglar breaks into your room and takes all your money, all your clothes, all your valuables. Do you prefer him to a burglar who only takes ten marks? Your big devil, whom you admire so, has broken into your house and taken everything—your heart, your conscience, your reason, your feeling for what is good. He's stolen everything you possessed, and for that you admire him? A theft of such magnitude was never before considered possible. Most people were unaware of it, because they no longer possessed anything that could have been taken away from them; they were empty. The big devil took advantage of that and gave them something: poison. He made them drunk on poison, and now they think they have something to die—if not to live—for. But you, Reinhold, you've got something in there'—he pointed to my heart—'don't let them take it away from you. Don't let them delude you, don't let yourself be infected with the drunkenness of the masses.' And so on, all the old bilge. You know, when they talk pathos, I can't help laughing. And up to a certain point he was knocking down a straw man. I was never a believer, either in the good or in the bad sense, and certainly not when it came to politics. Then Diebold started in: 'That is the consequence of systematically keeping the young people away from church, of knowingly withholding the truth from them. Since your confirmation, Reinhold, you have never been to church, although your father and I have repeatedly urged you. One couldn't even speak to you of God. But the kingdom of God is not of this world. You have sunk so deep into the mire, into the filth of the street, you are so befouled, that today you wouldn't dare to set foot in a church, even if you wanted to. You are so immersed in sin that every word spoken by the pastor would make you blush for shame. You should cast down your eyes when you pass a church and stop your ears at the sound of a hymn and . . .' "

"Good God," said Teichmann. "That's enough."

"No, the best is yet to come: 'And that's why you're afraid to go to church. But I say unto you: the day will come when you will lie in the dust before God's altar and beg for mercy. The day will come when you will be called to account for your actions, for your actions today when the Antichrist seems to triumph. I say seems. For the day will come when everything created by human hands will fall into ruins. When the Lord of Hosts will make his entrance amid drums and trumpets. And he will shatter the walls of your hearts; he will take them by storm, and ye will stand defenseless before him, the victor, and you will plead for mercy. Yea verily, ye will plead for mercy. You too, Reinhold. Even if you are defiant now, even if you close your heart like a fortress against the Almighty. But no fortress will help you. When he storms the fortress, the most obdurate heart will quail—and open.' At this point I interrupted him. It was too bad, he was going strong. 'Were you ever a soldier, Herr Diebold?' 'I? Never. Thou shalt not kill, saith the Scripture.' 'I only ask because for a clergymen you have a remarkable knowledge of military tactics—it may be a little out of date, but it's remarkable just the same. In the Middle Ages it would have been possible to storm a fortress in the manner you describe, and actually your predecessors did besiege people that way, or storm them as you put it. Spiritual rape, one might call it. I don't think you'll have much luck with my generation with your Lord of Hosts and his regimental band. But enough of that. I have something else to say.'

"And now, Hans, listen carefully. I turned the blade around. I asked Diebold, 'You reject the regime under which we are now living?' 'Yes.' 'Its philosophy? Its ideas?' 'Yes,' 'Its aims?' 'They are the aims of a criminal.' 'Its Führer?' 'He is the incarnation of the Antichrist. His philosophy is godless, a backsliding into heathenism. I am not deceived by the hypocritical words with which he winds up his speeches: The Lord God protect our people.' 'Your fellow clergymen are of the same opinion?' 'Yes, like every true Christian.' 'Then you fully share my father's opinions?' 'Fully and absolutely.' 'I wanted to hear that again from your own mouth today. You said before that I hadn't been to church since my confirmation. That was true up to a few days ago, when I did go to church. I went out of curiosity. I wanted to see if I'd still be as unimpressed as before. There were lots of people there; older people, most of

397

them, more women than men, and to tell you the truth the women were no beauties: I noticed that even as a child. The organ played. The congregation sang "We come to pray" . . . you know the hymn?' 'Of course.' 'I listened to a sermon on the second chapter of Revelation. If I remember rightly, it goes, "Fear none of those things which thou shalt suffer. Behold, the devil shall cast some of you into prison, that ye may be tried; and ye shall have tribulation ten days. Be thou faithful unto death, and I will give thee a crown of life." You know the passage?' 'Yes.' 'After that the congregation sang "Rock of Ages" . . . You know the hymn?' 'Yes.' His 'Yes' came out very softly, almost inaudibly. I went on, 'Then I saw the pastor fold his hands and heard him pray, "O Lord, today we stand once more before thee with our most fervent prayer. Bless and protect our beloved Führer and his brave soldiers and give us victory over our enemies. Amen." Do you know that pastor?' "

"Not bad," said Teichmann.

"In Diebold's honor it must be said . . ."

"What do you mean by honor?"

"Well, let's call it that. In any case, he turned red. Not with anger. No, he blushed for shame."

"That was the least he could do."

"But there are people who don't even blush. But that's not the end of my story. It took Diebold a minute or so to recover, and then he said, 'We are all of us mere mortals.' 'And that's why we call ourselves ministers,' I said. And Diebold: 'It is written: Render unto Caesar the things that are Caesar's.' 'But what if, as you yourself have said, Caesar is a criminal? And you call yourself a Protestant? Where is your protest? Luther would turn over in his grave if he knew what the so-called Protestants are doing to his teachings.' Diebold was very upset: 'I have been through a hard inner struggle as to whether to resign my pulpit. What good would it have done? Another pastor would have taken my place, or the congregation would have been left without a pastor. A flock without a shepherd.' Diebold was on the verge of tears. I said, 'No, you shouldn't resign; you should protest, man of God. And besides, your explanation of your conduct is not the truth. The truth is that you and your kind are afraid of death, and the ironic part of it is that you need death and particularly the fear of death for your business; without it your churches would be empty. Without men's fear of death and of what allegedly comes after it you couldn't get along, you'd starve. You've blown up death until men have become terrified of it. You've set up a whole cult of death. And you too'—this was to my father—'you've glorified it in hymns and poems, as something great, as the crown and culmination of existence; it was you religious men who developed the cult of death and called it depth of soul: yearning for death, the inner life, unworldliness, and so on. And this was just what Hitler needed. What better soil for him to sow in? And now you yourselves are afraid. Not of losing your calling, your family, your congregation— no, you're afraid that they might take your life, the life that you despise so. That's what you're afraid of.' I pointed to those sabers up there. 'With all that claptrap you played the strong men when you still had sap in your bones. You bragged; you talked about honor, freedom, manly dignity, the fatherland; you drank beer to work up courage. You read the ancient poets: *Dulce et decorum est pro patria mori.* Do you remember? You coquetted with death. And now? Apparently it no longer strikes you as sweet and honorable to die for your country. Or for the truth. You're so afraid of death that you haven't even the courage to die for your God.' Diebold jumped up: 'That is not so. I am not afraid of death. I am at all times prepared to stand before my God if he calls me.' 'And to stand before the Gestapo?' 'Yes, the Gestapo too.' It went on like that for a while. I called Diebold a drawing-room hero of Christianity. 'With Christians,' I said, 'it's always the same old story. They don't practice what they preach. And besides, what is one to think of a church that says, Thou shall not kill, and then produces fighting bishops and army chaplains, and blesses the armies? What is one to think of a church that prays to God for victory in battle? Off helmets; we shall pray.' "

"You're right. But to me it's sad. I see nothing to laugh about."

"To change the subject, my father started in on politics. He said that power is fundamentally evil because it's always abused. I said, 'God's power has taught us that. The stronger tree crowds out the weaker one and takes away its sunlight; the weakest always go to the wall. And it's the same in the animal world; the stronger animal eats the weaker. There's your glorious creation, you nature lovers. You climb around in the mountains to feel the breath of God, and at the same time, without knowing it, you trample out the life of a worm that crosses your path. You praise the Creator who created all things and at the same time you kill one of his creatures. Killing just seems to be part of God's trade. I see nothing to worship in that, and nothing to love. And if you argue that power attracts the weak like a magnet, but the strong stand firm, let me ask you this: Who was going to make us young men strong? You, I suppose. Well, are you strong? You sit around here, philosophizing, marking up paper, writing little tracts that no one reads, and discussing among yourselves while other people kill and are killed. You huddle together like frightened animals and crawl into your holes, because there's thunder and lightning outside. You should take off your hat to the youngest soldier at the front. He is risking his life for what he thinks to be right, for what he can't help thinking to be right, because you neglected to tell him the truth. And what are you risking? Man is not judged for his ideas, knowledge, convictions, but for what he is willing to sacrifice. Is my generation to blame if its sacrifices are made for an idol? Who enthroned the idol?' Well, that was what I said, more or less. Opposition at any price, you might call it. Anyway, it made me feel better, and that was my only excuse for it."

"I didn't know you were that much of an oppositionist."

"Neither did I, but I am. I'm too young, I think, to have much of an opinion in political matters; we're all of us too young. Sometimes I think I would be against any government, against any regime, no matter who was in power. But now I want to tell you the last act, as briefly as possible. This discussion must have had an effect on my father. That means I was the indirect cause of his death. Two days later a student told me my father had delivered a lecture on the concept of power and that he had been pretty outspoken. I didn't take the matter very seriously, but when I got home that night my father had been arrested. I put on my uniform and went to Gestapo headquarters. I didn't get to see my father. They told me he had already been taken away and that I would be kept informed. They were very polite—on account of my medals, I guess. Then they asked me if I had a moment's time—just a little confrontation; it wouldn't take long. They were right; it didn't take long. They had him brought in—I didn't even look at him—and asked me if I knew this gentleman. I said yes, by sight. They asked me if he often came to see my father. I said I didn't know; I had been away, fighting the war. 'Did you often visit Professor Heyne?' the Gestapo man asked him. 'No, very seldom. Only as the pastor of my congregation. Very seldom. My calls were purely official.' 'What do you do on official visits?' 'My activities are entirely of a spiritual nature. I comfort people in times of misfortune, where there has been a death in the family, for instance; I console them, I admonish them to persevere, to be brave. I do my utmost to improve the morale of the members of my congregation. I . . .' 'Very well, my morale-building friend; keep right on,' said the Gestapo man, and dismissed him. He was permitted to go. He was a free man again. 'Heil Hitler, Herr Kommissar,' he said. 'Heil Hitler, Herr Pastor,' said the Gestapo man. I followed him for about fifteen minutes. I didn't do anything to him. But he kept walking faster and faster. I still didn't touch him. Then he ran away. Next day I received orders to report at the Submarine School in Pillau. I was able to write my father twice, but I wasn't allowed to send him anything. In March a letter came from the administration at Belsen, saying my father had died suddenly; if I wished to claim his body, the transportation charges would be so many marks, to be sent to Postal Account No. So-and-so; the body could be released only on receipt of the money. Heil Hitler. That's the end of the story. Exciting, eh?"

Heyne turned on the radio. It took a while to warm up.

401

They heard the tail end of the news and a repetition of the Army communiqué. They heard words such as "heroic," "extreme bravery," "heroic sacrifice," and they thought, Do we need that? Then a set of chimes rang out the first bars of "Be loyal e'er and true." That was the intermission signal of the Deutschland radio station. Then a sultry female voice conveyed the people's greetings to the boys at the front. A few light pieces were played on the piano. Then there was dance music.

"My father wasn't the only one in the family. My mother's whole family was sent to concentration camps."

"What did they do?"

'Nothing, except for being alive. They were Jews, that's all, or rather half Jews. I'm a quarter Jew, you know, or maybe only an eighth; I'm not quite sure. All I know is that if I don't marry a Jewess, my children will only be sixteenth part Jews; they'll be allowed to live. I don't think they do anything to sixteenth Jews."

"Where are they now?"

"Same place as my father."

"No—that's not possible."

"But it's true."

"But they can't kill people just because their parents were Jews?"

"Oh yes they can."

"But they must have done something?"

"I didn't want to believe it at first, but that's how it was. Help yourself. We'll open another. The wine is good, isn't it?"

Heyne opened another bottle and filled the glasses. The wine was wonderful. They drank it in little sips and let it lie on their tongues. It tasted of honey and warm sun and earth, with a tinge of iron. The taste was so good that they neglected to smoke.

"I can't believe that, Gerd. I can't . . ."

"But, man, it's so," Heyne shouted.

He raced up and down the room as though looking for a window, stirring up the dust that lay on the books and the

Greek busts. A woman's low voice came out of the radio: "Don't cry over love. . . ."

"Forgive me, but that's just what riles me. Nobody believes it, and that's the worst part of it. It's driving me crazy. Do you understand that?" said Heyne sitting down.

"Yes, I understand."

"Just imagine if I told Wegener about it. He'd say I was drunk. Or my dear uncle, the general. He'd say, 'I forbid you to make up horror stories, or . . .'"

"Do you think the top generals, the marshals, the bigwigs know about it?"

"No, I don't think so. The commander of the Air Force, yes. But I'm convinced that the Commanding Admiral of the Navy has no idea of it. And that's what no one will believe later on when the war is lost. . . ."

"Are you so certain that we're going to lose it?"

"Don't be silly. At any rate, no one will believe that we didn't know about something that was our government's systematic policy."

A songstress informed her unseen audience that she didn't like to be alone at night, and then came an air-raid warning. Teichmann lit a cigar. It was a bit mangled; he had to paste it together with spit, but it burned. He said, "After the war we'll settle accounts with those boys. You can be sure of that."

"We?"

"Yes, we. Suppose we front-line servicemen—of the Army, Navy, and Air Force—should get together. And I can promise you that even the combat troops of the SS would join in. That would be the end of Himmler's gangsters. Do you think a single German soldier, not to mention the professional officers, would risk his life at the front so that Herr Himmler can murder innocent people at home?"

"After the war we'll be dead. Or digging ditches for the Allies."

"Dead, yes, if they keep us in submarines, but . . ."

"America's in the war now. That means that from now on it's sheer quantity that counts. In the air and on the seas they are already twenty to one. We can't fight against such odds. We can only die."

"And you think the top brass know that?"

The radio played the "Tritsch-Tratsch Polka." Then a eunuch's voice sang, "You're a lucky man with women . . ." Heyne seemed to be listening, but suddenly he cried out, "Yes, *that* they know. Unless they're pure idiots."

"You see things too black. . . ."

"Just a minute. How are you going to conquer Russia? How are you going to conquer England and America? Can you tell me that? They will conquer us. Our generals know that. But they'll go right on fighting."

"The Allies are talking about unconditional surrender."

"What else would you expect? Do you mean it's better for Germany to come out of the war with nothing but corpses? That's a fine kind of patriotism. No—our military leaders are perfectly aware of all that, and nevertheless they will keep on fighting to the last shell. And do you know why? Because they are good soldiers. And after the war . . ."

"You expect them to come through alive?"

"Top-ranking generals usually survive; they have the greatest chance of survival. And that too is very important for them, especially when the war is lost: because they've got to write their memoirs. And in their memoirs they'll tell us how clever they were, how brilliantly they led the troops. They'll tell us that if this and that measure which they allegedly recommended had been taken on time, the war would have been won. But they weren't able to do as they wished, and for that a certain corporal was to blame; the very same corporal for whose benefit they had stood like ramrods, shouting, 'Heil mein Führer!' if he was good enough to decorate them or give them a marshal's baton. And in those memoirs they will speak very profoundly about strategy and tactics. And of course they will say that they were motivated at all times by patriotism and nothing else. But they won't write a single word about what they did or didn't do at the time of the Roehm affair, when the corporal openly showed himself to be nothing but a mass murderer— I guess they were all on leave at the time. And they will not waste a single word to tell posterity how they stood looking on in 1938 when women and children and old men were rounded up by the SS thugs, herded through the streets, insulted, beaten. Hans—I ask you—is that a German way to behave? Since when have Germans attacked defenseless people and set fire to their temples? Since when?"

Heyne lit a cigarette. He had to strike the match on the box several times to produce a flame; then he inhaled deeply, let smoke filter through his nose, and put the cigarette down. "I always thought that it was up to the officer corps to set an example—where were the German officers that night in November, 1938, when the synagogues were burned?" Heyne took another drag at his cigarette. "I waited for them to speak up. So did my mother. Next morning she committed suicide."

A preliminary air-raid warning came over the radio. Large fleets of bombers, said the announcer, had been sighted over northern France, heading for Germany.

Heyne crushed out his cigarette. "I don't want to play the prophet, but I can tell you one thing: that night is going to cost us more dearly than anything else in our whole history."

"Then what are we still fighting for?"

"I'll tell you. We are fighting so a handful of men can go on governing and commanding a little longer. . . ."

"That is not true, Gerd. You are unjust. I can understand that. You have a right to be. But you forget that we also have officers who take their profession as an ideal. They will not stand by while the German people goes to the dogs. . . ."

"You forget that officers are specialists—narrow-minded, stubborn specialists. Experts in their field, oh yes. For that reason it will take the Allies a little while to defeat us. But what is outside their horizon does not interest them, or only in passing, such things as the Roehm putsch, the burning of the synagogues, the Fritsch plot. They will say, 'We didn't persecute the Jews'—and that is a typical German argument: in Germany when the bakeries are on fire, the butchers stand looking on, and vice versa. And the captains of industry will say, 'We didn't want the war'—no, they only financed it and made good money doing so. And the pastors will say, 'We didn't want Hitler.' But now I ask you: Who did want him, anyway? Can you tell me what these people ever did to oppose him? Today the concentration camps are crowded. Well, I don't know how many clergymen there are in Germany, but I'll bet you anything that there aren't five per cent of them in the camps. And what would you think of an infantry regiment if only five per cent of its men were willing to risk their lives?"

Outside, the sirens screamed, rising and falling. For a change the radio provided a march.

Teichmann felt overcome. Heyne's words stuck in his brain like barbed arrows. They had come quickly and with deadly aim. He had been defenseless, and now he was powerless to pull them out. They stuck fast. He's right and he's wrong, Teichmann thought. It isn't as simple as it sounds; there is no such thing as black and white; there are only varying shades of gray.

"But that's how the Germans are, Hans. We have outstanding religious leaders and brilliant philosophers; we have gifted musicians and soldiers; we have smart bankers and remarkable whoremasters; we have everything—except human beings. Aha, here they come."

"Yes, it's all typically German."

They heard the deep, steady droning high above them. They switched off the radio and listened in silence. They took it as a natural phenomenon, the work of a higher power. The dispersed yapping of the flak seemed absurd, like shooting a revolver at the moon. And the droning went on undiminished.

They left the bottles and went up to Heyne's room on the second floor. In the searchlight beams the falling bombs looked like pearls. Over the city the whole sky was blood-red.

They stood by the window breathing in the acrid smell of fire borne on the wind, and listened to the crash as the bombs landed. And then a great flame shot sky-high, as though someone were signaling with a giant searchlight.

Later, as they listened to the phonograph, the sky turned a sulphurous yellow. The planes were gone. The fires were still raging; the air blowing into the room bit their eyes and caught in their throats. But they left the windows open and went on listening to the music.

It was growing light outside while the music was still playing. Teichmann could see Heyne. He sat motionless in his chair, his haggard face bent forward. Teichmann thought of the polite little professor and of Heyne's mother who had poisoned herself, and of her family who had died in the gas chambers, and he glanced shamefacedly at Ensign Heyne, who in a few hours would be putting out to sea in a submarine. Suddenly the cruelty of this war seized hold of him, harder than when he had been in the midst of it.

On one of the records a woman sang, "Now ye have conquered sadness . . ." and it was very lovely to listen to. When Heyne had to turn the record, everything was as before; the music gave comfort only as long as you were listening to it. Teichmann didn't know whether or not he should be grateful for that. There was one more record, then the Requiem was ended.

"What we have been doing," said Heyne, "is typically German too."

"What do you mean? We haven't been doing anything."

"That's just it." Heyne laughed.

"You're a stinking sophist. And I want to tell you this: I'm going to go on fighting the same as before. And all this stuff about losing the war is rot, that's all I . . ."

"Poor little fellow. Did I break your toy?"

"You jackass, you. Once and for all, you can kiss my ass," said Teichmann, trying to be angry. But he didn't quite succeed, and then he thought of Heyne's father. "But about your father, Gerd . . ."

"Shut up, and sing the 'Watch on the Rhine.'"

"Stop it!" cried Teichmann, and now he really was furious. "You've got no call to talk like that."

"But what can I do?"

They celebrated their farewells at Dora's. The drinking began right after lunch. Despite Dora's organizing ability, the food was not what it had been. They were soon drunk and talking nonsense. Toward evening Heyne laced into Teichmann without the slightest provocation. "You're all bone and muscle and no brain," he said. "That's why you're such a brawler. You do everything with your fists. You try to use the small amount of brains the Lord gave you, but there's not enough of them, so you take to your fists. That's all you've got. Nothing to be so conceited about."

"I'm not."

"You're just like Emil, except that Emil was more naïve and more decent. He didn't know any better, but you do; yes, sometimes you know better, but you won't take the consequences. A good pork chop and a bottle of wine are enough to put your brain out of commission. That's your strength, if you want to look at it that way. It's all you have to offer. And the women, of course . . ."

"I suppose they're nothing to you?"

"I take them as a necessary evil. Something one needs from time to time. But you make a cult of . . ."

"That's enough, friend. Shut up now . . ."

"You just live to amuse yourself. That's all you've got in you. A bull. Tough, full of vitality. And that's all."

"It's something."

"And you've got taste like a . . ."

"That's enough, now . . ."

"Oh no, it isn't. You half-wit, you . . ."

"Gerd!" Dora cried.

"You half-wit. You enjoy life, don't you?"

Before Teichmann could answer, Heyne struck him twice in the face.

"Gerd, for God's sake!" cried Dora. "He'll make hash out of you."

"You keep out of this," said Teichmann. "You don't understand."

"But you, you . . ." Heyne bellowed. Then he fell back in his chair. Teichmann acted as if nothing had happened.

A little later Heyne disappeared. Teichmann thought he must be feeling sick and went looking for him. One of Dora's girls said he had gone home. It was after midnight when Teichmann left Dora.

It took him almost two hours to get to Blankenese. The house door was locked, and that worried him; it must mean that Heyne wasn't home yet. Unlocking the door, he felt for the candle they had put there—since yesterday's air raid there had been no electricity. He couldn't find the candle; no, he assured himself, he wasn't drunk; the candle was gone. He groped his way up to Heyne's room. When he opened the door, he saw a little candle stump burning in the middle of the floor. Gerd is here, he thought; he was so drunk he forgot to put the candle out. Teichmann went in and closed the door behind him. The draft blew the candle out, but he had already seen Heyne hanging by the wall opposite the door, where the bookshelf had been.

He lit a match. Heyne had hanged himself with a sword belt. He had passed the free end through the buckle; then he had burned a hole in the strap and fastened it to the big nail from which the bookshelf had hung. It was good German prewar leather; the hole had scarcely been stretched when Heyne, standing on the bookshelf, had put his head in the noose and kicked the shelf away.

Only Teichmann, Dora, and three of her girls went to the funeral. There was no pastor, for Heyne had been a suicide, and for the same reason the general did not attend. Dora was very grieved that a pastor hadn't been there.

Heyne's house was confiscated. Teichmann packed up all his personal belongings, mostly books. There were books by Schopenhauer, Dostoevski, Pascal, Hölderlin, Nietzsche, Gogol, Kierkegaard, Baudelaire. Teichman hadn't read any of them, and he had heard of only a few. But he packed them up carefully and sent them to the general in Nienstedten. All he kept for himself was the belt buckle with which Heyne had hanged himself. "God be with us" was inscribed on it. He put it in his pants pocket. Then he took the train for Gotenhafen, where he was to take a course at the Submarine School.

409

17

Lüttke's submarine put out on her last mission.

The captain had asked for and obtained Teichmann as first lieutenant. Petersen was exec. He still spoke softly, because of the splinter in his throat. But in speaking to the captain, he exerted himself and his voice rasped like a file. Langen was still engineering officer. His rumpled hair had turned gray, and that improved his looks, lending him a certain air of dignity. His hair distracted one's attention from the extraordinary homeliness of his features. Otherwise, he was still the same. Of those who had cracked up on the last trip, only the radioman remained. He had missed one trip, but now he was back again. The auxiliaryman was in a sanatorium. The old exec was dead; no details were known.

During Teichmann's term in Submarine School, the boat had done eighty days in the North Atlantic. She had undergone no fewer than forty-two air attacks. She had battled fog and icebergs and winter storms of hurricane strength. And she was still afloat.

Teichmann stood on the bridge as the boat silently left the pen with electric motors at one-third speed. Out in the basin she turned. It was raining, a fitful wet spring wind was blowing, and the empty pier looked as if it had been swept clean. Because of the frequent air raids there was no one outside the pen. Suddenly he felt the absurdity of this kind of warfare. Out of five submarines, three or four were regularly lost, and no enemy ships were sunk. Yet those that returned went right out again. Lüttke's vessel was accompanied by two others; the officers waved at each other, hoping that once again it would be the others who failed to come back. Bitterness rose up in Teichmann over this in

410

human obstinacy. It was not the fear of death—that was bad enough, but everyone was resigned to it—but the senselessness of dying in this way. There is no country in the world, thought Teichmann as the rain dripped down on him, where men are so docile about dying, and they call it bravery. The propagandists in Berlin boasted that the fighting spirit of the submarine fleet was unbroken. And that was true. But Teichmann began to doubt whether this was so worth while. It struck him now as a perverted kind of courage. And what if it were mere stupidity? Or a matter of false pride?

The Bay of Biscay gave them a harsh reception. It drove over the boat with its mountainous seas, green and black and gleaming white at the summits. For a moment the waters released the steel tube, only to seize it again, shaking it, stamping on it, sweeping the four lookouts from the bridge. Because of the weather, the sky was empty of planes, and any submarine chasers that might have been patrolling those waters could congratulate themselves if they didn't capsize.

The homing device jammed, and Bolz, the radioman striker—the one with the Bible—fell overboard as he was trying to repair it. A torpedo started to roll and crushed the arms of Seaman First-Class Brenk. And just before the captain dived so his arms could be set—yes, Lüttke was getting soft-hearted in his old age—the motor machinist's mate reported that the port engine was out of commission.

Twenty-five fathoms down, the storm was unnoticeable. There was peace and quiet to set Brenk's arms while the firemen were working on the Diesel. They removed various parts and cursed because they could not agree on how to repair it, and the seamen who were trying to set Brenk's arm under the guidance of the radioman, who didn't stir a finger, argued about the best way to go about it without driving the poor fellow mad with pain. Each man wanted to show his skill in setting crushed bones, for this was a special kind of fracture. They took hold with their delicate fists, and when Brenk let out a yell they said: "Does it hurt? It won't be long." And then the next one gave it a try. The radioman kept as far away as possible and commented after

411

every failure, "Wrong. They'd knit crooked. They'd have to be broken again."

When the captain had his bellyful of the screaming, he came out and gave the radioman such a blast that he was close to cracking up again. Finally Petersen and Teichmann took over and set Brenk's bones, using two slats from the potato crate for splints.

Two hours had passed. The port engine had been taken almost completely apart. Another hour later Langen informed the captain that the engine could not be repaired with the materials available on board; there were several cracked camshafts. Sabotage.

In his rage the captain made a mistake: he sent off a radio message and ordered the helmsman to steer for home. But when he reached the rendezvous point he went right on instead of waiting for the escort ships to arrive.

The submarine crawled homeward submerged, at a rate of two knots, ninety screw revolutions a minute. Some of the crew, particularly the married men, were not the least bit dismayed over this course. All those who had time went to the engine room for a look at the dismembered engine. Uninvited, the firemen gave their comments, pointing here and there with their grease-blacked arms, and feeling very important. The seamen made disparaging remarks about the firemen. The married men cursed loudest. The engineering officer stood by. In his great hands he held the parts of a broken camshaft, which he examined gloomily, muttering and shaking his head. Those who were close enough to him could make out the words "They've been sawed." And those words rung in the seamen's ears even after they had left the engine room. They knew that a brand-new engine had been destroyed by the enemy, an invisible enemy—in Germany. That upset them, even the married ones. But they showed no sign of it. "It won't take long to mend," they said. "Sure, those fellows in the drydock will do it in no time. Those firemen of ours are too dumb . . ."

Suddenly all life froze in the boat.

They didn't believe in ghosts; their nerves were pretty ragged but still more or less in hand; none of them was exactly hypersensitive. But everyone heard this sound—a metal object out there in the water, scraping against the side. And then despite their reduced speed a jangling so loud as to drown out the whirring of the motors.

No one moved—or even breathed. Out there, scarcely a yard away, steel struck steel and every single man heard it. Death had laid his bony hand on the hull. As it passed, the men's eyes followed as though an unknown commander were passing them in review. It had started behind the bow plane, and now it was moving slowly, slowly along the side.

The captain spoke. "Right full rudder," he commanded, hoping to clear the after plane. But the helmsman didn't have time to carry out the order.

The mine exploded next to the motor room. It tore open the pressure hull and killed the men in the motor room and the engine room, and the cook in the galley, and some of the men in the petty officers' room. In less than three seconds all these rooms were flooded. The exec bolted the after water-tight door; the rest of the men in the petty officers' room were drowned.

It was black and the boat stood vertical in the water; the men forward and in the control room fell off their feet and rolled down to the watertight door where the exec lay. His lower jaw was smashed, temporarily blocking his jugular vein. Then a dull thud was heard as the keel struck bottom.

A flashlight went on. The captain held it, directing the beam on the depth gauge in the control room. The blinding light remained in place, much longer than was necessary for reading the gauge. And then again total darkness. The needle of the depth gauge stood at sixty-eight meters.

The silence was complete, both inside and outside the boat. There was something unearthly about that silence, as though everything that had ever lived had gone out of existence. Never had the men's ears heard anything like that silence.

It was a relief when sounds came from the radio room—a crack-crack as of smashing flowerpots. And then a long pause. The men were glad when the sound started again.

Teichmann groped his way to the radio room. He could

413

hear someone inside. But he couldn't get the door open. He tried several times, passing his hands along the door frame; he felt the smooth wood under his fingers and the places where the paint had peeled, but he couldn't open the door. The strange noises continued. Teichmann went back to the control room.

The captain stood leaning over the chart table; the chief quartermaster held the light for him. The captain's left hand was bleeding, and the chief quartermaster's temple had been bruised. Across the room Teichmann made out the auxiliary-man in the half-darkness. He was standing upright, his hands on the main valve of the compressed air manifold, waiting.

"I need a flashlight," said Teichmann.

"Make a check of survivors," said the captain into the void.

"I need a flashlight," said Teichmann.

"We haven't got any more, sir," said a voice from the corner.

"I need a flashlight quick," said Teichmann.

"Why quick?" said the captain without turning around. "We've got plenty of time."

"We haven't got any more sir," said the voice from the corner.

"You've got a whole pile of them," said Teichmann.

"What for?" the chief quartermaster asked.

"We haven't got any more," said the voice from the corner.

"There's somebody in the radio room," said Teichmann.

"He's all right in there," said the chief quartermaster.

"We haven't got any more, sir," said the voice from the corner; it belonged to the torpedoman. Teichmann crossed over to him, took his flashlight, and went back to the radio room. He tinkered awhile, and when he finally had it open he flashed his light into the room. The radioman sat at his table; he had on the earphones and was working the transmitter key.

"Come on out of there."

The radioman went on tapping at his key. Teichmann watched him. He was tapping Morse code at a furious rate; beads of sweat stood out on his forehead. He reached under the table with his free hand, took a phonograph record out of the holder, and bit into it. He spat out the pieces and threw the record down. He had already used up quite a pile of records; his tongue was cut and bleeding freely; when Teichmann caught a glimpse of it, he was reminded of raw hamburger.

"Come on out, man."

The radioman kept on sending his messages and fumbling for more records with his free hand.

"Come on out, you idiot."

The idiot's right hand went on tapping out messages while the left hand searched for records. Teichmann tore off his earphones; the radioman fell forward, and his forehead struck the transmitter. Teichmann carried him into the control room and laid him on the deck among the others. When Teichmann left him, the radioman began to knock the deck plates with the knuckles of his right hand. He kept tapping out the letters *K* and *R* and got no further. The men moved away from him as if he were a leper. No one spoke.

The auxiliaryman still stood motionless by the main valve of the compressed air manifold; he had his hands on the wheel and was waiting for the command to blow out the tanks. The captain and the chief quartermaster were also motionless. Teichmann was reminded of the tableaux that he had once seen at an evening entertainment as a child. The ladies and gentlemen had stood just as still, but their poses had been deliberately theatrical.

The only noise came from the radioman, but his tapping was nerve-racking. Teichmann saw the men kicking at him. He kept right on tapping.

"Hey, you," said Teichmann to the auxiliaryman. "What are you hanging on to that wheel for?"

"Mr. Teichmann," said the captain, "must you always make so much noise?"

When the auxiliaryman let go the wheel he squatted like a little girl on a curbstone, and then he sat down. Another crack-up, Teichmann thought. Three or four times he laughed. His laugh was short, dry, and unnaturally loud.

"What was that?" the captain asked. He turned around and looked at Teichmann. "Aren't you feeling well?"

"I'm feeling fine, sir," said Teichmann. But he felt like crawling through the deck.

It was quiet again. The radioman's tapping could no longer be heard; they had shoved a leather jacket under his hand. The kicking had stopped too.

Only the chief quartermaster could see what the captain was doing at the chart table, and he said nothing. He held the light in such a way that it fell only on the captain; his own face was in the darkness, as was every other living face on board. Most of the men huddled on the control-room deck and did nothing, and the strange part of it was that they seemed quite content. Every bit of life in them was concentrated on watching their captain's back.

Teichmann looked around for the engineering officer. He had been trapped in the engine room with his sabotaged camshaft; the wonderful, ugly fellow was gone. Teichmann forgot him at once and looked at the others. He wondered how they managed to breathe so silently; it seemed to him that he himself was wheezing as though each breath were his last. Yet he didn't feel the least bit moribund—though he couldn't quite see how the future was going to shape up.

He regulated his breathing and then his brain began to speak up. What it told him was this: First, the boat is lying on the bottom; second, she can't rise; third, you are shut up inside. That was all his brain told him.

The silence was unbroken. And now that everything around them had ceased to live, they realized that they were no longer afraid. They looked into each other's faces and suddenly knew more about each other than in all the years spent fighting side by side. The fighting was over now. They lay at the bottom of the sea, in the place to which they had sent so many enemy ships, the place where all ships ultimately go. The others had been dead, but they too had come here alive.

Never had they been less afraid. Their minds and bodies had got used to fear as you get used to a job. Death could not have come more easily, more peacefully or pleasantly. There was something splendid, almost luxurious, about this kind of death. They knew how evil death could be, with what subtle cruelty it could strike, promiscuously and unjustly, and now

416

it had come so gently. They had learned long ago that the main thing in war is the way death comes, not the mere fact of death. They saw no ground for complaint. They had known it would come one day; it was easy to figure it out, and secretly they had done so. Now they found it perfectly acceptable. Even the boundless silence around them was soothing. No more depth charges, the war was over, they had made their peace. This was how they felt when the captain said, "Stand by to step ashore."

The captain had spoken in the same tone as he had used hundreds of times to command, "Stand by to surface." But the men cowered as though he were holding a club over them.

"It's perfectly simple. We have plenty of time, and there's no need to hurry. We have plenty of escape lungs. So it's all perfectly simple. I will explain everything in detail. Anyone who has questions may ask them. Incidentally, the depth presents no problem. . . ."

The men did not listen. They understood nothing. They gaped at him, as bewildered as children listening to a new, ununderstandable funny story: and that was the tone in which he spoke. He kept his injured hand in his pants pocket, and he tried hard to make his expression friendly and reassuring. The chief quartermaster held the light on him.

The captain broke off. He saw that he was not understood and his face changed. His lips became lines and his eyelids turned to slits. Teichmann expected an outburst of rage. But the captain fell silent and turned around to the chart table. He untied the string holding the chart pencil, first the end attached to the table, then the end holding the pencil. The men watched him.

The captain climbed up into the tower. They heard him undogging the tower hatch, pushing back the catch, and making it fast. Then he climbed back down and said, "Get your escape lungs ready. Petersen, stand by to flood tube three."

The men jumped as if they had been sitting on a hot plate. Teichmann despised them for a moment, and then he himself was afraid of what was to come. In Submarine School he had learned something about escaping from submerged

417

boats. He had been instructed in the technique of escaping at great depth; but the great depth hadn't amounted to more than twenty fathoms.

"Do you understand me, Petersen?"

The exec went toward the captain but said nothing.

"Do you understand?"

The exec was now standing right in front of the captain. He made no sound but shook his head and pointed at his throat. When he opened his mouth a bit it could be seen that his front teeth were missing, and the captain nodded. He had understood that the exec was unable to speak.

There were twenty-one survivors. The captain told them that they would not have to swim very long; they were on the route regularly taken by the flotilla and the escort vessels; possibly they would even see the Île de Ré with their naked eye; they were only a little way from the harbor mouth.

This time they listened. And after he had explained how the tower hatch could be opened in spite of the high pressure, they were convinced that escape was a relatively simple matter even at this depth. They went forward for their escape lungs and hurried back to the control room.

The captain divided them into three groups of seven. The first group would be led by Teichmann because the exec was partially disabled, the second by the chief quartermaster, and the last by the captain himself. Then he had the well of the periscope opened and the canned goods taken out. He ordered each man to eat a can of peaches. Some of the men complied. They ate because they had been ordered; the peaches were juicy and succulent, but they could barely get them down. The exec and the radioman made no attempt to eat. Some of the men poured out their cans. They weren't hungry and there seemed to be no point in eating now.

Nothing could be done with the radioman. He could not hold the mouthpiece of the escape gear between his lips; there was nothing to do but to shoot him. That was better than letting him float on top with burst lungs.

The captain did it while the others were still eating their

peaches. He did it so skillfully that no one noticed at first. But later, when the terrifying escape maneuver began, they envied his easy ending.

At 0800 the flooding began.

Teichmann went alone into the forward torpedo room. For a few seconds he remained hesitant in the darkness, as if to think the whole thing through one last time. He looked toward the tubes, where the water would stream into the boat; and he suddenly realized that he was starting off a process that could not be reversed. Then he looked back into the control room. A few of his shipmates, themselves illuminated by a flashlight, were peering after him, unable to see him in the darkness of the torpedo room.

He turned the wheel, opening the outer door of tube three. Then he let compressed air into the tube and fired the torpedo. He could hear the torpedo bouncing along the bottom and waited for all to be still. Then he closed the outer door, opened the breech, and removed the piston from the tube. For reasons of safety the tube was so constructed that the outer door could not be opened when the breech was open. He closed the breech, then he opened the outer door a little, and then quickly reopened the breech.

The water poured in with the shrill note of a steam whistle, which deepened to an ear-shattering howl. It seemed to Teichmann that the water had been waiting the whole time to come in and drown them. He ran back to the control room. The captain stood by the watertight door, holding the flashlight for him.

For the first time the men were seized by a kind of panic. They moved together like a herd of frightened animals, fingering their escape lungs, breathing as if they had just completed a cross-country run.

The captain turned out his flashlight. The gush of water sounded hideously loud in the darkness. But above it the words of the captain could be heard: "Don't be afraid of the water, boys." Then he flashed the light from face to face. The men were too frightened to move a muscle. Normally they would have hated their captain fiercely at a moment like this, but even for that they were now too frightened. They wanted nothing but to remain alive. When the light went out, the howling of the water was twice as loud as before.

Each group was tied together with a line slung around their waists in case anyone should lose his nerve and rise too quickly. The group that was to go first stood in a circle under the control-room hatch; the second and third groups stood behind them. But when the water reached the lower edge of the hatch and rushed into the control room, they squeezed together and tugged at the lines; a few fell down screaming.

The water rose quickly. When it was knee-high, the captain had to flash on his light while the lines were being disentangled. Just then a howling was heard from the forward torpedo room. A second wave of panic came over the men. They had never heard anyone howl like that.

They knew that it was too late to close the tube and that the man with the crushed arms had been forgotten. The captain realized that he had been to blame; he forced his way through the half-submerged passage and, up to his hips in water, waded through the wardroom and the chiefs' room into the forward torpedo room. Teichmann was barely able to follow him. They lifted up Brenk, who was lying in one of the upper bunks. He was still howling. Teichmann laid him over his shoulder, picked up the nearest available escape lung, and carried it in his teeth. The captain went first, lighting the way. To get back through the passage-way they had to dive, but they managed to get Brenk through. In the control room they adjusted their escape gear and instructed him to follow Petersen, who would unscrew his oxygen bottle. Then they tied him to the line between Teichmann and Petersen.

"Do potatoes float? Go on, throw one in the water," cried the captain when the water was chest-high and flowing over the potato crate. The water was already up to the necks of the smaller men, and they adjusted their nose clamps. There was pure terror in their eyes. "If they sink, they're fresh," said the captain. Now they had all put on their nose clamps. Through the din of the onrushing water, the whistling of the oxygen could be heard as the men tested the valves. They tested the valves about every ten seconds. "If they float," said the captain, "they're old potatoes." "That's only true of eggs,"[5] said Teichmann, and those were the last words spoken. They pulled the goggles over their eyes. The captain put his flashlight in his mouth and leaned his head back to make the light shine as long as possible. Some of the men grimaced and reeled because of the pressure in their ears. The rising water had pressed all the remaining air into the tower hatch. They waited for the air pressure to open the lid of their coffin.

When the light went out, Teichmann put the mouthpiece between Brenk's lips and opened his oxygen bottle a little. Then he did the same for himself. Almost at the same time there was a crash of lightning and Teichmann's head was pushed against the deck of the control room. A peal of thunder followed and then the whole boat was full of water. Teichmann had almost bitten through the mouthpiece of his escape gear.

The tower hatch was open. There was no more air in the boat. Theoretically, there should still have been some under the control-room deck, or so he had learned at Submarine School. Well, that had been book learning.

But the escape lungs functioned. Teichmann breathed gingerly; he didn't dare to breathe deeply, because he was afraid that he might suddenly find himself breathing water. The first breaths tasted of cold rubber and copper, but then the only taste was oxygen, and the breathing was easier than he had thought it would be.

He sensed that Petersen was drowning. He had seen him gagging, unable to hold the mouthpiece between his lips, massaging his throat. A quiver went through Petersen, his hands moved convulsively. Then he lay down slowly on the control-room deck—all movements are slow in the water. It was as if he were tired and wanted to sleep.

Teichmann had to untie him. He bent over and found the knot, but it had pulled tight when Petersen sank down and he couldn't undo it. Teichmann needed all his nerve to take his knife from his pants pocket and open the long blade. He was frantic to get out of the boat as quickly as possible or else to stop living; his terror was so great that he didn't want to live any more. He cut the line and tied the loose ends together. He hadn't the strength to close his knife and put it away. He simply let it drop and groped for the rungs of the ladder.

He found them at once. Slowly he climbed up into the tower, taking care not to damage his escape lung and life jacket. He drew Brenk after him and along with the leading seaman, who took Petersen's place, he passed Brenk through the conning tower hatch to the bridge.

Up top he waited. With one hand he held fast to the periscope standard and waited for the rest of his group. He was surprised to realize that there should still be oxygen in his bottle; he expected it to run out at any moment. He held his hand over the hatch and felt for the heads of the men. When they came, he gripped them by the hair and pulled gently to let them know he was there and waiting for them. And each time he touched a man, he felt lighter, as if he had stripped off a weight. He took each man by the arm and directed him to the place behind the periscope. Two of them clapped him on the shoulder.

When the group was all assembled, he felt better. He opened Brenk's oxygen bottle and his own a little more and felt himself floating. He gave three tugs at the line as a sign that they were going to rise, and felt the others passing the signal along. Then he lost his sense of direction.

Everything around him was liquid and soft and there was nothing to hold on to. But the line was still there. When he looked up, the water was green. He let air bubbles out of his mouth in order to slow down the rise, and at once the line tautened; the others were ahead of him. Without knowing what he was doing, he let more oxygen out of his mouth. The line grew rigid and pulled him into a slanting position. Then it occurred to him that he had let out too much air and that there would be none left with which to blow up his life jacket. He flailed about with his legs, but the line remained taut. He opened the oxygen bottle again and the water around him became light green. For fear that his lungs might burst, he let out some more air. The line tautened. He had a feeling that the others were already up top. Suddenly he was able to think calmly and clearly, and he knew it. He also knew that it would be best for his lungs if he rose as slowly as possible; but his sense of time had abandoned him completely. He couldn't say whether a minute or half an hour had passed since he had left the boat; he only knew that the oxygen in the bottle was supposed to be enough for half an hour if you breathed sparingly. At this thought he began to make swimming movements in order to save oxygen. Then he saw dark spots.

He was so frightened that a tremor ran through his whole body. He vaguely remembered that once he had seen dark spots and then lost consciousness. He beat wildly around him, tugged at the line that was still taut, and kicked. In this way he used up a good deal of oxygen. It did not occur to him to open the valve any further. He had lost all power of reflection.

The panic passed. Suddenly he was calm again and thought the dark spots might be air bubbles on his goggles. He closed his eyes and passed his fingers under the goggles. The spots were still there. He could see clearly above him and thought the spots might be jellyfish.

He had read somewhere that masses of jellyfish could burn off your skin and kill you if you came into contact with them. He mustn't rise now. There were large jellyfish above him.

He felt ice-cold. Up until then he hadn't noticed how cold the water was, but now it bit into his body and he shivered. The dark spots had grown larger. If he didn't want to collide with them, he would have to let out the air and swim away. But it didn't do any good to let out air; the line held him fast and he had thrown his knife away. He was much too excited to untie the line. He looked up again, and the dark spots were straight above him.

He counted them and reached five. Then he felt ashamed and exasperated. He had been acting like an idiot.

He made more swimming movements, a kind of breast stroke with a crawl kick, and suddenly he saw the sky and his shipmates. The skin of their faces was gray. He closed the air valve, took out the mouthpiece, opened the oxygen bottle full, felt the life jacket filling and pressing against the back of his neck. And then he felt miserably cold.

"On deck!" he heard someone calling. He tore off his goggles, got a noseful, and spluttered. Now the men's faces looked red. One of them must have opened Brenk's bottle; Brenk's life jacket was full.

"On deck, sir."

"On deck."

"On deck."

"On deck."

And then the others called "On deck." They repeated the cry like parrots, and then when seven heads popped out of the water close by, they called again, "On deck." Teichmann called out too. The chief quartermaster and his men called back. They bobbed up and down in the swell and cried out as though toasting one another. Then, shivering miserably, they waited for the next seven.

The chief quartermaster swam over to Teichmann and joined their lines.

"There are thirteen of us, sir; that's no lucky number. But the others are coming."

"Oh, yes, they're coming."

"Where's the exec?"

"Couldn't make it. His throat."

"Hell. Of all the rotten luck!"

The captain bobbed up with his six men. "On deck!" called the newcomers in chorus. They were greeted on all sides. It sounded like the chattering of geese.

"Where's the exec?"

"He couldn't keep the mouthpiece in, sir."

"Damn stupid business!"

Now there were twenty men up top. Each man seemed to feel the need to tell each of his mates personally that he too was present. There was no sign of the Île de Ré. Aside from water and twenty heads, there was nothing to be seen whatsoever.

"Why do they send me such men? The poor fellow deserved a desk job. I'm going to tell the admiral that. Those skunks in personnel will have this man on their conscience. Yes, I'm going to talk to the admiral."

"Yes, sir."

"What do you suppose he'll do to them? As I know the old man, he'll make it plenty hot for them. I wouldn't like to be in their shoes, Teichmann. No, I wouldn't."

"Nor I, sir."

"It's those pen pushers in Kiel. Once a month they turn their hotel ship around at the pier, and that entitles them to seagoing pay. That's the sort they are."

"Yes, sir. I could never stand their guts, either."

"They're shopkeepers in uniform, that's all they are. It's their fault. Sending me an invalid. The idea! Sending me an exec that's half dead."

"Yes, sir, they're to blame."

"Damn cold, eh?"

"Yes, sir, it's getting cool."

That was the end of the colloquy between Lüttke and Teichmann. They watched each other for a while bobbing up and down in the swell, and then each turned back to his own worries.

They were all joined by lines now. They had formed a circle and were waiting for something that didn't come. Some had begun to turn blue in the face.

The sun warmed their heads, but from the neck down they were frozen. They felt that a crust of ice was forming around them. When they moved, the crust grew thinner. But when they stopped moving, their limbs grew heavy and numb.

By noon the first began to give up. They wanted to sleep. They tried in vain. It wouldn't work. When they laid their heads against the cushions of their life jackets, the water washed into their mouths and noses—the sea was moderately rough—and when they leaned back, the sun shone into their eyes. It was straight overhead and very white. There was nothing to do for the present but go on living; the sea kept them awake.

The captain shouted a few words of encouragement, but

425

only the leading seaman, a particularly tough customer, reacted. He even managed to sing a song. The song was about the most obscene that had ever struck Teichmann's ears.

"I'm wondering whether to blush," Teichmann called out to him.

"You're red already, sir," the leading seaman answered. He was right. Teichmann's nose was bleeding.

"If you must sing," said the captain, "can't you sing something a little more appetizing?"

"Sure thing. I can sing 'We'll deck you with the virgin's crown,' if you like."

"I don't give a damn. Sing your *Magic Flute* if you want to."

"It's not from the *Magic Flute*, sir. I don't know what it's from, but it's not the *Magic Flute*. Anyway, it's called 'We'll deck you with the virgin's crown.'" The text that followed was completely new.

Teichmann's watch was watertight. It said 1400 when the gulls came. He watched them coming as a paralytic left alone in a burning house watches the fire. And at that moment something snapped inside him. He felt that his head had been parted from his body, that the connection between him and his head had been broken.

The others were glad to see something alive. For them the gulls were a distraction. The gulls' legs were red beneath their white plumage, and the underside of their wings shimmered steel-blue in the sun. They cried only intermittently. This, Teichmann thought, meant that they had already talked the situation over and knew what was to be done. Or maybe they're harmless. No, they're harmless only when their bellies are full, and right now their bellies are not full. At any rate they are curious.

When the first gulls came down to Brenk, Teichmann felt that he was gradually growing mad. He saw that Brenk was crying and paying no attention to the gulls, but when one came down, Teichmann jerked at the line; Brenk's head was toppled into the water and then shot up again as though he had made a quick bow. He was crying like a little

426

boy. Before Teichmann's eyes there was a strange shimmering. For a time he saw a hundred heads sticking out of the water, and then there was none. He saw the shadows of the gulls on the water. He struck at them. He struck the water with his fists like a child trying to swim. But the shadows were not concerned with him, and he could not chase after them.

The shimmering ceased when the sun went behind the clouds. The sky was as bleak as sour milk and seemed farther away than before. The gulls waited.

Their cries became more frequent. They're getting impatient, Teichmann thought. But it won't be long. You'll get your dinner. He jerked the line; Brenk tilted forward and wagged his head as if making fun of Teichmann, but actually he was weeping and the gulls barely grazed him.

Teichmann felt that the sea was slowly killing him. He kicked at it, and then he counted the bobbing heads. He no longer saw faces but only red balls lying on the yellow rubber cushion of their life jackets like flour-dusted apples on a plate. The flour was salt. Finally his eyes came to rest on Brenk, who tilted forward with every wave. The sea had grown rougher.

The gulls came down lower and their cries grew louder. Teichmann drew the line; Brenk bent forward and wobbled and wept. And Teichmann cried, "Hiya, Brenk. Hiya, my feathered friends."

The strange part of it was that Teichmann knew he was mad, just as a drunken man knows he is drunk. But that didn't trouble him. He kept calling out to the gulls, though not a sound issued from his mouth, "Hiya, my feathered friends. Give God my regards and good wishes. If you see him, tell him he'd better watch out, because if I run into him I'll kill him. Best regards from Teichmann. And tell him to watch out." He tugged at the line, and Brenk, who had been dead for some time, wobbled. "Hiya, Brenk. Chin up. Hey, you up there, come down and fill your bellies if the old boy isn't giving you enough to eat. Plenty of eyes down here. Come and get 'em." He tugged at the line. Brenk wobbled. "Hiya, Brenk. Chin up. You won't have any

trouble with Brenk, my feathered friends. His arms ar
gone. You can peck away to your hearts' content. No mor
fight in him than a head of cabbage. Two warm little huma
eyes in the brine. Help yourselves." He tugged at the line
and Brenk wobbled. "Hiya, Brenk. Chin up. Come on dowr
my feathered friends, and help yourselves. I wouldn't wan
you to go hungry. And give God my regards—the dirty dog.
He tugged at the line. Brenk wobbled. "Hiya, Brenk, chi
up. And you, my feathered friends, have a good feed. And m
regards to the old boy, Brenk, and chin up and chin up an
chin up . . ."

At dusk two patrol boats found the twenty men an
fished nine of them out of the water alive. The gulls ha
shown them the way.

The most macabre elite in modern history

THE ORDER OF THE DEATH'S HEAD

The Story of Hitler's SS

Heinz Höhne

Now, their complete story is told for the first time in superbly documented detail, with the aid of secret papers never before available. Absorbing, terrifying, true, this account of the Hitler SS has all "the fascination of a nightmare."

—*Los Angeles Times*

"A monumental achievement."

—*New York Times Book Review*

Aboard the German submarine U-124 in World War II

GREY WOLF, GREY SEA

E. B. Gasaway

With a Foreword by Grossadmiral Karl Dönitz Commander German Submarine Operations in World War II

Based on official German records and the vivid recollections of those who served on U-124 and survived, GREY WOLF, GREY SEA is as close a picture as we will ever have of the men who fought and died in the German U-boat service.

With 8 pages of photographs

For a complete list or to order by mail, write to: Dept. CS, 36 West 20th Street, New York, N.Y. 10003

A nightmare voyage
100 feet below
mine-infested waters

SEND DOWN A DOVE

Charles MacHardy

Not since *S.M.S. Ulysses* has a novel delivered such "Force Ten" impact—or received such stunning praise from the critics.

"The finest submarine story to come out of either world war—remarkable."
—Alistair MacLean

"A top drawer effort . . . MacHardy has made the dangerous, confining and claustrophobic atmosphere of the sub chillingly real."
—*New York Times*

"Will be compared with THE CRUEL SEA—just as fine a work of fiction."
—*Hartford Times*